EXODUS TO
ARTHUR

CATASTROPHIC ENCOUNTERS WITH COMETS

The Author
Professor Mike Baillie is an Irish palaeoecologist and an acknowledged expert in the field of dendrochronology – tree-ring dating. Based in Queen's University, Belfast, he is one of the first researchers to have access to long tree-ring chronologies from around the world, and to view the environmental information they contain from the perspective of both a scientist and an archaeologist. Some of his controversial proposals, on the effects of volcanic dust-veils, have already given rise to active debate in archaeological circles worldwide.

EXODUS TO ARTHUR

CATASTROPHIC ENCOUNTERS WITH COMETS

MIKE BAILLIE

B.T. BATSFORD LTD; LONDON

Dedicated to my mother, Hester

By about the sixth century AD, Christian beliefs included the dogma that nothing that happens in the heavens could have any conceivable effect on the Earth.

Fred Hoyle and Chandra Wickramasinghe, 1993

© Mike Baillie 1999

First printed in paperback 2000

B.T. Batsford Ltd
9 Blenheim Court
Brewery Road
London N7 9NT

A member of the Chrysalis Group plc

ISBN 0 7134 8681 3

A catalogue record for this book is available from the British Library

Printed by Biddles Limited, *www.biddles.co.uk*

Illustration credits
The author and publisher would like to thank the following for kind permission to reproduce copyright illustrations: David Hardy/Science Photo Library for page 52; Hulton Deutsch Collection for page 217; Novosti Photo Library for page 123; Private collection for page 45; Professor Barry Raftery for page 42; Somerset County Museums Service for page 35; South American Pictures for page 23; The Ulster Archeological Society for page 40.
The illustrations on pages 16, 17, 22, 24, 49, 55, 56, 57, 58, 63a, 63b, 67, 68, 97, 119, 120a, 120b, 124, 127, 200 and 201 are courtesy of Mike Baillie.

Cover picture by Fletcher Sibthorp

CONTENTS

PREFACE

This book grew out of the apparently simple question, asked by Charlotte Bickerstaffe and carried on by Monica Kendall at Batsford, 'Could you write a popular version of your recent book *A Slice Through Time*?' That book was about the building and completion of the first long oak tree-ring chronologies in Europe, and about some of the applications of those chronologies to archaeology, building history, trade and environmental studies. At the time I thought a popular version would be possible simply by expanding a few of the more interesting aspects of that existing book; what actually happened was quite different. As I wrote, at every turn I started to find new hints of a much bigger story. Spaced environmental events already observed and dated in the tree-rings appeared to be reflected in spaced events in ancient histories and mythologies. The new text started to take on the form of a 'what if' story. If the comets recorded in ancient China were the same as those alluded to in biblical sources then logic suggested something special about those particular comets, or something special about the periods in which they were observed. If the similarities in happenings in the sixth century AD and at the time of the Exodus were real, that logic suggested something too. By following the path 'but if that is the case then surely that means...' the text of this book was born. Thus the book was not conceived as a complete text but grew as the links were made and the logical questions were asked.

Several people contributed to useful discussions, notably Richard Warner, Valerie Hall, Peter Francis, Chris Lynn and Gerry McCormac. I should also mention the contributions made by Bob Kalin, Don Carleton Peter Pritchard, Leroy Ellenberger and Bob Kobres, each of whom supplied information which triggered new lines of enquiry. I am grateful to Ruarí ÓhUiginn for saving me from the worst pitfalls of the Rosualt sea-monster legend. Ian Tyers and Janet Ambers sat patiently through renditions of the basic story, while Jim Mallory, Tony Farrell and Ken Burnett bravely read drafts of the text to assist with ironing out some of the worst howlers. I would hasten to add that I am solely responsible for the text and any errors of fact or interpretation, in the many fields where I am not a specialist, are mine alone. In writing the later chapters, with their hints of cometary interactions with planet Earth, I found that the developing story had distinct similarities to the earlier writings of the contentious catastrophist, Immanuel Velikovsky. I therefore felt obliged, under the rules of prior work, to make use of a fraction of Velikovsky's work even though it is normally totally disregarded by scientists. After the book was written, Benny Peiser pointed out that much of Velikovsky's thesis contains striking echoes of the extremely strange works of Comyns Beaumont, an Englishman who was writing in the 1920s, 1930s, and 1940s. I had never heard of Beaumont, and it was not until July 1997 that I was able to obtain inter-library loan copies of his books, *The Mysterious Comet* and *The Riddle of Prehistoric Britain*. In the Foreword of the latter book Beaumont states, in bold capitals,

THE FLOOD IMMORTALIZES THE COLLISION
OF A FALLEN PLANET, LATER TERMED SATAN.
ACTUALLY A COMETARY BODY,
WITH OUT EARTH.

Anyone reading to the end of this book will see why I bother to quote Beaumont's prior statement here. Mixed in with many completely crazy ideas, for example, Britain being Atlantis, Beaumont correctly identified comets as a major hazard; he suggested that the dragon image was the description of a fireball, and that diseases come from space. He even suggested, in a roundabout way, and for all the wrong reasons, that meteoric impacts can trigger volcanic eruptions. If the rules of prior work really do apply, people in a wide variety of disciplines may find themselves citing Comyns Beaumont in the future. However, as with all such work, Beaumont was not actually the originator of many of the ideas about comets. Authors too numerous to mention, dating back at least to the seventeenth century, had discussed the possible hazards associated with cometary interactions. It is surprising how effectively such thoughts have been expunged from mainstream science; it seems that for most of this century concern about comets has been confined to eccentrics. It is fair to say that things are beginning to change in this regard.

In terms of conventions, I have used AD and BC to indicate dendrochronological dates and historical dates. CalAD and CalBC are estimates of real age based on calibrated radiocarbon dates. I have used 'AD' and 'BC' for other calendars which in my opinion are not well related to real time (eg, Irish prehistoric annals). I have chosen to use mostly old Chinese nomenclature when referring to historical Chinese characters, simply because it relates the text better to the quotes of prior authors such as Legge or Sagan and Druyan. Finally, much useful information used in this book has been gleaned at conferences on dendrochronology, radiocarbon, vulcanology, clathrates and catastrophism attended as part of more mainstream environmental research funded by the EC Environmental Research Programme, Contracts EV5V-CT94-0500, and ENV4-CT95-0127 Climatology and Natural Hazards, 2K and 10K.

Update to Preface

When the original text of *Exodus to Arthur* was written, the acid record relevant to the sixth century AD allowed me to state that 'there was no good evidence for a layer of volcanic acid at AD 540'. Subsequently, with the publication[1] of the detailed record from the European Greenland Ice Core Project and Dye3 Greenland ice cores (comparing the volcanic records over-the past 4000 years), it was evident that nothing much had changed. Although there were acid layers with mean dates of 533 and 528.5 (all +/- 1 per cent of age), it is interesting that neither was singled out for detailed analysis of their chemistry, whereas layers elsewhere in the sixth century were. So, while there is no evidence that either of these acid layers relates directly to the AD 540 environmental event, we now know, in addition, that they did not stand out in any way to the ice-core scientists.

Thus it can still be stated that there is no good evidence for an exceptional volcanic event in the immediate vicinity of AD 540. That statement is not altered by the occurrence of a layer of acid in the Antarctic ice at AD 504 (+/- 40)[2]. Nor has it been altered by the fact that this inherently weak evidence has been used elsewhere to support a hypothesis involving the eruption of a supervolcano in February 535[3].

Mike Baillie, June 2000

[1] (H. B. Clausen, C.U. Hammer, C.S. Hvidberg, D. Dahl-Jensen, and LP. Steffensen, 1997, *Journal of Geophysical Research* 102, No. C 12, 26, 707-26, 723)

[2] C U. Hammer, H.B. Clausen, and C.C. Langway 1997, '50,000 Years of Recorded Global Volcanisrn', *Climatic Change* 35, 1-15)

[3] D. Keys, 1999, *Catastrophe: an investigation into the origins of the modem world.* Century, London.

Tree-ring events	Europe	Near East	Hebrew	China
3195BC		Start Egyptian civilization		
	Henge at Stonehenge constructed			
2354 BC	Bronze Age starts, Britain and Ireland	Akkad	Flood of Noah (Ussher date)	Emperor Yao famous for floods
		Middle Kingdom		Start Xia Dynasty
1628 BC		Start Second Intermediate Period	Exodus of Moses Plagues of Egypt	Comet End Xia Dynasty (King Chieh) Start Shang Dynasty (King T'ang)
	Stonehenge abandoned			
		New Kingdom		Shang Dynasty
1159 BC	Comet Troy ends Middle Bronze Age	Comet Babylon Start Third Intermediate Period	Comet Jerusalem David Plague	Comet End Shang Dynasty (King Chou) Start Zhou Dynasty (King Wu)
207 BC	Stones fall from sky Cybele brought from Asia Minor to save Rome			Famines Stars not seen Start Han Dynasty
44 BC	Death of Caesar			Famines
540 AD	Dark Age Arthur/Merlin Beowulf	Justinian Plague		Famines

INTRODUCTION

What is the purpose of this book? It is an introduction to dendrochronology, or tree-ring dating, for the interested reader who may not have come across the potential of this quite remarkable dating method. However, if that was all the book was about it probably would not have been worth writing; any one of a number of pre-existing books would have sufficed, including my own *A Slice Through Time* (1995). In fact, to understand just what this book is about it is necessary to say a few words about some previous work.

A tree-ring chronology is a year-by-year record of what trees thought of their growth conditions in the past. The lengths of the records are not restricted to the lifespans of the oldest trees. By overlapping the patterns of wide and narrow growth rings from living trees with the patterns of successively older and older timbers from historic buildings, archaeological sites and natural sources, really long tree-ring records can be produced. The international tree-ring community now have such annual tree-ring records running back for thousands of years, from areas as diverse as Ireland, Germany, Fennoscandia, northern Russia, North and South America and Tasmania. Thus we can look at any year in the past several thousand years and see what trees, widely dispersed around the globe, thought of conditions. It turns out that when we interrogate some of these records in this way we find some positively alarming evidence of extreme environmental events in the past which also 'seem' to be recorded in human history. I use the word *seem* because much of human history is not very well dated in comparison to the tree-ring records which are precisely dated to exact calendar years. So we know the exact dates of the environmental downturns and these fall close to the dating estimates of human trauma deduced by ancient historians and archaeologists. Because of the way these extreme events showed up, with tentative links to volcanic acid in Greenland, the initial hypothesis about their cause was that they were related to the environmental effects of large explosive volcanic eruptions.

We have known about this story for about the last decade and it has been a matter of accumulating information to try to get a handle on the exact sequence of events and to prove the actual cause of the environmental downturns. However, as research has continued the story has started to turn strange, and to contain hints of an extraterrestrial component. Things are still highly speculative but already the outline of a new story can be put together. It is not the story I set out to write because at every turn new pieces of information have slotted in – in some ways making more and more sense, in others becoming stranger and stranger. The purpose of this book is to share with the reader the outline of what this story may ultimately be. Put another way, it would be easier to believe that the story you are about to read is true than to believe that all the apparently logical steps could just be one big mistake. You, the reader, will have to judge. All I can say is that there is no fiction in what follows, although there are some quite big leaps of faith. I make use of facts and I add in myths – other people's ancient myths – and still other people's interpretations of those ancient myths, but all the logic steps are obvious and nothing is made up; in many cases I use the dates and linkages others have already committed to print. I quote extensively from published sources and, if I were asked, I could document just about every statement made in this book. In fact, to aid anyone who wishes to check or follow up the sources, most principal authors cited are given in a bibliography at the end of the book. It may be fitting that as we approach the millennium this book could at last be written – the story as far as I can see has been waiting to be told.

So, what is new about this book? Well, people previously trying to make sense of the last several millennia have had to rely on ancient history, archaeology and mythology. Of these three sources mythology has had the worst press and has been mostly relegated to the sidelines; suitable for literary but not for scientific study. However, in each of these disciplines, time control has been, to say the least, limited. When it comes to chronological issues, ancient history, archaeology and mythology share similar problems. For example, poor chronological control has stopped workers trying to relate happenings in the East and West; while relatively little, almost no, use has been made of environmental markers to link distant but contemporary happenings. In this work I have introduced some independently dated environmental downturns, deduced from the precisely dated tree-ring chronologies, and have then attempted to show that a plausible case exists that dynasties in the East and West suffered at the same times as the trees. The new linking factor is the occurrence in both East and West of references to comets or cometary interactions at or around these same environmental events. The result is a scenario which is amenable to testing and which, if it turns out to be correct, will give a core of real meaning to much mythology. Indeed, if the cometary scenario is true, recent human populations, and most scientists, have been missing a significant global hazard. If that is the case, then it is truly imperative that we know the score well in advance of the next such episode so that we have adequate time to work out a mitigation strategy.

Now, that said, I need to explain a couple of other points. I am not schooled in mythology or the study of ancient literature. What has astounded me is that even with no specialist experience I have been able to access, and take some broad hints from, the analysis of such sources as the Grail Legend, tales about Arthur and Merlin, Anglo-Saxon poetry and classical mythology. On the more historical side I use evidence from Chinese and Hebrew literature. Now, either myth is so wide a concept that you can find in it anything you want to reinforce any idea, or, more realistically, myth is partly based on real memories, no matter how distant and distorted by re-telling. Common sense would suggest that some of the deep-remembered tales would relate to important events which may also have been recorded in ancient history; catastrophic events could very well fit the bill. The problem in the past is that poor time-control has normally stopped people from seeing the links between the different sources. With the fixed points provided by dendrochronology, we can begin to see the *possible* links between ancient history and mythology and real environmental happenings. My personal feeling of success in having found evidence in these areas to support the hypothesis developed in this book is tinged with the knowledge that I have merely scratched the surface of fields which have exercised scholars for centuries. My only defence for intruding into the complex areas of history and myth is the fact that, through dendrochronology, I am one of the first people to have access to aspects of the previously missing environmental story. The implication is that there is much more evidence to be located by specialists in those other fields; hopefully this text will be the starting-point which will trigger some fresh understanding. This feeling would also be consistent with the following observation. As I put together the text of the last few chapters I found that new and interesting pieces of information were being discovered every few days – colleagues would say 'have you seen this …' or 'did you know that …' Every trip to the library or the literature turned up more usable tit-bits. In fact, where this book ends is an essentially arbitrary point in the accumulation of information; if I had gone on writing for another month or two there would have been another new chapter, in six months maybe two more; certainly that is the current feeling. So this book is a launching pad for anyone interested in Dark Ages, myths, Arthur, the Exodus, abrupt environmental change, comets and even 'fire from Heaven'.

Once you have read the book you can judge for yourself whether it makes sense. I am sure that a lot of people will want to prove that it *has to be* wrong. That will be ironic because, as far as I can see, it does not matter how the scenario was arrived at, it is the scenario itself that is important – and it was the trees that pointed out the dates which made the scenario possible. Finally, it is important to remember that the real driving force behind this study is to try to derive hints from ancient sources that will help us to better understand those fairly impenetrable environmental events in the past. Since the story suggests that at key dates the Earth has had some interactions with comets or their debris – we could call them cometary near-misses, for we certainly have not been hit by a full blown comet in recent times (the simple fact is that if we had we would not be here) – we may now know where and when to look for the real scientific evidence necessary to prove, or disprove, the case.

M Baillie
Belfast 1998

PART I

CHAPTER 1

·

INTRODUCTION TO DENDROCHRONOLOGY

Nearly everyone has at some stage looked at the cut surface of a tree-stump and noticed the patterns of concentric growth rings. A good proportion of us have learned that the circles we can see and count on these tree-stumps represent 'a ring for every year that the tree grew': usually that is correct. In most regions trees do develop a new layer of woody tissue each growing season. Even in the tropics, where people used to say, 'trees have growth rings but they may not represent actual years, because of the lack of distinct seasons' it is becoming increasingly clear that the trees do put on one growth ring relevant to each calendar year of their lives. It has been possible to prove this by checking that the growth ring for 1963 – dated by counting rings back from the felling date – coincided with a huge spike of radioactive carbon in the tree-ring for 1963. This anomalous quantity of the radioactive carbon isotope was produced in the atmosphere by the uncontrolled nuclear testing at that time. So the presence of the radioactive 'spike' in the growth rings for 1963 proved that, even in the tropics, some trees were putting on one growth ring per year.

This recognition of annual growth goes back a surprisingly long way: scholars have searched through the literature of the past to reveal that Theophrastus, a student of Aristotle, worked out that fresh growth formed on the outer circumference of a tree. Even Leonardo da Vinci had thoughts on the matter of tree-rings. Da Vinci had not only deduced that there was a relationship between ring width and moisture availability but had used this to reconstruct past weather from earlier ring widths. By the eighteenth century people were using the annual character of the rings to count back from known felling dates to look at specific growth years. By the nineteenth century Babbage appears to have got right to the heart of the matter by suggesting that cross-dating (ie, overlapping the patterns of wide and narrow rings from tree to tree) would eventually allow the construction of long chronologies back to the ancient trees in bogs and lakes, for dating purposes; something which, of course, we can now do. In fact if Babbage really made this proposal in 1837 he would only have had to wait about 145 years to see his proposition fulfilled – the first prehistoric bog oaks were fitted into chronologies and precisely dated in 1982. So tree-rings were pretty well understood in the past but it was not until the beginning of the twentieth century that someone actually decided to develop the idea and create a long chronology of tree growth. The original stimulus came from Andrew Douglass, an astronomer at Flagstaff, Arizona. Interested in solar cycles, he made a simple series of judgements. Working in semi-arid Arizona, he saw sunshine just about all day every day in most years. Douglass deduced that Arizona trees must get more or less the same number of hours of sunshine every year. He also knew that tree growth in the semi-arid area was very closely related to the amount of moisture available to the trees – if there was moisture the trees grew well and developed a relatively thick growth band; if there was effectively no moisture the trees grew hardly at all and sometimes, in extreme cases, they could miss a ring altogether. So when Douglass looked at the ring patterns of Arizona trees he noted that the patterns contained two components: rapid short-term 'year to year' variations due to the changing amounts of rainfall from year to year, and also longer-term growth 'trends'. What was causing these trends in growth over time? Douglass decided that because the number of sunshine days was more or less equal each year, the long-term changes in the tree-ring patterns might be due to changes in solar output. By separating the effects of rain and sun, he had deduced a way to look at changes in solar activity over time. The Arizona tree-ring record appeared to give evidence of the 11-year solar cycle.

Douglass arrived at the conclusion that the 11-year solar cycle was clearly there in the tree-rings, back to about AD 1700, and not there for the century before, when it was replaced by a ten-year cycle. This was rather a curious observation: people recognize the sun as the mainstay of life, and yet the tree-rings hint that it is not the same all the time. Not only does it vary in a series of cyclic ways, but it appears to have been very quiet across most of the seventeenth century. Just what was going on? Douglass was worried about this breakdown in the 11-year cycle. However, eventually he was contacted by Maunder, from the Royal Observatory at Greenwich, with the information that there was a general absence of sunspots in the seventeenth century – now known as the Maunder Minimum. From the time when Galileo first popularized the use of the telescope, back in the early seventeenth century, people had fairly systematically counted and recorded the number of sunspots – black blemishes on the surface of the sun's disc. This count dropped steeply in the seventeenth century and only became clear again after 1710. The change in solar activity as indicated by Douglass' tree-ring record appeared to be well substantiated by the direct scientific observations.

Douglass got very little credit for these observations. Scientists are not

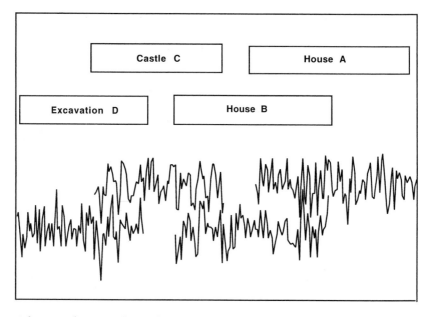

Schematic diagram of procedure for building a master chronology. Sections of ring pattern, from trees of the same species, from successively older sources, are overlapped to produce a continuous record.

very fond of cycles because they can tend to become a bit of a fetish. However, Douglass decided to extend the tree-ring record by hundreds of years by overlapping the wide and narrow growth-ring patterns from living Arizona pines to the patterns from ancient archaeological timbers. If the trees were growing over some common period he could match their ring patterns over their common years. He acquired timbers from ancient Pueblo ruins in the dry American Southwest and encouraged archaeologists to dig on certain sites which might contain key pieces of wood for his chronology building. In the later stages of this quest, in the late 1920s, several so-called 'Beam Expeditions' were organized where archaeologists, using their knowledge of the pottery types occurring in the ruins, could pinpoint sites of just the right period to give the maximum chance of linking across the thirteenth century AD. By 1923 Douglass, working in the Flagstaff area, had extended his living-tree chronology for yellow pine back to AD 1284. He had also constructed a 'floating' chronology – one that is not tied to the present but floats in time, from archaeological sites at Aztec, New Mexico, and from Pueblo Bonito some 50 miles to the south. The easiest way to refer to a floating chronology is to assign it relative dates (RD), so as his chronology was 314 years in length Douglass called his floating chronology scale RD 230 to RD 543. He hoped

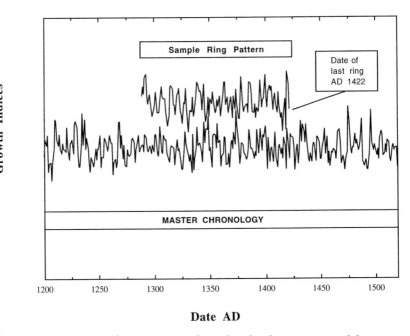

Date AD

Once a continuous year-by-year master chronology has been constructed for a region, the ring patterns of individual trees or site chronologies can be compared with the master. Where a reliable visual and statistical match is found the exact calendar years of the sample can be read from the master.

to be able to assign a calendar date to RD 543 and thus date the whole sequence.

While piecing together his chronology Douglass noticed that there were short runs of tree-ring pattern which were almost always present in particular periods. He called these *signature patterns*, for example, a set of four narrow rings followed by two wide rings with a noticeable narrow ring seven years later occurred in the years from 1215 to 1227 – if he saw that particular pattern in a new piece of wood from a site he could immediately tell the date of those rings. Then he would count the rings forward to the outside of the sample and he could give the felling date. Douglass, having memorised all the signature patterns in his chronologies, was eventually able to pick up a wood section, study the rings with a hand lens, recognize a signature pattern, count the rings to the bark surface and announce to the archaeologist that, for example, the tree had been felled in AD 1312!

However, let us return to the time when he had not yet managed to find any link between his modern chronology back to 1284 and his floating 314-year section. In 1923 the National Geographical Society became sufficiently interested in the potential of Douglass' work to fund the first 'Beam Expedition'. Large numbers of timbers were collected from historic buildings, ruins and archaeological sites throughout the Southwest. Though the length of the floating chronology was extended, nothing turned up to bridge the gap between the two chronologies. A second Beam Expedition was funded in 1928. It is now known that timbers from Hopi villages had been cross-dated to the older end of the modern chronology, that is, to the fourteenth and fifteenth centuries. So effort was put into sampling early Hopi sites. Unfortunately, most samples dated against the modern chronology and only one extended it back to 1260.

It became apparent that this random sampling strategy worked to some extent, but was failing to turn up timbers relating to the gap. A more systematic approach was required. About 30 archaeological sites fitted into the, by now, 585-year floating chronology and a better understanding of the prehistoric archaeology was beginning to emerge. Sites dating to the later part of the 585-year chronology were characterized by particular types of red background, polychrome pottery, while sites dating to the older part of the modern chronology tended to have orange and yellow background wares. However, the sites which produced the right colour of pottery were just those which tended to produce few, if any, useful timbers. The chronological gap was a real gap, not just a sampling gap.

The prize – precise dating for prehistoric sites – was such that Douglass and the archaeologists had to keep going. In 1929 a series of excavations were undertaken on 'orange pottery' sites. Excavation was the only possibility because there were no timbers in the ruins and only charred beams were likely to have survived buried in the deposits. One site chosen was the Whipple ruin at Showlow, which had all the right criteria to turn up charred timbers of the right date range.

On the fifth day of excavation, 22 June 1929, a charred roof timber turned up with most of one radius preserved. Douglass arrived at the site in time to assist with the lifting of the beam. Preliminary examination of the ring pattern of this timber (HH-39) showed that its outer rings ran out to around 1380 and extended back to 1237. Would this timber cross-match with the floating chronology? There was a recognisable overlap of 49 years between HH-39 and the floating chronology, specifying the 585th year as 1285 … In fact, an overlap between 1260 and 1285 had been discovered, but it had been too short to allow definitive matching.

This linking of the modern and floating chronology gave Douglass a yellow pine chronology for Arizona back to AD 701. Immediately all those relative archaeological dates could be converted to calendar dates. Suddenly the American Southwest had the best archaeological chronology in the world. However, by this time the whole issue of cycles had become so muddied that Douglass was never able to demonstrate a satisfactory conclusion. The irony is that the very thing which had stimulated him to build the chronology came virtually to nothing; it is only in very recent times that new analysis has demonstrated good evidence for solar cycles in certain tree-ring series. What did become clear was the fact that dendrochronology as a discipline had become important as a chronological and environmental indicator. The very act of building the chronology and dating the Amerindian ruins proved the potential of the method.

Let us consider this original gap-bridging exercise a little further. Douglass set out to build a long chronology and that chronology turned out to have two easy bits, with many timbers, separated by a difficult bit, the gap, The gap, as we have seen, took much effort to bridge. Why? A possible answer to this question may lie in the short overlap, from 1260 to 1285, when there was a 'Great Drought'. In the 1970s Martin Rose and colleagues at Tucson undertook a detailed climate study based on tree-ring chronologies from Arroyo Hondo in New Mexico; ring patterns from fourteenth-century phases on the site ran back across the thirteenth century. According to the trees, a great drought from 1276 to 1299 almost certainly made it impossible to sustain agriculture in the area. People probably had to abandon settlements and there may have been an increase in raiding for scarce food supplies – certainly a period of stress. The first tree-ring gap ever discovered actually indicated a period of environmental stress. This was the first hint that gaps, although they seem to be just a nuisance to dendrochronologists building chronologies, usually indicate something going on.

Arroyo Hondo is a classic example of what a detailed dendrochronological analysis can show. Rose and his colleagues noted the drought episode from 1276 to 1299, then surmised:

Arroyo Hondo was established about AD 1300 when precipitation was increasing after a 50-year period of mostly below average values. It may be that by making desert farming possible ... the increased rainfall made this location attractive to settlers for the first time. Initially a small group of farmers constructed an alignment of rooms along the edge of the canyon.

From the tree-ring response it was possible to deduce that rainfall remained above the long-term average for about the first 35 years of the fourteenth century. This in turn implies that agriculture was probably productive and population could expand. That is also implied by the archaeological findings.

With ...favourable climatic conditions, the pueblo grew to nearly a hundred times its original size in the first three decades of the 1300s ... The settlement reached its greatest size around 1330, comprising 24 room blocks constructed around ten ... enclosed plazas ...

The dendrochronologists actually charted the development of this expanding site in real time and inferred the population density from the number of rooms as the construction grew. However, in the Southwest conditions can turn marginal very quickly, and again the combination of dendrochronology and dendroclimatology tells us what happened next:

about AD 1335 the pattern of precipitation shifted toward high annual variability, with severe droughts separated by brief wet intervals ... soon after 1335 the town's population began to decline even more dramatically than it had increased ... by about 1345 the pueblo was virtually abandoned (for the next 30 years) ... Then, sometime during the 1370s, a second phase of settlement began.

Thus in the decade before 1347, when the plague known as the Black Death arrived to kill one third of Europe's population, changing environmental conditions in the American Southwest precipitated the abandonment of what were effectively agriculture-based towns. Two totally independent populations suffering at the same time does smack of a common cause. The only vector that can possibly be common between Europe and America at that time, if we ignore Fred Hoyle and Chandra Wickramasinghe's theory about diseases from space, is climate upset. Reconstructions from Huon pines on the island of Tasmania indicate that AD 1345 was the third coldest year in the last three millennia: something interesting was happening globally at that time. Other widely spaced tree-ring chronologies, from Fennoscandia to New Zealand, show reduced growth in the 1340s. More of these synchronous global events will be discussed later.

ANASAZI DEVELOPMENT AND DROUGHT

In the arid Southwest one cultural group of prehistoric agriculturists were the Anasazi who colonised canyons which today are very inhospitable. They built huge multi-storey pueblos and developed agricultural irrigation systems. One group, the Virgin Branch Anasazi, lived in the Southwestern Great Basin where the states of California, Arizona and Utah meet. From the tree-rings Dan Larson and Joel Michaelsen found evidence of two significant droughts. During the first, between AD 1000 and 1015, the relatively low population, deduced from the size of the dated buildings, appeared to have survived by concentrating more on agriculture and storage as reliance on hunting and gathering became too risky a strategy. Following

Poignant reminder of the effects of environmental change. The Cliff Palace ruins in Colorado abandoned by the Anasazi agriculturists around AD 1300.

this first drought the climate became wetter and the population expanded for about a century. The second drought, between AD 1120 and 1150, although not as severe as the first, affected an expanded population fully reliant on agriculture. During this second drought they seem to have suffered several consecutive failed harvests and the area was abandoned.

Another Anasazi group lived at the same time in Chaco Canyon, New Mexico, some 700 km (435 miles) due east of the Virgin Branch area. Julio Betancourt and colleagues, in another detailed study, found evidence for the large-scale importation of fir and spruce into the presumably tree-less canyon in 'the period of major construction between AD 1030 and 1100', that is, the wet period between the two droughts. In this case, with favourable conditions, the increasing population built huge pueblos and thought nothing of carrying thousands of logs over distances of more than 75 km (50 miles) along 'logging roads'. (Apparently the use of the word 'carrying' is literally true; as the timbers showed no signs of drag marks it would seem that a typical 'primary beam 22 cm [8 inches] in diameter, about 5 m [16 ft] in length and approximately 275 kg [600 lb] in weight' was literally *carried* over 75 km (50 miles).

The Anasazi were a highly organized and sophisticated agricultural society maintaining widespread networks over long distances. Yet as they consistently let their population rise to levels which could not be sustained in a crisis, they were highly vulnerable to changing environmental conditions. Their abandoned ruins and the timbers they left bear witness to their experience. However, the drought between AD 1120 and 1150, which forced the Anasazi to abandon the southern Great Basin, was not an isolated phenomenon. Keith Briffa and colleagues, analysing temperature-sensitive pines in Fennoscandia, have reconstructed past summer temperatures for this northern European region. One of the coldest 20-year periods in the last 1500

The extensive ruins at Chaco Canyon, New Mexico, mostly constructed in a period of increased rainfall between AD 1030 and 1100, and subsequently abandoned.

years was AD 1127–46, which had a mean temperature anomaly of almost one degree Celsius. Drought in the American Southwest and cooler conditions in Fennoscandia: both point to a period of global dislocation in the northern hemisphere. In one of Briffa's analyses, the twelfth-century cold episode is bracketed by two warm periods, 1087–1106 and 1158–77, which were on average anomalously warm by one-half to three-quarters of a degree. A global picture begins to emerge as these various tree-ring chronologies are deciphered.

THE GIANT SEQUOIA

Douglass had not restricted himself to the Arizona region: early in the century he went to the massive logging operations at the groves of sequoia – the giant redwoods – in California. Sequoia National Park, situated in east central California, contains many giant sequoias more than 2000 years old, including the 'General Sherman Tree', 83 m (270 ft) tall, with a diameter of 11 m (36 ft), which may be as much as 3000 years old.

These trees can weigh up to 6000 tons with recorded heights of 117 m (385 ft). Douglass collected sections from the huge stumps left by the loggers and measured up their ring patterns in a sequoia chronology which eventually was to run back to 1200 BC. Because their ring patterns were relatively complacent, compared to the arid yellow pines of Arizona, his principal use of the sequoia chronologies was as a dating control for his other chronologies.

More recently other workers have realized the wealth of environmental information in these majestic Californian trees. Malcolm Hughes and Peter Brown, studying sequoia ring widths, have found that distinct low-growth events in these trees can be related to severe drought years; they have produced a regional reconstruction of the Palmer Drought Severity Index back to 101 BC. In their Californian study area they found that extreme droughts occurred on average 4.5 times per 100 years over the last 2000 years, though these averages can be deceptive. The number of droughts in a century could range from as few as one to as many as twelve; twelve severe droughts in a century would be challenging for any human inhabitants of the region. One of the lowest 100-year periods, that is, the period with the least severe droughts, is 1850–1950. It seems that modern settlers in the area may have a totally false impression of just how dry the area can be.

Hughes and Brown note in passing that sequoias can show extreme growth release – anomalously wide rings – after fire damage and they mention a very severe fire which caused this effect at their Mountain Home site in AD 1297. This opens up another research area. The wood of the large sequoia is sufficiently fire resistant that trees are rarely killed by a low-level fire, though they may well record the fire in their ring record. Tom Swetnam has developed a whole fire history for these trees by identifying and dating the fire scars in trees from five separate groves. He records that the earliest fire scar to be identified had occurred in 1125 BC. From an environmental standpoint he found that the frequency of fires varied with time, as had the severe droughts. Moreover, by comparing the dates of fire years and non-fire years with tree-ring estimates of past precipitation he was able to confirm that multiple-grove fire events tended to occur in dry years: years when fires were recorded in three, four or five groves were increasingly dry, whereas years when no fires were recorded in any of the groves were wet.

So the giant sequoias are gradually giving up their secrets to the dendrochronologists. Before moving on, I want to use one of the dates just given as a 'taster' for things which we will come onto later in the book. That very severe fire in AD 1297 may just seem to be a random date, but is it? Once you know that 'lightning and meteors destroyed the corn' in Ireland in 1294, 'ten fireballs the size of houses' fell in China in 1295, and there was a notable extraterrestrial impact in Russia in 1296, then maybe that fire-induced growth release in 1297 was not just random; maybe it had a quite exotic cause. One of the tree-ring phenomena noted after the extraterrestrial impact at Tunguska in June 1908 was growth release in many of the surviving trees (the growth release can be due to removal of competition and/or release of nutrients). Precise dating allows one to see hints of patterns that were not there before. Critics would say that such connections should not be made without proof of causal relationships; however, no proof will ever be forthcoming if such interesting clusters of information go unrecorded.

THE BRISTLECONE PINE

The early American story would not be complete without making some reference to the longest-lived trees yet discovered on the planet: the

Ancient bristlecone pines in the White Mountains of California. Individual specimens live up to 4900 years. Dead trunks and snags survive up to thousands of years in the same vicinity.

bristlecone pines which live at high altitudes in some mountain ranges in California and Nevada. It is ironic, given the environmental information now being squeezed out of the sequoias, that it was the sequoia's apparent lack of environmental signal that drove people to look for other environmentally-sensitive tree species. In the 1950s, Edmund Schulman heard about bristlecone pines growing at the upper timberline, about 3000 m (9500 ft). He discovered that the previously unknown trees were very old. He soon found several specimens that had been growing for more than 4000 years. Moreover, the conditions at these high altitudes, combined with the very resinous nature of the bristlecone pine wood, meant that there were many dead trees simply lying on the ground surface. Conditions are very dry, with almost no ground cover – the bristlecones grow out of the rock scree. At these altitudes the high level of ultraviolet light inhibits most decay organisms. The end result is that all around the living trees are ancient specimens, some still standing, others fallen, which have been dead for hundreds, sometimes thousands, of years. Apart from their great age, one of the strangest things about these trees is their shape. They start out fairly bushy with small circular trunks, but as they get older and are subjected to damage of various sorts they tend to lose much of their bark, often ending up as mostly dead wood with just a thin strip of bark. Since it is the cambium below that strip of bark which forms the new ring each year, they grow into an elongated rectangular shape. Each bristlecone pine growth ring is about 0.25 mm.

Obviously dendrochronologists do not want to harm these incredible trees, so felling is out of the question. However, one great advantage of their rectangular shape is that the ring patterns can be extracted without killing the trees; a hollow borer is drilled in from either the centre or the bark end and a core extracted with all the rings running across it. Dendrochronologists have aged still-living specimens up to 4900 years; the location of the oldest tree is kept secret to stop souvenir-hunters taking bits home for the trophy wall. Unfortunately, human folly knows no bounds and in the tree-ring laboratory they have a black museum which includes a slice from one of the oldest trees in the world. This tree was growing on a scree slope and a geomorphologist cut it down to get a minimum age for the scree – he felled a living thing which was almost 5,000 years old just to see how old it was! What can one say? The only hope is that if there is a Hell, he'll have a long time to think about he issue. But then he would be spending his time with the Tasmanian who felled the tallest tree in the world just to measure how tall it had been!

The work of building a bristlecone pine chronology, started by Schulman, was taken up by Wes Ferguson. By overlapping the patterns from the living trees to older and older dead specimens, the year-by-year chronology was eventually pushed back more than 8000 years. There were some problems; for example, these trees are so stressed that they can miss rings. Thus the patterns from many trees had to be compared to construct the complete chronology. This is probably the point to bring in the factor which makes dendrochronology such a wonderful technique. The process of comparing the growth patterns from tree to tree to tree, ironing out problems, and building a chronology which is a perfect annual calendar, is really a process of *replication*. But dendrochronology is not just limited to individuals checking their own work. Often completely independent workers build tree-ring chronologies in the same or neighbouring regions. Then these independent chronologies can be compared to see if the patterns are consistent through time or if they go out of phase, allowing a still higher level of replication. Consistently, dedicated dendrochronologists get the same answer when they compare independent chronologies.

Douglass had recognized the importance of replication and had checked his Southwestern pine chronology against the Californian sequoia chronology. Similarly in the Tucson laboratory, Val LaMarche and Tom Harlan built a bristlecone chronology high up at the extreme tree-line: this matched perfectly with the Schulman–Ferguson chronology for more than 4500 years. LaMarche reckoned that the trees right at the tree line would be the most sensitive to changes in temperature through time and assumed that long-term changes in mean ring width were basically a record of long-term changes in temperature. Thus, these chronologies were built purely for their potential use in environmental reconstruction. Equally, the very existence of the long bristlecone chronologies meant that Ferguson could supply precisely-dated samples of wood for the purpose of calibrating the radiocarbon timescale. The applications just continued to grow. In the 1920s, Douglass embarked on dendrochronology to study solar cycles, but his work on cycles never achieved any significant result. However, his successors built very long chronologies which were used to provide calibration curves for radiocarbon. Radiocarbon is produced in the upper atmosphere by incoming cosmic radiation. The amount of cosmic radiation reaching the earth is modulated by solar activity – appearing as 'wiggles' in the calibration curve. By studying the calibration wiggles solar physicists were able to detect various solar cycles, including those around 200 years and 2400 years. Douglass got his cycles in the end.

It is possible to see in the development of the American work how the progression from interest in solar cycles to radiocarbon calibration represents the maturing of the subject. As the potential of dendrochronology has become widely recognized it has spread through many applications, as well as many geographical areas. LaMarche and other American workers moved the work into the southern hemisphere, where it has taken firm root. The remainder of this chapter will look briefly at Europe – in many ways the course of dendrochronology in Europe replicates what had taken place in America.

EUROPE

In Europe dendrochronology was initially rather more limited. Most early tree-ring work related to the study of living pines from a forestry perspective and only Bruno Huber in Germany in the 1930s made any determined attempt to conduct research after the American fashion, though this effort was frustrated by World War II. However, by the mid-1960s Huber, along with Veronica Giertz, had produced a 1000-year central German oak chronology, while Ernst Hollstein, working at Trier to the north-west, had built another which was almost identical. This chronology-building had been relatively straightforward: both had access to long-lived modern oaks and Germany was full of well-dated medieval buildings with many available oak timbers. Chronologies back to AD 832 and AD 822 were produced. Of the two operations, only Hollstein collected substantially older timbers from archaeological contexts, putting together what would eventually be a 2700-year oak chronology.

It was only in the late 1960s with the arrival of computing power that the European oak work could really begin in earnest. Huber and Hollstein had been working in a fairly safe tree-ring environment; they knew the felling dates of their living trees and they had excellent documentary evidence for the likely dates of their building timbers. They were searching for overlaps between ring patterns within very narrow time ranges – they could not go very far wrong. To build very long oak chronologies, with lots of consecutive overlaps, using many timbers of unknown age, computers are necessary to run the correlation programs which are needed to check the similarity of the patterns at every possible position of overlap. The dendrochronologist then checks the most likely matching positions indicated by the computer, looking all the time for replicated matches as a control. However, it was not just computers that made the difference. In the late 1960s major assemblages of naturally preserved sub-fossil oaks were extracted from peat bogs, fens and river gravels. These are labelled 'sub-fossil' because if they had been left in the ground, eventually after millions of years they would have become fossilised into lignite or coal. The reasons behind the recovery of these ancient trees were socio-economic. Everywhere in northern Europe there were intensive drainage, farming, road-building and extraction operations; thousands of ancient trees were uncovered. Moreover, they were from post-glacial deposits which were all within the last 10,000 years.

The expansion of European universities in the 1960s supplied many young scientists who were hungry for research projects on which to work. So this threefold configuration of computers, ancient trees and scientists produced a spurt of activity on the building of prehistoric chronologies. The European work did not have the advantage of the very long-lived trees like the sequoias or bristlecones; it had to make do with oaks which on average grow for only two or three hundred years (very occasionally specimens with five hundred years' growth are found). However, one great advantage was that oaks were available from many periods, having been widely used by builders in the past; thus the wood appeared commonly in buildings and on archaeological sites as well as in natural contexts. Building a prehistoric chronology, in particular, was rather like putting together a huge jigsaw puzzle – with no picture on the box. Thousands of 'pieces' existed in the form of individual ring patterns but they had to be ordered and cross-matched in time. As it turned out, the jigsaw analogy was not strictly accurate for the prehistoric period. What saved European oak dendrochronology from chaos was the concept of the 'site chronology'. Large groups of oaks, whether from bog contexts or river gravels, tended to represent regenerating populations of trees. Instead of one hundred oaks having one hundred different dates, the tendency was for trees from a site to be broadly contemporary. Thus, even though the individual ring patterns might only be from 150 to 300 years in length, a typical site group might give an overlapping set of ring patterns that would end up as a 500-year chronology, or sometimes a 1000-year chronology. In one extreme case, oaks from one field at Croston Moss in

Lancashire, England, provided a continuous chronology from 3200 BC to 970 BC with just a single gap between 1680 and 1580 BC. European oak dendrochronology was saved ultimately by dealing with site chronologies which were of the order of millennia long; the same order of magnitude as the individual American sequoia and bristlecone patterns.

Two different groups of European workers were able to find all the pieces necessary to complete two versions of the 'jigsaw' in Ireland and Germany in only just over a decade. The Belfast and Göttingen chronologies were in precise synchronization back to 5000 BC – an observation made possible by the stepwise correlations from Irish to English to German chronologies. By the early 1980s, dendrochronologists had constructed chronologies covering the whole of the last 7000 years. Since then German workers have pushed back chronologies to 9000 years, even longer than the bristlecone record. The principal motives for all this chronology construction were basically twofold. In central Germany Bernd Becker wanted to date the many oak trunks which came out of the river gravels. By dating them and noting their positions he could trace the development of the river valleys through the Holocene. In the course of doing this he was able to supply samples to radiocarbon workers who were anxious to calibrate their method (that is, to check it against real dates) and to check if the shape of the original American calibration was correct. This was also the primary reason for the initiation of the Irish tree-ring work. The University in Belfast had its own radiocarbon laboratory, and a plentiful supply of Irish bog oaks; it was thus decided in 1968 to attempt to build a long oak chronology and supply precisely dated samples of oak for recalibration of the radiocarbon timescale.

There would be other bonuses from the chronology-building. If dendrochronologists used timbers from historic buildings or archaeological sites in their chronologies, and dated them, then those dates would be of interest to building historians and archaeologists. The dendrochronologists needed timbers just as much as the building historians and archaeologists needed dates; so a symbiotic relationship built up within these disciplines: exactly what Douglass had found in the 1920s. Unfortunately, once the chronologies were complete the dendrochronologists started to make a commercial charge for the dates and the symbiotic relationship was truncated.

But dating archaeological samples was only one bonus. The other was the potential to extract environmental information from the tree-ring patterns. Year-by-year records of what trees 'thought' of their growing conditions in some ways allow us to investigate a parallel history which has little of the bias present in human history. All we know in detail about the past is basically conditioned by what historians have access to – those things which various humans, for various reasons, over the years, have left as a record. We can divide the last 5000 years into two sections. The 2000 years since the time of Christ, when we know quite a bit about quite a lot of areas, and the 3000 years BC when we know something about a few areas and almost nothing at all about huge swaths of the Old and New Worlds. As we will see in later chapters, there is little certain information and some pretty severe Dark Ages or 'gaps in the record'.

When it comes to recording environmental information, history really does not make a very good job of it at all. Yet historians and ancient historians only can deal with these incomplete records, and, as a consequence, may attribute human causes and motives to effects which may have been environmentally determined. Famines and plagues are undoubtedly mentioned, but seldom is there any attempt, either by the original writers or by historians, to seek the physical causes of such phenomena. In most cases the physical cause will have been remote from the affected population, for example, some distant phenomenon dimming the sun, affecting the climate and causing famines and population dislocation. For the most part such secondary phenomena were not recorded. So deep is the conditioning that the environment is not a significant factor that no attempt is made to understand the causes of famines and plagues which are perceived as 'acts of God'.

To see how this works in practice let us look briefly at the outbreak of bubonic plague in Byzantium, in AD 542, during the reign of the emperor Justinian. John Norwich tells us that the plague began in Egypt. Judith Herrin elaborates by telling us that the same plague arrived in 'Egypt from the Far East'. No question of why it began or why it moved. No hint of any environmental trigger. Yet the same books mention the effects: 'the number of its victims was estimated at 300,000', or the plague 'may have reduced the entire population by as much as a third'. Effects are mentioned, causes are not: the original documents only tell of the effects. Environmental triggers were not mentioned then, or now.

But plagues do not just happen; something *causes* them to break out and spread – some physical cause. Because none is mentioned, it is as if there was no physical cause. This is not just a problem for the historian. More generally, just about everyone is conditioned to think the following: 'If something really significant had happened, surely it would have been recorded'? There are several points about such thinking that are worth exploring. It is assumed that:

- The historical record is more detailed than it actually is – the record from earlier times was never complete and much has been lost or deliberately destroyed.

- Early writers deployed a critical faculty, something which may or may not have been the case – some ancient writers were very observant, but they are probably the exception.

- Conditions were always conducive to the setting down of records – this may or may not have been the case. Witnesses to truly catastrophic events may have been in no position to make a record, having had other priorities such as survival.

- The historical record has not been selectively edited to remove evidence for certain types of phenomena – while that sounds needlessly conspiratorial, as we will see, there are hints of selective editing of evidence relevant to one of the catastrophic events in the very era of the Justinian plague

In addition to these assumptions, for more than a century, in recent times, the idea of environmental determinism has been more or less summarily dismissed. Even today there is still a strong lobby against it. So historians and archaeologists tend not to think in terms of environmental causes for events, even though common sense tells us that there must have been environmental causes in most cases.

By the end of this book, readers will be aware of the traumatic environmental events between AD 536 and 542 which serve to cast a whole new light on the Justinian plague. They will also be aware of the likely physical cause of the outbreak. They will also see that the key information comes from the unbiased tree-ring records. Many will ask the obvious question – why did history miss the answer? More importantly, if the historical record missed out on the causes of the Justininan plague, what else has it missed out? It begins to become apparent that there may be some gaps in our knowledge relating to possible environmental factors on planet Earth.

It is into this situation of quite appalling environmental ignorance that tree-rings, and the information gleaned from their analysis, now begin to intrude. In the next chapter I will look at other uses for the tree-ring chronologies, once compiled. Then we will look at some issues relating to those environmental changes in recent millennia, where either human history has failed to record what went on, or, where historians and archaeologists have, until now, largely chosen to ignore the issue.

CHAPTER 2

◆

SOME EXAMPLES FROM DENDROCHRONOLOGY

We have now looked at how dendrochronology came about and how, and where, some of the first long chronologies were constructed. Apart from their primary use for calibrating the radiocarbon timescale, the most obvious application of these chronologies is in dating timbers as they become available from ancient sources. These sources can be buildings or archaeological sites, art-historical boards – the boards used by medieval artists to support oil paintings – or timber used in sculpture, furniture, or even musical instruments. Naturally preserved timbers from bogs or lakes or river gravels can be dated as well as ship or boat timbers, though of course in this case dating can be more difficult as the timbers may have been removed far from their place of growth. In addition, we should not forget living trees. Worldwide there are now numerous instances of dendrochronologists deducing information from recent ring patterns anchored at the present. Often a pencil-thin core is extracted from the living tree with a suitable hollow borer; in this way the growth pattern can be investigated with little effect on the tree. In this chapter we will look at some examples of these dating activities and show how the very act of dating often throws up new or unexpected information as well as how the accumulation of tree-ring dates allows us to see patterns from the past.

DEDUCING ENVIRONMENTAL INFORMATION FROM LIVING TREES

The aim of dendrochronological activity is to produce absolute calendrical dating. It is not good enough to sample a tree, count the growth rings back in time from the last ring under the bark, and assume that the exact date of each ring has been established. Trees can miss or duplicate rings and problem rings can occur where it is difficult to maintain an accurate ring count. So dendrochronologists measure the ring patterns of numerous samples and painstakingly check that all the sequences are in phase through time. This procedure, called cross-dating, underpins all dendrochronological study, ironing out any problems presented by individual trees and producing an overall master sequence which is calendrically precise, that is, there is one ring for each year and the calendar date of that ring is known. This robust procedure is further checked in most areas by comparing among chronologies to ensure absolute consistency of dating control.

There are now whole grids of living-tree chronologies across northern Europe, western America, northern Russia, etc, which can be interrogated on a year-to-year basis as part of climatological or environmental studies. Only with all trees precisely dated can any sense be made of such macro-scale studies. It is now technically possible to choose a year, or a decade, in the last few centuries and look at tree growth across vast areas in literally hundreds of replicated site chronologies. We can look at the ages of trees, see when forest stands were established, see regeneration phases. We can observe changes in mean tree-ring width, or density, through time. Individual ring patterns can be interrogated looking for phenomena such as 'light rings' – rings of low wood density in conifers associated with cool growing seasons. International studies on light rings show that there is a notable tendency for these to occur in the year of, or the year following, explosive volcanic eruptions which are known to cause cooling through dust and sulphur loading of the atmosphere and stratosphere. Recent studies from northern Canada and northern Russia have shown notable light-ring occurrence in key years such as AD 1601, 1783 and 1816, all volcanic dust-veil years.

In oaks, people are studying a phenomenon called 'small early vessels' or SEVs. Particularly in central and eastern Europe this effect, which shows up as very notably reduced spring vessels at the start of the year's growth, is observed to be associated with severe frosts. It is thus possible to read off the dates of winters exhibiting extreme cold; for example, in northern Europe the intensely cold year AD 1740 shows up not just as extremely narrow growth rings in oak, but is accompanied by SEVs in both Ireland and Germany. SEVs occurring a discrete number of years apart are a regular feature in Baltic timbers and can be used as an aid to dating, for example, the pair of SEVs which occur in a large percentage of trees for the years AD 1437 and 1454 – a bit like Douglass' signature patterns.

Dendrochronologists also regularly use damage scars on trees as a means of tracing anything from earthquakes, floods, rock falls, glacial advances, even hailstorms. When a tree is physically damaged it immediately begins the process of healing over the scars. Where a winter flood or a glacial advance scars a tree, the date of the scarring will often be preserved in the ring pattern in just the same way as the fire scars mentioned previously. Thus the dates of extreme events can be established. Damage does not have to take the form of scarring. Trees pushed over from the vertical will tend to put on reaction wood in an attempt to straighten themselves. Thus the date of the onset of reaction wood is a useful clue to phenomena such as past earth movements and glacier advances.

Human interference can also be recognized. Repeated evidence of branch-lopping, often on a regular cycle, indicates pollarding practices – best seen in France where old oaks show no substantial side branches; their ring patterns end up as an artefact of human behaviour, obscuring any climate signal.

DATING EXERCISES

As chronologies have been completed dendrochronologists have been dating samples from many different contexts. Basically, in any given area where a local chronology exists the ring patterns of samples of the same species can be dated by comparing them with the master chronology and checking for matching at every possible position of overlap. In area after area this procedure works well as long as the samples have long ring records, say 100 growth rings or preferably more. When Ernst Hollstein sampled oak timbers from the cathedral in Trier, Germany, he was able to compare their ring patterns with his completed German oak chronology; he could just as well have used Huber's oak chronology which covers the same time period and looks very similar. Hollstein was able to date many timbers from the cathedral, tracing the history of its construction through the early AD 1040s up to the 1070s. Now you might ask 'if those were the felling dates of the oak timbers, would there have been an interval before they were used; would they have been seasoned?' Hollstein could answer this question too. He went to a whole series of well-dated buildings in Germany – where historical records are often very complete – and showed that the difference between the tree-ring dates for the buildings and their known building dates usually numbered between one to three years. Many other workers have found the same thing, so it is now generally accepted that for buildings seasoning is not a serious problem. There are two pieces of evidence which add to the understanding of the seasoning business. Many oak timbers now found in buildings have distorted *in situ*. Peg-holes, which would have been straight when originally drilled, are now found to be curved, making removal of the pegs very difficult. Similarly, original straight-sawn surfaces on beams now have distinct angles. These observations indicate that the timbers were originally put into the buildings while 'green', that is, unseasoned. I believe this was deliberate on the part of the builders. They knew that the timbers would warp and season *in situ* and this would have the effect of 'tightening' or 'locking' the joints; it is probably this very fact that accounts for the survival of so many ancient timber-framed structures.

We have already seen the widespread survival of timbers in the arid conditions of the American Southwest. In more humid Europe the surviving power of oak timbers can also be remarkable. In standing buildings which have been roofed continuously since they were built, as is common in many

European countries, timbers can survive for up to a thousand years or more. What is more surprising is the discovery of timbers in ancient ruins. Trim Castle is probably the most important Norman castle in Ireland and was known to date to some time between AD 1170 and 1250. Like most medieval buildings in Ireland, with its troubled history, the castle is a ruin with no surviving timbers inside. However, in the course of exterior renovations it was discovered that timbers did survive on the *outside* of the walls. During original building, timber frameworks were built into putlock holes in the walls to assist the builders. As the building rose the protruding ends of the timbers were cut off flush with the walls and quite possibly plastered over. In the 1990s during restoration it was found that the stumps of these timbers survived, exposed to the weather and much visited by nesting birds. Several of the timbers even preserved their sapwood and bark, so that when their ring patterns were cross-dated against the Dublin medieval oak chronology it was possible to see that those timbers were felled in various years between AD 1195 and 1203. Even in Ireland, notorious for its humid climate, these pieces of oak had survived on the outside walls of a castle for 800 years.

Dendrochronologists have dated buildings and their different phases in many countries. They have been equally successful with dating archaeological timbers. Dendrochronologists are called upon to date everything from eighteenth-century shipwrecks to medieval timber-lined pits, right back to Neolithic structures such as trackways, lake dwellings and even the occasional burial chamber. Success depends only on the survival of timbers of the correct species, with long ring records; after that, dating is just the same as for those above-ground timbers from buildings giving dates precise to the year for samples which are thousands of years old. In Britain one of the first, and best, examples is the famous *Sweet Track* from the Somerset Levels, published by Hillam *et al.* Early in the Neolithic, just after agriculture had been introduced to the British Isles, people built an artificial wooden trackway across this very boggy area. They felled a series of old oak trees and cut the trunks into sections; then, exploiting the radial character of oak wood, they split them longitudinally into 'riven oak' planks. From just a few trees the settlers were able to obtain a large number of planks which were laid out as a raised plank walkway across the extensive wetland. Many of the radially split planks ran right out to the underbark surface and when these were dated by the dendrochronologists at Sheffield and Belfast it was found that the trees had last grown in 3807 BC. Unfortunately, Neolithic oak timbers are, so far, very scarce in Britain or Ireland. This becomes clear when we compare our few early dates with the lists of precise dendro-dates from Swiss and German archaeological sites. The third and fourth millennia BC, in central Europe, are now littered with absolute dates, with sufficient available to allow occasional

Dendrochronological dating of the split oak timbers which make up the Sweet Track in Somerset, England, last grew in 3807 BC and were felled either late in 3807 or early in 3806 BC. The track allowed humans to negotiate the inhospitable levels, probably at a time when the surface was relatively dry.

long-distance connections to be glimpsed. For example, there is an abrupt two-year decline in Irish bog pines at 2911–2910 BC which is not recorded in oaks growing in the same area – that deciduous trees were not affected while evergreens were, may imply a winter event. Let us use this as a typical example of what dendrochronology has in store for prehistoric studies.

THE 2911 BC EVENT

This event is interesting as an example of how tree-ring information can draw attention to a point in time in prehistory. Nothing in the original oak chronologies hinted at anything special at this date. Then, when a pine chronology from Garry Bog, Co. Antrim, was being constructed by David Brown, it was discovered that it could be cross-dated with the oak chronology. Once dated, it became clear that there was an abrupt growth reduction in virtually all the pines at 2911 BC. Subsequently the same event showed up in pines from a second site 50 km (30 miles) away. This slightly peculiar, species-specific, event suggested perhaps severe frost, or a winter storm, or acid damage, that defoliated pines but left oaks unscathed. In 1995 one bog oak found at Ballymurphy, Co. Down, some 110 km (70 miles) to the south of Garry Bog, provided a ring pattern which extended from 3016 to 2576 BC. This tree showed a dramatic growth *release* just after 2911 BC. The tree, Q8991, had been growing extremely slowly from 2989 BC, never exceeding 0.4mm in ring width. In 2910 its ring width bottomed out at 0.08mm, thereafter rising rapidly to 0.8mm by 2902; by 2886 it achieved growth of 2.0mm. The release was dramatic, with ring width increasing by a factor of ten in the decade following 2910 BC. A standard explanation for such a release would be the demise of neighbouring trees with a subsequent spurt of growth in a suppressed individual. This additional strand of evidence could support the storm hypothesis although it could be that the release was due to humans felling neighbouring trees. However, the observation serves to reinforce the idea of something going on which adversely affected trees in the north of Ireland at the date 2911–2910 BC.

The event also appears as a distinct growth decline in LaMarche and Harlan's temperature-sensitive bristlecone pine series from Campito, California. So 2911 BC is actually part of a more widespread tree response to some environmental event. But the beauty of those Swiss archaeological dates is well represented by timbers from a Neolithic village at Portalban on the shore of Lake Neuchâtel, reported by Alain Orcel and colleagues. After some building activity on the site in 3085 BC, there is no felling for almost 170 years, until a short episode of construction takes place between 2917 and 2912 BC. This building episode at Lake Neuchâtel, which began at 2917 BC, may well have been truncated by that same 2911 event. You can almost imagine the lake level rising! So these dates really come into their own when we begin to add in other deductions on precisely dated environmental issues from the tree-ring chronologies themselves, just as we saw with the original work in the American Southwest.

As noted, there are now many Neolithic dates from continental Europe and only a few from Britain. In Ireland, wet as it is, there is only one trackway with a tree-ring date even close to the Neolithic and that is the Early Bronze Age Corlea 6, from County Longford, which dates (allowing for missing sapwood) to 2259+/-9 BC. Evidence is definitely thin on the Neolithic. However, more exists for the later Bronze Age. In Ireland the very first prehistoric timber structure to be given a specific date was a rather enigmatic lakeside 'hunting camp' at Cullyhanna, Co. Armagh. This site had been excavated in the 1950s when there had been essentially no dating evidence. It was interesting, therefore, when the site was ultimately dendro-dated to 1526 BC. The date sat in the middle of nowhere and was assumed to be 'random'. However, we had not been dating prehistoric sites very long in Ireland before something interesting emerged. Of the first five oak-bearing prehistoric sites to be dated two fell at almost exactly 95 BC: the ritual 'temple' at Navan Fort, Co. Armagh, the ancient capital of Ulster, and part of 'The Dorsey', a peculiar enclosure which forms part of the linear earthwork which appears to be an ancient boundary-marker known as the Black Pig's Dyke. It is really quite puzzling when one first comes across these landscape divisions. We are now pretty sure that around 150–200 BC one Irish tribal grouping constructed a major linear earthwork which effectively runs across Ireland from Newry to Ballyshannon, separating the 'north' from the 'south'. When people first studied the earthwork they assumed it was copied from Hadrian's Wall, which dates to *c.* 100 AD. It was thought that the sophisticated Romans brought in the idea of marking tribal boundaries with linear earthworks and hence the Black Pig's Dyke should be 100 AD or even later. Now we know the earthwork dates some 250–300 years further back in time, putting it much more in line with other European linear earthworks. For example, in Spain archaeologists think that they have found remains of a wall of *c.* 140 BC which the Celtiberians built to defend the town of Numantia against the Romans. The most impressive linear 'earthwork' on Earth, designed specifically to keep people out, was, of course, the Great Wall of China, consolidated by the emperor Shih Huang-ti (died 210 BC). This boundary-marker, constructed by linking the earlier walls of states along the northern frontier, runs for some 2400 km (1500 miles) along the edge of the Mongolian plateau. Is it just coincidence that within a space of less than a century the idea of building defensive dividing walls crops up from China in the East to Spain and Ireland in the West? Could word of the Great Wall have filtered through to the West?

To return to Ireland, of the first five prehistoric sites dated by dendrochronology, two were initially at around 95 BC, another was around 970 BC (planks associated with a dug-out boat at an Irish lake dwelling) and two were around 1500 BC, namely Cullyhanna at 1526 and Imeroo, Co. Fermanagh, another possible lake-edge dwelling, at 1478+/-9 BC. That distribution, given the large span of time which we had to play with, did not look random. And so it was to prove. Ten years later we could report dates for some 25 prehistoric sites and structures which have produced oak timbers. Of these 25, no less than seven fall between 1526 and 1475 BC, ten between 980 and 880 BC and five between 150 and 95 BC. Yet again dendrochronology surprises; we would have expected oak-bearing sites to be spread uniformly through time, but that is exactly what we do not find. In fact we find a distribution so non-random that we need to explain somehow what was taking place. The most likely explanation seems to relate to environmental conditions. These clusters point to periods when humans were felling oaks and putting them into wet contexts where they survived for us to find them. However, in a wet country, just putting oaks into wet places would be close to random. What happens when short *dry* episodes occur in an otherwise wet environment? In a drying-out situation people would find new areas open to them, for example, if lake levels drop, new lake margins become available; if bogs start to dry out they become more accessible. It looks as if these clusters of oak-bearing sites actually tell us when there were periods of relatively dry conditions. We can hypothesize that around 1500 BC, around the tenth century BC, and around the second century BC it got drier. How can this be confirmed? Malcolm Grant, who studied trees and pollen records from bogs in central England, identified a colonization by pine just around 1500 BC. Pine likes dry conditions to colonize bog surfaces, so it looks as though in this case 'dry' may be the answer. Parallel German work carried out by Andre Billamboz dates a bog settlement called Siedlung Forschner in the Federsee marsh. An intensive series of building dates span 1511–1480 BC, essentially duplicating the dates of the *c.* 1500 BC cluster in Ireland: virtual proof of a widespread drying event across northern Europe at that time

Just as with the droughts in the American Southwest, even a preliminary excursion into prehistoric tree-ring dating leads us rapidly into environmental issues. Environmental factors are invoked to explain the observed date clusters. Historians and archaeologists simply have not been taking sufficient account of environmental change in human affairs. The reasons for this are quite simple: until recently there was very little environmental information, and, until we can accurately date human activity and environmental change it is impossible to see the relationships. Once we can date these things the relationship with environmental change starts to become evident.

RELATIONSHIPS

One of our best-dated prehistoric Irish sites is the major Iron Age trackway, Corlea 1, from Corlea, Co. Longford, excavated by Barry Raftery. This massive roadway is approximately 3 m (10 ft) wide and 2 km (1.2 miles) long and is made up of split oak logs laid side by side on top of longitudinal poles and pegged into position. By sampling especially for complete timbers with bark surfaces it was possible to establish that, within the limits of the method (that is, allowing in some cases for damaged sapwood), the track was built from timbers which last grew in 148 BC and were felled either late in 148 or early in 147. While the track is testimony to the building exercises being undertaken in Ireland in the second century BC, it raises as many questions as it answers. Where was it leading to and where was it coming from? Was it, as Richard Warner has suggested, part of a major route way from Uisnead, the ancient navel or 'centre' of Ireland to Rathcroghan, the ancient capital of Connaught, in the West? Was the track actually heading towards the fording point on the Shannon River, north of Lough Ree? Unfortunately any discussion of archaeological sites 'lining up' raises a chorus of 'Oh no, ley lines!' from most archaeologists. However, unlike most proposed ley lines, which tend to have sites of different dates from medieval cathedrals to Dark Age wells to Neolithic barrows all supposedly lined up across the countryside, Uisnead, Corlea and Rathcroghan all have definite Iron Age affinities. Moreover, they do all lie on a single line.

But it was not just this alignment that caught Warner's attention. There are other key Iron Age sites in Ireland which appear to be perfectly aligned. The discovery of the other example was actually prompted by information in the Irish tale *Mesca Uladh*, the 'Drunkenness of the Ulstermen'. A line from Temhair (Tara), the ancient capital of Ireland, to Dun da Beann, an important archaeological site close to the north coast, runs through the enclosure of Emain Macha (Navan) the ancient Iron Age capital of Ulster. We have a dendro-date of 95 BC for a major buried temple on Emain Macha. In this case, at least two of the three aligned sites have definite Iron Age associations. According to Warner, Emain Macha lies 79.9 km (49.6 miles) from Temhair and 80.2 km (49.8 miles) from Dun da Beann – exactly half way! Even if one does not believe in ley lines one has to admit that this is a strange, equi-spaced, linear configuration.

Taken together, these alignments hint at a fairly massive landscape reorganization by Iron Age kings or chieftains. Who were these people? Were they part of the indigenous Iron Age peoples of the island or were they an invading elite? From the dendrochronological dating we know that Corlea was built in 148–147 BC, and that some timbers from the northern section of

The ritual 'temple' at Navan Fort - Emain Macha, the ancient capital of Ulster. This symbolic structure contained a huge central oak post which last grew in 95 BC and was felled either late in 95 or early in 94 BC.

The Dorsey – that defensive earthwork just to the south of Navan (Emain Macha), mentioned above – date to around 150 BC. We could ask if in fact this other routeway from Tara, the capital of all Ireland, to Navan, the capital of Ulster, had to pass through a defended 'gate' in the Black Pig's Dyke on the way? A picture could be appearing out of the prehistoric mist if only we could find datable timbers at Tara or Rathcroghan or Dun da Beann.

However, just when it looks as though we have completed the Navan–Dorsey–Corlea story, two further strands of evidence appear from disparate sources. First, in one of the ancient Irish mythological tales – the 'Wooing of Etaín' – there is a description of a magnificent trackway built by a particular Irish king, Eochaid Airem, whose capital was not that far from County Longford. In the way of all the Irish king lists, this king's reign is dated 'from the beginning of the world'. These dates have been interpreted by

Richard Warner and it seems that the king who built the great track is supposed to have reigned 'between *AM* 5058 and 5084, equivalent to 142–116 BC', that is, around 140 BC! Is it possible that there is even a surviving memory of the building of the Corlea track from prehistory? The real value of this question lies in turning it around. If there was a relationship between this dendro-dated track and the mythological reference then perhaps there is some factual basis to some of the Irish mythological tales – this is not to suggest that they are all true, just to pose the question whether some of them may contain a kernel of truth.

There are other Corlea-type trackways in Saxony, in Germany, where archaeologists have excavated roads which are almost identical in scale and construction to the Irish examples. The great surprise is in the dates; one dates to the range 190–170 BC, another 135–129 BC – actually bracketing the date of Corlea. People in Ireland and Germany were building the same style of massive trackways at essentially the same time. Was there any connection between these peoples?

It may be hard to imagine that there would have been contacts over long distances in the distant past. It is easy to forget that people had very adequate boats; that Mediterranean traders and possibly even geographers were travelling around the coasts of Europe. Only a century after the trackways were constructed Caesar arrived on the shores of Britain with a massive invasion fleet. People, armies and navies were on the move in the second century BC; we shouldn't be surprised if there were contacts between tribal groupings in Ireland and Germany. Barry Raftery has pointed out that the name of the seafaring tribe which occupied the area in Lower Saxony where the tracks were found are called the Cauci. In Ireland, on Ptolemy's famous map, there is also a tribe bearing the same name. In addition, in both areas there are neighbouring tribes called the Menapii. We should not underestimate people in the past, nor the scope of their activities.

In some cases the dendro-dates support existing history, in others they call conventional history into question. Take a recent example from Roman Britain. For several years Cathy Groves worked on oak timbers from the important Roman town of Carlisle. Conventional wisdom, based mainly on the writings of Tacitus, had suggested that the first fort at Carlisle was constructed in AD 79. This date was backed up by coin and pottery evidence, but this type of evidence is not really capable of dating right down to a year; it was more a question of the coin and pottery evidence being 'not inconsistent' with a date of AD 79. Grove's tree-ring dates changed all that abruptly. Using timbers with complete sapwood she discovered that the first wooden fort was constructed either late in AD 72 or early in AD 73 with alterations and additions right through to AD 82 followed by a major

The massive oak roadway across Corlea Bog, Co. Longford, Ireland, which dates to 148 BC. Richard Warner has suggested that this is the same roadway which is referred to in the ancient story the 'Wooing of Etaín'.

rebuilding in AD 83–5. This latter episode apparently coincides with a major reorganisation within the Roman Empire. In a separate exercise the ramparts were found to have been constructed originally in AD 72–3 and repaired in AD 84–5. So Tacitus may not have been correct in his dating of the foundation of Carlisle. As Jennifer Hillam has written of this exercise:

[the dates] also confirm that the writings of Tacitus are not always reliable. His date of AD 79 coincides with the time when his father-in-law Agricola was governor of Britain whereas it was in fact founded under Petillius Cerialis six or seven years earlier. It had long been suspected that Tacitus was economical with the truth so as to improve the image of Agricola.

Ancient writers are not always trustworthy simply because they may have had their own agenda. Sometimes they record the facts, but sometimes they get things wrong, or make it up as they go along – they certainly leave things out. However, we should not be too hard on history and historians. The dendrochronologist Ernst Hollstein came unstuck when he allowed the historical date for the Cologne bridge to influence his placement of the relevant tree-ring series. The result was that for some time his tree-ring chronology was wrongly dated by 26 years. As the first person in Europe to build a chronology across the Roman period he was out on a limb. Hollstein's mistake meant that the Roman section of his chronology was all *too old* by 26 years. This in turn meant that timber dates from sites with 'known' historical dates did not make sense. In a classic example, he dated one definite Roman structure at Cologne to 24 BC; a full decade before the Romans had even arrived in the area. The German Roman scholar Baatz was quick to pick up on this blatant error and suggest that Hollstein's chronology was too old by 'about 30 years'. In fact shortly afterwards Bernd Becker used his independent oak chronology to show that Hollstein's error was exactly 26 years.

To redress the balance, a good example of highly refined Roman dating has been provided by Burghart Schmidt. In the course of dating sites in Germany, Schmidt came across timbers from a Roman legionary fort historically dated to 11 BC. Within two years of the legion moving into the area the soldiers were massacred and the forts destroyed. There was no question of later phases or timber re-use on a site like this, a narrow Roman excursion into hostile territory ending in failure. As confirmed by tree-rings the timbers had indeed been felled in 11 BC. We already knew that the tree-ring chronologies were correct because of the levels of independent replication: even if the forts had given felling dates at odds with the history, it would have been the history in this case which was inaccurate. It is the fact that the dendrochronology is an independent method which gives it the power to check history.

ADDITIONAL APPLICATIONS OF TREE-RING DATING

We have looked at several applications of direct tree-ring dating as applied to houses and archaeological sites, but it is possible to date anything from panel paintings to violins. Furniture made with oak panels can be dated as can paintings from the Middle Ages. It was common practice in the days of artists like Raphael or Holbein to paint on the prepared surfaces of wooden boards. Raphael painted on lime panels which came from trees so fast-growing that the rings are hugely wide and very few in number; basically there is not enough pattern to date them. However, in Northern Europe oak was the preferred wood and as it splits radially, as noted with the Sweet Track, the panels usually contain almost the whole ring pattern of the parent tree. Since the late 1960s dendrochronologists have been building up art-historical chronologies by measuring the edges of panels. The method worked remarkably well for paintings from England and the Netherlands and soon two closely matching chronologies had been built, in Oxford and in Hamburg. However, there was a snag. It turned out that although these chronologies matched each other they did not match anything else. The art-historical oak chronology built in England did not match any other British or Irish oak chronologies, while the art-historical chronology from the Netherlands did not match any of the established German chronologies. It turned out that the bulk of the wood panels used by artists in England and Flanders was all imported from the Eastern Baltic. This had been suspected for some time on the basis of historical records about the Hanseatic League, but was not proven until Thomas Wazny built a Polish chronology, and it was discovered that the 'English' and 'Flemish' chronologies actually matched directly to Poland.

Even before Wazny's chronology was available, we had found several quite good correlations pointing to the art-historical chronologies dating to the key reference date AD 1550. When we compared the art-historical chronologies against everything in Europe at this new reference position we noticed that the correlations got steadily higher from the British Isles as one moved east; the highest correlation being for Delorme's German chronology. The correlation against Polish timbers was even higher and we are now pretty sure that the art-historical timbers actually came from Lithuania. The outcome of the exercise is that art-historical oak panels are now dated on a fairly regular basis. However, all anyone can do is date the panels. No dendrochronologist can tell who painted on them or when. Care needs to be taken when attempting to authenticate panel paintings by dating them – you can date the panel but not the painting. The method only gives definitive authentication results when those results are negative; obviously if the tree was still alive when the artist died he or she cannot possibly have painted on a panel from that tree and the painting is a copy or a fake.

Small, high-quality objects like carvings, pictures and furniture are inherently portable: this is very obvious in the case of musical instruments. Peter Klein, among others, has established that violins can be dated (if you can date violins you can date anything). For places like England or Ireland violin wood had to be imported in the first instance and after manufacture, musical instruments could find their way around the globe. Despite this, it is becoming clear that dendrochronological links can be found between different makers who shared timber sources.

These examples of the past movement of timbers open up the prospect of studying trade. This was difficult in the early days simply because there were too few available regional chronologies. Now most laboratories have whole ranges of chronologies in their archives making it possible to compare the ring patterns of portable timbers against, for example, 'every chronology in northern Europe'. Frequently the results show steadily increasing correlation values as one approaches the source area. Good examples include the location of the source of oak barrels at the mouth of the Rhine; the barrels were made from oaks several hundred kilometres upriver and shipped down

The Vejby ship found off the coast of North Zealand, Denmark, in 1976 has been dated by dendrochronology to 1372. The source of the oak timbers could be narrowed to the Danzig Region.

full of wine; once obsolete they were buried in the ground to act as wells. Longer-distance travel was uncovered when it was found that one of the famous Viking blockships from Roskilde fjord in Denmark had actually been built of wood which had grown close to Dublin in Ireland. Niels Bonde had been unsuccessful when trying to date the ring patterns of the ship's planks against various Scandinavian and German chronologies. Eventually it was pointed out that the ship's construction had British–Irish characteristics. Bonde examined some published Irish chronologies for the Viking period and immediately found excellent cross-dating around AD 1060 against the Dublin chronology. Subsequent analysis against other local Irish chronologies showed that this was the highest correlation, thus allowing an attribution of the ship to Dublin itself.

Bonde and Crumlin-Pedersen have some of the best examples of ship dating in the world. They have dated boat burials, establishing how old the boats were when they were put into the ground with their dead owners by separately dating the timbers of the burial chambers, which were erected within the ships themselves. They have also dated shipwrecks and discovered, among others, one striking example: a north European trading vessel known as a cog. This trader, the Vejby ship found on the coast of North Zealand in Denmark, was oak-built and the trees used in its construction were felled between AD 1369 and 1372. The best match of the ring patterns against north European master chronologies indicated that the timbers had originated in the coastal region of Poland. In addition, a hoard of English and German gold coins was recovered from the wreck. On numismatic grounds it was argued that the wreck had to belong to the period 'after 1369' and most probably to the interval between 1370 and 1375. This very narrow window of time then allowed a search of historical documents relating to ships lost at sea. A cog was discovered to have foundered in the Denmark Sound in 1377 carrying cloth, oil, rice and almonds from Flanders to the Baltic; maybe even the same cog.

OTHER TYPES OF INFORMATION FROM DATING

As more dates become available, we can begin to see patterns within the dates we produce. I noted above the clusters of Bronze Age and Iron Age activity starting to show up in Ireland. When Hollstein published the volume of his life's work in 1980, he accumulated all his dated buildings through time. His distribution of felling dates shows the clear building pause in continental Europe immediately after the arrival of the Black Death in 1347. He effectively found no buildings which dated between AD 1347 and 1440, and one has to assume that when the population is sharply reduced there is less pressure for new buildings. There was also related information from Ireland

and Britain. Great difficulty had been experienced when building the Irish chronology because of a notable regeneration of oaks in most areas immediately after AD 1350. It is now clear that this regeneration was due to a reduction of human pressure as the population declined, allowing some land to go back to forest. When first noted, it was assumed that this regeneration meant that trees colonized abandoned land. Now it seems more likely that it was actually due to previously managed woodland, such as coppice, being abandoned as there were not enough people to tend the woods. We now know that the Black Death also appears in Greece where a pattern broadly similar to Hollstein's hiatus has been observed. When these three different observations are considered together it is clear that the Black Death left a discernible imprint on the dendrochronological history of Europe; even without the historical record we could have suggested a pandemic as a likely cause. The Irish example of regeneration after AD 1350 shows that dendrochronologists do not just date the last rings in a tree, but all of them; they can date when the tree starts to grow as well as when it dies. Thus by looking at the clusters of start dates and tree ages, it is also possible to look for management practices and to work out some aspects of woodland history.

Dendrochronology's progress can be measured in the number of dates produced and the emergence of patterns. As Douglass first discovered, dendro-dating rapidly introduces an environmental dimension into the dating picture. There is probably no way back, but, as we will see, there are some surprising ways forward.

CHAPTER 3

◆

VOLCANOES AND TREE-RINGS

BACKGROUND

In the previous chapters we have been looking at the direct dating applications of tree-rings. The method is based on matching up the long patterns of wide and narrow growth rings – the 'good' and 'bad' years – and we have already seen how some of the 'bad' information can be related to environmental factors such as drought or cold. Some trees can record truly notable effects of cold induced by volcanic eruptions, for example, many northern pine species exhibit so-called 'light rings' at or just after big explosive eruptions. These rings are called 'light' because the density of the summer wood is reduced due to unusually cold conditions during the growing season. Good examples of such rings occur in the years of known volcanoes such as Laki in AD 1783, and Tambora in 1815. In the Irish oak work it had been noticed very early on, while we were working with living oaks, that the growth rings for AD 1816 and 1817 were always narrow and this could be attributed to the widespread cold conditions in this so-called 'year without a summer'. The cause of the reduced growth appears to be well explained when one reads the Irish weather records for 1816:

In 1816, the spring was unusually late; the summer and autumn excessively wet and cloudy ... There were 142 wet days, principally in the summer and autumnal months. The mean temperature of the spring summer and autumn was three and a-half degrees below that of the preceding year ...

However, in some ways this is jumping the gun; when this reduced growth–volcano relationship was first noticed, we had no idea that environmentally effective volcanoes would prove to be so important. The first good evidence for volcanic effects in tree-rings was discovered by Val LaMarche. In the early 1970s Val LaMarche and Tom Harlan at Tucson produced that upper tree-line bristlecone chronology back to 3435 BC, using material from Campito Mountain in the southern part of the White Mountains of California. (See pp25) LaMarche noted that in the long, sensitive, bristlecone records there were some growth rings which exhibited

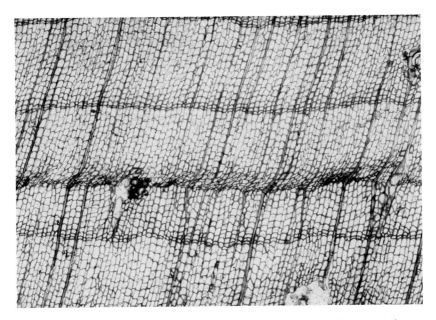

A bristlecone pine ring exhibiting frost damage in 1627 BC as first pointed out by LaMarche and Hirschboeck. Their original observation gave rise to much of the story in this book.

clear frost damage; the cellular structure in these rings having been disrupted by the freezing of the liquid in the cells. It was apparent that in these high-altitude trees the frost rings were caused by anomalously low temperatures during the growing season. There was widespread occurrence of frost damage in the growth rings for AD 1884, 1912 and 1965: these years were in or just after the dates of the large explosive eruptions of Krakatoa (1883), Katmai (1912) and Agung (1963). LaMarche had good grounds for believing that some of his trees were recording the climatic effects of at least some large volcanic eruptions. Large explosive volcanic eruptions inject ash and chemicals high into the atmosphere, which is divided into zones. The lowest 14 km (9 miles) is called the troposphere; the zone above the troposphere is called the stratosphere. Large explosive volcanic eruptions inject their debris into the stratosphere. The fast winds in the stratosphere spread the debris around the globe. It is not known just how high an eruption column can go but heights of about 50 km (30 miles) and even as much as 80 km (50 miles) have been proposed. The essential thing about putting debris into the stratosphere is that it tends to stay up for quite a long time.

After a big explosive volcanic eruption the Earth is 'veiled' by a layer of fine debris made up of dust and tiny droplets of sulphuric acid, as well as ice crystals, circulating in the stratosphere. The overall effect of this 'dust veil' is to reflect away sunlight and cause the Earth's surface to cool. This has been well observed by satellite observation of recent eruptions such as Pinatubo in 1991, though one should stress that Pinatubo was not all that big an eruption in terms of output. The cooling effects around the globe are not uniform – some areas are more severely affected than others. In the case of LaMarche's high-altitude trees, after large volcanic eruptions, freezing winds blow down the Rockies from the North and chill the bristlecone pines during the growing season resulting in the appearance of frost rings.

Although LaMarche published a paper on frost rings as early as 1970, his most important discovery was not published until 1984. In the meantime another important record of past volcanic activity was appearing: the ice-core record. Underneath the Summit in Greenland is as much as 3000 m (9800 ft) of ice which is essentially an annual record of compressed snowfall. Snow falling each year buries previous layers and eventually compresses them into ice. This process continues for tens, even hundreds, of thousands of years – the Greenland ice-cap contains an enormously long record of past snowfall. Within the layers of ice, stable isotopes, dust and acid, all derived from the atmosphere, provide a record of past variation right down to seasonal resolution. If we were to drill down from the surface and examine a core taken through the ice-cap we could examine the annual layers of compressed snowfall; in many cases the annual banding in the ice is actually visible. Ice-core workers who have drilled into the ice-cap can count back through the layers of compressed snow with almost the same level of accuracy as tree-rings (though not quite as accurately because, of course, snow can melt or blow away or be a bit hard to interpret at times). The ice-core records are an incredibly important source of information about the past and, to put all other methods into perspective, in recent cores ice-core workers can actually see the annual layers for more than 40,000 years.

Volcanoes leave very characteristic signs in this ice record. From time to time the scientists studying the cores identify distinct layers of acid, principally sulphuric. These acid layers are the result of the sulphur emitted in large eruptions; so it is possible to identify and date big ancient volcanoes in the Greenland and other ice records. The first really important ice-core paper, using results from the relatively short, 400 m (1300 ft) Crête core, provided a list of dates for major volcanic eruptions back to the sixth century AD. This record was believed to have dating accuracy to 'within a few years' in 1500 years: the date of the deepest layer in the core was given variously as 548+/-3 or 552+/-3. Other significant dates from Crête included the Laki eruption in Iceland in 1783, significant unknown eruptions in 1601 and 1257–8 and Eldgja, again in Iceland, in 934+/-2; interestingly, the well-known Krakatoa eruption in 1883 would hardly have been picked out in the ice record if it had not been known about historically. However, in ice-cores a mere 1500 years is as nothing. The first very long Greenland core was from Camp Century. This core, about 1400 m (4600 ft) in depth, was of poor quality towards the top, but provided a significant record of compressed snowfall from around the time of Christ, back to more than 100,000 years ago. For the Holocene period the error estimates were of the order of one to two per cent, that is, about +/-30 years in 3000 rising to about +/-100 years in 6000, pretty good though not up to replicated tree-ring standards.

The core showed a relatively small number of significant acid layers (often referred to as acidity peaks) in the first six millennia BC. Given the assumption that some volcanoes erupt somewhere around the Earth every year, it was surprising how few large acid layers there were:

          50 +/-30 BC
         210 +/-30 BC
         260 +/-30 BC
        1120 +/-50 BC
        1390 +/-50 BC
        2690 +/-80 BC
        3150 +/-90 BC
        4400 +/-100 BC
        5400 +/-100 BC

From this list of nine large acid layers, the ice-core workers singled out just one volcanic event for its possible archaeological significance: the 1390+/-50 BC layer which they attributed to the Bronze Age eruption of the Aegean volcano Santorini (Thera). This eruption, of extreme archaeological importance, had affected the Minoan civilization, centred on the island of Crete. As late Minoan deposits were buried at the site of Akrotiri on Thera, the eruption marked an important horizon in the history and archaeology of the Aegean. What exactly were the effects of that eruption and exactly *when* did it take place?

The possible ice date for Santorini fell into a somewhat controversial archaeological area. In the middle of the second millennium BC, Santorini was an outpost of the Minoan civilization, with the real power base on Crete 120 km (75 miles) to the south. For many years it had been assumed that the cataclysmic volcanic eruption had put an end to the Minoan civilization. The date of this collapse was generally accepted to have been around 1450 BC – a date arrived at by archaeological linkages to the historical (and apparently well-dated) civilization in Egypt. Two issues provided complexity. First, it had become apparent that the Santorini eruption did not come at the end of the

Schematic illustration of how Santorini may have looked before and after the cataclysmic eruption in the mid-second millennium BC. Although the exact date of the eruption is not yet known for certain, it may have been in 1629/28 BC if it was a contributor to the environmental event which shows up in European oaks in 1628 BC and in the bristlecone pines in 1627 BC.

Minoan period. On various Aegean islands debris from the eruption was found stratified between the Late Minoan 1A (LM1A) and Late Minoan 1B (LM1B) archaeological horizons. On Thera itself, where everything was terminated by the eruption, the deposits ran up only to the end of LM1A; there was no trace of LM1B material culture. This led to debates on the duration of the LM1B period, as this was the time buffer between the date of the eruption and the end of the Minoan period. These debates were further complicated by radiocarbon dates from Akrotiri which were originally seen to suggest a seventeenth-century date for the eruption. The end result was that workers who were happy with a 'low' or 'short' Egyptian chronology were quite happy with the 1390+/-50 BC ice acidity date. In fact, the Danish workers had no hard evidence to link their acid layer to the Santorini eruption; Santorini was just the best-known large eruption in the mid-second millennium.

A general acceptance prevailed that the ice-core date of 1390+/-50 BC for Santorini was correct. However, in 1984, LaMarche published a paper with Kathy Hirschboeck documenting the bristlecone frost-ring story in detail and announcing their observation of a dramatic frost-ring event in 1627 BC. This 1627 BC event was widespread in their trees and was the most severe frost ring in the second millennium. It seemed reasonable for them to suggest that this event might possibly have been due to the Santorini eruption: ' … it offers the intriguing possibility of dating precisely the cataclysmic eruption on Santorini …'.

I have likened this 1984 paper to an intercontinental ballistic missile. Fired from western America it arrived in the world of Aegean archaeology and blew apart all the old certainties about the previous dating, which was conventionally believed to be *c.* 1500 BC, dated against Egypt. The chronology of the Egyptian civilization has been studied in depth – based on lists of kings and the lengths of their reigns. Egyptologists frequently give the impression that the chronology of the New Kingdom in Egypt in the second millennium BC is 'absolute'. It is easy to find references to specific dates, for example, Desroches-Noblecourt, referring to the death of Tutankhamen says 'Amenophis III's last son died some time in January 1343 (BC)'. Thus it appears that a truly historical calendar exists. In fact, back in the second millennium BC the Egyptian historical chronology is *not* absolute. The Tutankhamen source referred to above also states that his nine-year reign may have been from 1369 to 1360, or from 1357 to 1350 or even from 1352/51 to 1344/43. Similarly, the eighteenth-dynasty pharaoh Tuthmosis III can be variously dated from 1504 to 1450 BC through to 1479 to 1425 BC, and so on. There are perpetual arguments about the detail of the Egyptian chronology and it is technically possible for the errors to be even greater than these statements imply.

The role of the scientist should be to provide some fixed points on which to hang the Egyptian chronology. LaMarche and Hirschboeck had set up a very definite and precise target date for Santorini around 1627 or 1628 BC. If they were correct the implications were profound. If Santorini had genuinely erupted in the 1620s BC, then either there was something wrong with the Aegean/Egyptian linkages, or, more devastating if true, there could be something wrong with the Egyptian historical chronology itself. The ongoing debate about the date of the Santorini eruption quickly resolved itself into two extremes – an earlier *c.* 1627 BC 'scientific' camp and a conventional *c.* 1500 BC archaeological camp.

IRISH TREE-RING EVIDENCE

1984, when LaMarche published the 1627 BC event, was also the year when Irish and German workers finally agreed that the European oak chronologies were complete back to 5000 BC. It was also the year the independent Göttingen chronology was announced by Axel Delorme and Hubert Leuschner. This chronology allowed the definitive replication of the chronologies for the last 7000 years. Thus, the time was right for the 1627 BC announcement: with the oak chronologies replicated it was possible to look with confidence at the oak growth rings for any year in the last seven millennia. In Belfast we could look at all the individual Irish trees spanning any given date and see what they 'thought' of conditions. Having seen the frost-ring article, the 1627 BC date and the resulting archaeological controversy (when the well-respected Aegean archaeologist, Peter Warren, sought to play down the bristlecone frost-ring evidence) it seemed appropriate to check the Irish trees covering the seventeenth century BC. Would we see a narrow ring in 1627 BC in Irish oaks? Or was the bristlecone frost ring just a local effect? It was impossible to predict what the Irish oaks might show (or not show).

What we found was interesting. Some of the Irish trees had narrow bands of rings in the 1620s BC, though not specifically in 1627 BC. Some exhibited colour changes and measurement difficulties where the rings became impossibly narrow. Obviously the Irish bog oaks had been affected by something in the 1620s BC – LaMarche's 1627 BC event was not just local to California. However, colleagues thought that the narrow rings might just be coincidence – they are not uncommon and the ring width in any year picked at random would have a 50 per cent chance of tending to narrowness. While such arguments were cautionary, the evidence was impressive enough to press on. Also, narrow bands of rings had been found in several German chronologies in the 1620s BC. The widespread character of the effects, starting in 1628 BC, seemed sufficiently significant to proceed with the study.

In order to satisfy the doubts of some colleagues, I was interested in trying to quantify the effect in some way. Eventually, what separated out this event was not just the occurrence of narrow rings, but the occurrence of *narrowest* rings. Several of the Irish trees, from different bog sites, showed their narrowest growth rings in the 1620s BC. Many things can adversely affect growth in an oak, for example, it could be cold, or physical damage, or insect attack. For several trees to show their worst growth at the same time had to be significant. Furthermore, this was an easy phenomenon to quantify – search each tree-ring record, pick out the date or dates of the narrowest rings, then sum these through time, looking for clusters. In the many hundreds of precisely dated bog oaks, how often would we get a 'narrowest ring' event?

The answer turned out to be that narrowest-ring events did not occur very often. There turned out to be only a handful of occasions between 5000 BC and 1000 AD where as many bog oaks from different locations showed narrowest rings as in the 1620s BC. There was an event in the 1140s and 1150s BC which was possibly even more impressive than that in the 1620s. Other events occurred at 2345 BC, in the 3190s BC, 4370s BC and coming forward in time others at 207 BC and AD 540. This list had to be astonishing; several of the dates from the tree-rings fell within the dating errors of some of the large Greenland acid layers mentioned previously. Clearly there had to be

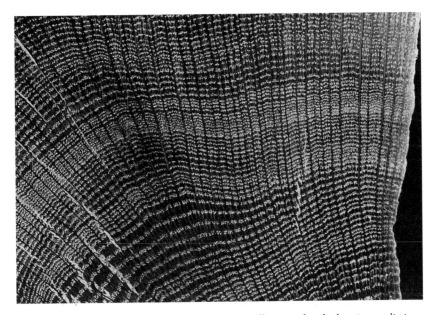

Cross section of a single bog oak from Sentry Hill, N. Ireland, showing a distinct band of seven narrow rings beginning in 1628 BC.

a story in these coincidences, the most obvious being that the Irish trees were showing the detrimental effects of large explosive volcanic eruptions!

Readers can assess for themselves whether there is any significance in the following observation – that when investigating Irish oaks to find support for one bristlecone frost-ring date, we turn up another series of dates for very poor growth conditions, which coincide, within the dating ranges of the ice acidity layers, with a list of volcanic acid layers (Hammer's 210+/-30 BC; 1120+/-50 BC; 3150+/-90 BC; 4400+/-100 BC). Logic suggests that this is a highly significant finding and that the extreme poor-growth events in the Irish oaks must be due to the same dust-veils which left the acid layers in Greenland. Claus Hammer and the other Danish ice-core workers had also footnoted a large acid layer at AD 540+/-10, again coincident with one of the narrowest rings events.

We could provisionally name a couple of these events. For the 1627 BC event LaMarche and Hirschboeck had already *suggested* Santorini. The Danes had suggested that their 1120+/-50 BC event might be the Hekla 3 eruption in Iceland. No one could prove that these volcanoes were specifically involved, but they served as a starting-point for discussion purposes. Vulcanologists normally use radiocarbon to date eruptions – for example, the reason why the 1159 BC event might involve Hekla 3 is because radiocarbon dates had been

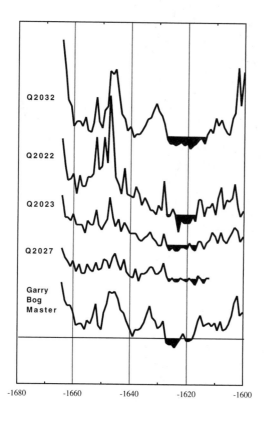

Q2032

Q2022

Q2023

Q2027

Garry
Bog
Master

-1680   -1660   -1640   -1620   -1600

Date BC

The original oak ring patterns from Garry Bog, N. Ireland, which exhibited narrowest rings in the 1620s BC. The Garry Bog master chronology contains the ring patterns of nine trees. The low points in the growth curves are highlighted for clarity.

obtained for peat in Iceland buried by that eruption; the suggested date range, after the radiocarbon date has been calibrated, is something like 1300–1000 CalBC. However, such a wide range does not prove that Hekla 3 really caused the events in the tree-ring patterns. It does suggest a possible eruption that might have been involved; the real culprit could be somewhere on the other side of the world and may not even be known – there could even be more than one culprit. A general principle must be stated: most ancient volcanoes cannot be related to their effects because they are too poorly dated. All we can do at the minute is make loose suggestions about which volcano or volcanoes

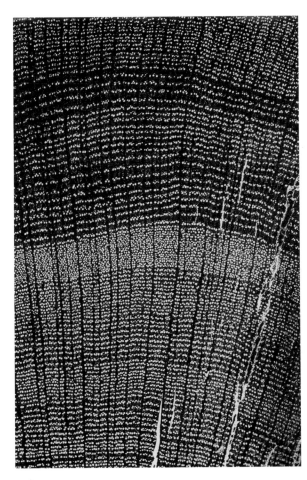

The band of eighteen narrow rings which occurs in many Irish bog oaks between 1159-1141 BC. This sample Q8001 comes from Garry Bog, Ireland.

caused which effects – a very unsatisfactory situation given that humans need to understand what types of volcanoes cause which configuration of catastrophic environmental change.

In the overall scheme of things, relating volcanoes to their effects is fraught with uncertainty. What is significant is the introduction of absolute calendar dates for some notable environmental downturns in recent millennia. This latter point is well exemplified by the 207 BC and AD 540 events, where the tree-ring dates fit extremely well with historical information. This observation in itself suggests that the earlier dates will also fit with effects on human populations when archaeological and ancient historical dating improves. It should be noted that the 207 BC event in the tree-rings stood out as the only really clear narrowest-ring event in the first millennium BC, while the AD 540 event, of which we will hear more later, stood out as the most profound event in the first millennium AD (the most

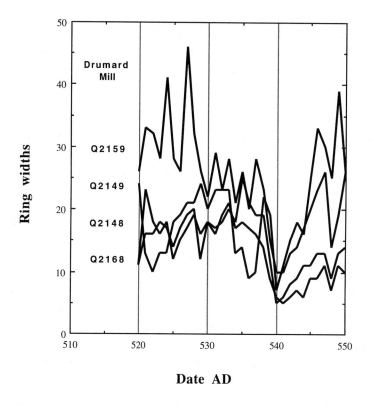

Individual ring patterns from the horizontal mill site at Drumard, N.Ireland, showing the dramatic tree response at AD 540.

recent millennium was left out of the initial narrowest-ring analysis, though this has no effect on the following discussion). Having thus established that we were in possession of a series of dates for potentially important environmental downturns, it is necessary now to digress in order to link in a series of other lines of evidence. We can start by considering two items: a revised ice-core date for the Santorini eruption and historical information from ancient China.

THE 'NEW' ICE-CORE DATE

In 1987, data regarding a new acid layer at 1645+/-20 BC, in the important Dye 3 ice core from Greenland, was published. Claus Hammer and his co-workers suggested that this new date might be Santorini, and this replaced their previously suggested identification of the layer at 1390+/-50 BC in the Camp Century core. From a tree-ring viewpoint this was good news, because all the lines of evidence for a major volcanic event now pointed to the later seventeenth century BC. Since 1645+/-20 BC brackets 1628 BC, this had to be confirmation of the 1628/1627 BC tree-ring date for a major volcano. From the point of view of a dendrochronologist, the evidence of the 1645+/-20 BC acid layer relates directly and specifically to the proposed dust-veil event which shows up in the tree-ring records at 1628 BC. However, one has to point out that the ice-core workers have a slightly different perspective. They regard their ability to identify and count the ice layers as more or less as good as a dendrochronologist dealing with tree-rings. Unfortunately, the count of ice layers in an unreplicated single core *cannot* be as good as a replicated tree-ring record. Ice-core workers as a group know this, hence the inbuilt +/-1–2 per cent errors on their dates. However, individual ice-core workers tend to believe that their record is better than the errors they quote. Unfortunately for them, some layers they see are structures within the compressed snowfall of a single year, while some layers are genuinely missing due to ablation or melting. Even dendrochronologists have problems with missing rings in some species, the difference being that dendrochronologists have lots of ring patterns to work with and can fairly easily get more if necessary; it is rather more difficult to fully replicate ice cores. So when the ice cores give us an acid layer at 1645+/-20 BC, which brackets a tree-ring event with volcanic associations at 1628/27 BC, it is the same event until proven otherwise. Whether or not that volcanic event was Santorini is a continuing debate which we will return to later.

ANCIENT CHINESE RECORDS

Some scholars in America, namely Kevin Pang and colleagues, and David Pankenier, were using references to planetary conjunctions and eclipses in the early histories of China in an attempt to improve the dating of the early records.China represents one of the world's greatest civilizations and its early history is intrinsically important. Around 2000 BC the Xia dynasty begins, continuing to about 1600 BC. The last Xia king, Chieh, is believed to have been corrupt and he was defeated and deposed by T'ang, the first king of the important Shang dynasty. The Shang then ruled until around 1100 BC when their last king, Chòu, is supposed to have become totally corrupt. He was defeated and deposed by King Wu Wang, the first king of the Zhou dynasty. The Zhou then lasted until 221 BC followed by the first emperor of all China, Shih Huang-ti. Shih Huang-ti, who ordered the consolidation of the Great Wall, ruled until 210 BC, with his dynasty lasting until 206 BC. Traditionally, Chinese history is exact to about 841 BC; before that there is some confusion, largely due to the activities of Shih Huang-ti who decided to eradicate all previous history because he saw himself as the first true emperor of all China. He ordered 'all the books to be burned'; although not totally successful he did a very thorough job of robbing China of ancient historical material. Almost the only early documents to survive were the so-called 'Bamboo Annals'. These documents had been buried before Shih Huang-ti came to power and were discovered some centuries after his death. These annals were written on strips of bamboo, one statement per strip, originally held together in a certain order. Unfortunately, when the annals were found the order had been lost to some extent, though Chinese scholars attempted to reconstruct the early history in the correct order. It is pretty certain that they have not got it all right, hence the doubts about the early dynasties.

In an effort to improve the chronological dating of the Xia, Shang and early Zhou dynasties, the Pang and Pankenier camps were attempting to interpret the dates of some of the ancient astronomical references. Years of study of the astronomical records in the Chinese histories had allowed these specialists to suggest dates for highly specific phenomena involving computation of eclipses, alignments, etc. A classic example of what is possible relates to a reference in the texts to a conjunction where Mercury, Venus, Mars, Jupiter and Saturn came very close together in the ancient sky. This is said to have taken place at the start of the Xia dynasty, in the reign of a particular king: 'at the time of [King] Yu the five planets were strung together like a string of beads.'

Using computers to back-compute the planetary orbits, Pang and colleagues settled on a date in late February 1953 BC when Mercury, Venus, Mars, Jupiter and Saturn came within only five degrees of one another (close enough that they could be blocked out by a thumb held at arm's length). This retro-calculation allowed the start of the Xia dynasty to be assigned to the twentieth century BC. (Although this sounds conclusive, and there is no doubt that the planetary conjunction did take place in 1953 BC, there still is some doubt about its assignment to the reign of Yu. History may have been re-written at some stage in the late Zhou dynasty to make it conform to certain beliefs regarding the concept of Mandate of Heaven: see Appendix.)

Another striking example of retro-calculation relates to a phenomenon, recorded several times by the ancient Chinese writers, which they refer to as 'the day dawned twice'. It is fairly evident that this should refer to a dawn solar eclipse, where the sun comes up, is eclipsed and, as the eclipse ends, the sun rises a second time. One such event has been identified as occurring at dawn on 21 April 899 BC. The ancient source refers to it: 'In the first month of spring of the first year in the reign of King Yi of the Western Zhou dynasty the day dawned twice.' Examples such as these form a very refined way of helping to pin down the dates of ancient dynasties.

These apparitions, and others involving both solar and lunar eclipses, have allowed a refining of the date range of the important Shang dynasty.

Pang and his colleagues suggest that the Shang started around 1600 BC and ended in the vicinity of 1100 BC. Pankenier differs quite markedly in his dating, which runs from the mid-sixteenth century to the mid-eleventh century BC (though see comments in the Appendix). However, from the point of view of the current subject-matter, with its suggestion of seventeenth- and twelfth-century BC dust-veils, along with reduced oak growth, Pang and Chou noticed that in the reign of Chieh, the last Xia king, *and* in the reign of Chòu, the last Shang king, there were references which would sit comfortably with dust-veils and their effects. At the time of king Chieh: 'The earth emitted yellow fog ... the sun was dimmed ... three suns appeared ... frosts in July ... the five cereals withered ... therefore famine occurred ...'

These descriptions would coincide well with the idea of a dust-veil blotting out the sun and causing extreme cold, leading to crop failures and ultimately to famine. The question is whether these extreme conditions – which seem to be definitely associated with the collapse of a whole dynasty, (an event which itself seems to be around 1600 BC on the basis of astronomical information) – are associated with the notable environmental downturn which the trees record in 1628 BC. Logic would suggest we are looking at the same event; proof is a more difficult matter. However, there is a similar piece of information in the reign of the last Shang king: 'In the fifth year of Chòu it rained dust at Bo. For 10 days it rained ashes, the rain was gray ... it snowed in July ... frosts killed the five cereals.'

Were these events at the start and end of the Shang dynasty actually associated with our tree-ring–dust-veil events of 1628 BC and 1159 BC? The answer is: probably. This is simply because we know that in the *later* events, those at 207 BC and AD 540, there is evidence which mimics those at the beginning and end of the Shang dynasty. Weisburd, writing about the catastrophic happenings in China at these latter two events, notes that in 208 BC 'the stars were lost from view for three months'. Again there were famines and a dynastic change. At AD 536 there was difficulty seeing the star Canopus and, subsequently, summer frosts followed by severe famines and widespread population losses. Although in this latter case there was no instantaneous dynastic change, there were major setbacks to what had been prosperous northern and southern dynasties. When this information is reviewed it is remarkable that four dates, which drop directly out of an interrogation of tree-ring series, should turn out to relate exactly to two well-dated episodes of human trauma and loosely to two other, less well-dated, such episodes.

This chapter has taken us to the point where we have seen the accumulation of tree-ring and ice-core findings and where some historical information suggests that these volcanic events had widespread effects. We will look in more detail at several of these events in later chapters.

CHAPTER 4

•

THE VOLCANO STORY
CONTINUES TO BUILD

From the moment that the narrowest-ring events in the Irish oaks were observed to reflect the same spacing as the high acidity peaks in the Greenland ice record, it was clear this was a significant correlation. LaMarche and Hirschboeck had introduced the issue of Santorini, while Pang and Chou had brought in the Chinese dimension, lifting the possibilities out of the ordinary. So although several of the other narrowest-ring events, such as 2345 BC, have interesting stories attached to them, from the original list of events there were four that had to be of particular interest: 1628 BC, 1159 BC, 207 BC and AD 540, their exact dates specified by tree-rings. The volcanic acid tells us they are in some way related to volcanic dust-veils (or some other sort of dust-veil which produces large quantities of sulphur). The Chinese historical information, even if not precisely dated in the case of the earlier two events, suggests that these environmental events may well have given rise to, or been seen as a manifestation of, 'the Mandate of Heaven' concept in China. The Chinese believed that an emperor could reign only while he enjoyed the Mandate of Heaven, that is, while he 'looked after his people'; if for any reason he failed to look after their well-being, Heaven would withdraw its Mandate and the emperor and probably his ruling dynasty would be deposed. The close proximity of the end of the Xia dynasty to the 1628 BC event, the end of the Shang dynasty to the 1159 BC event, and indeed the end of the Ch'in dynasty and the start of the Han dynasty to the 207 BC event, suggests that perhaps the effects of these dust-veils were tied up with the Mandate concept. Heaven would have been seen to withdraw its Mandate when the sky darkened, the crops failed and famine ensued bringing death to large numbers of people. The emperor, guilty or not, gets the blame for failing his people. In the aftermath of a calamitous dust-veil event the political upset could easily lead to the deposing of the ruling regime.

Right from the start of these investigations the story seemed so interesting that some popular articles were published asking the question, among others, 'do Irish tree-rings date the Shang dynasty?' These articles in turn evinced information from individuals around the world and this chapter looks at several of these in a little detail. To me they suggest support for the

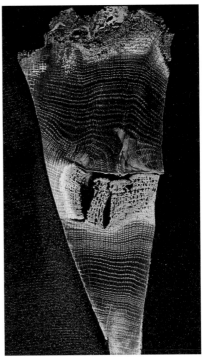

A bog oak section from the fenlands to the south of Lough Neagh, N. Ireland showing the anomalous band of 'diffuse porous' rings associated with the 2354-2345 BC narrowest-ring event. This anomalous physiology is most likely due to raised water levels at the time.

A bog oak section from Ballymacombs More, N. Ireland, which lies beside the northern exit to Lough Neagh, exhibiting dramatic damage with included sapwood in the year 2354 BC.

idea that in the last few millennia major, presumably volcanic, dust-veil events had profound effects on human populations which were recorded in various natural and human archives.

OTHER TREE-RING EVIDENCE 1628 BC

As stated previously, several German oak chronologies showed notable narrow rings following 1628 BC. Then, as prehistoric English bog-oak chronologies was being pieced together, two long chronologies were found both of which started around 3200 BC and ended in the seventeenth century BC. Another bog-oak chronology started around 1580 BC, so there was a distinct gap in the English oak record right across the century, centred on 1628 BC. Quite a lot of random sampling failed to bridge this gap, and it was not until Jennifer Hillam produced a chronology from Hasholme bog that it became possible to see what an English chronology showed in the seventeenth century BC. It transpired that there was an extreme growth reduction starting at exactly 1628 BC. So now the effects of this apparently volcano-related environmental event could be traced, not just from Ireland and Germany, but from England, and, of course, from the American bristlecone pine record.

1159 BC

It quickly became apparent that the worst event in the Irish tree-rings – the mid-twelfth century BC 'catastrophe' – was in fact the least well-substantiated event. There was no supportive bristlecone pine frost-ring evidence. The ice-core date 1120+/-50 BC was too loose to help significantly and the Chinese references at the end of the Shang dynasty were poorly placed at c. 1100 BC. There was, however, one tantalizing piece of information. During the 1980s Peter Kuniholm had been putting together long tree-ring chronologies in Greece and Turkey. One source was the Midas Mound Tumulus at Gordion, Turkey, which provided an enormous 806-year juniper chronology which was known to span the approximate period from the eighth to the sixteenth centuries BC. The dating was arrived at by a combination of archaeological chronology and radiocarbon evidence. Kuniholm noted that in this chronology there was one 20-year period 'where annual growth was abnormally large, accompanied by abnormal fluctuations both up and down'. Given the likely archaeological age of the chronology Kuniholm knew that this anomaly probably fell in the twelfth century BC. As the chronology was not yet dated by dendrochronology, and in order to tighten up the dating of the chronology, Kuniholm commissioned a series of high-precision radiocarbon dates on samples of wood from the chronology. These spaced dates were then 'wiggle-matched' to the Irish–American radiocarbon calibration curve to pin down the age of the tree-ring chronology to within a few decades in real time. We now know that Bernd Kromer's successful wiggle-match on the Gordion chronology showed that the 20-year growth anomaly was located within 20 years of 1159 BC. These two findings offered some serious tree-ring support for the 1159 BC downturn recorded by the Irish oaks. Though a positive growth anomaly in Anatolia and a negative growth anomaly in Ireland sound contradictory, Anatolian trees normally suffer from very dry summers. Increased summer growth indicates that conditions were either wetter or colder (or both) in Anatolia, apparently consistent with a downturn in Ireland.

207 BC

Moving to the third century BC, Hollstein's German oak master chronology showed a dramatic narrow event from 208 to 204 BC, while a major erosion phase in German river valleys appears to have started around 200 BC; in this case deduced from Becker's work on river gravel oaks. Interestingly, the Irish bog-oak chronology stopped at around 200 BC or so, implying that in this area some environmental alteration had made bogs incapable of supporting oak trees at this time. From the other side of the Atlantic, Val LaMarche wrote in 1987: 'We've just finished up tabulations of frost-ring dates from … recent collections. *Re* the Chinese famine date of 207 BC, we have a significant frost ring on both Sheep and Campito Mtn. sites in California at 206 BC.' The evidence was building up that this event was also seen in a fairly wide spread of chronologies.

AD 540

In the original Irish work, this sixth-century event showed up very clearly as an extreme growth reduction in timbers from several sites. The event can also be traced as a notable growth reduction in southern Scottish and northern English timbers. Looking at relevant European oak chronologies, the event is not so extreme, but it can be seen as reduced growth in just about every chronology. However, AD 536 was noted as the second coldest summer in 1500 years in a temperature-sensitive record from Fennoscandian pines. Keith Briffa and colleagues had compared recent tree-ring widths and wood densities with climate parameters, and had established a relationship which allowed them to reconstruct past growth temperatures. That the second coldest summer in that record coincided with an extreme growth reduction in oaks suggested that it had to be an exceptional event. In fact, AD 536 was not alone. In this Fennoscandian record AD 541 was also notably cold and, indeed, both years fit into a period of reduced temperature lasting until 550. The recognition that the tree-ring effects were not just in the oak chronologies caused us to go back and take another look at the European chronologies. While virtually all chronologies showed reduced growth in the AD 536–45 period, different chronologies responded somewhat differently through time. For example, a chronology from northern Germany, constructed by Hubert Leuschner at Göttingen, exhibited a narrow band of rings starting as early as 531, which raised the question whether the AD 540 event was actually superimposed on a longer-term downturn. It appeared that in this case there was a lead-in to the event. Normally one would expect a big volcanic eruption to come out of the blue; in most recent explosive eruptions the precursor activity has not been sufficient to cause an environmental downturn, only the explosive eruption itself, with its stratospheric loading, has caused significant effects. The possibility of a lead-in actually raises questions which we will return to later.

However, with regard to AD 536–45, nothing in the original Irish chronologies suggested precursor activity. This in turn called into question the nature of environmental effects in widespread chronologies. Would we expect a whole range of chronologies, from different areas, to all do exactly the same thing at any time? Probably not. Individual site chronologies can represent a wide variety of growth environments, and some will undoubtedly respond differently to local effects. It seems best to avoid over-concentration of individual idiosyncratic behaviour and to concentrate on overall response, that is, combine a number of chronologies to discover a mean and see what the 'common' response is. For the century centred on AD 540 there are many oak chronologies, from Ireland to Poland. Thus it was possible to view what might be called the European oak response to the environmental effects around 540. The resulting European oak master chronology indicated that overall there was little lead-in to the start of the AD 536 event. On average, in that year oak growth dropped to about 85 per cent of normal. Interestingly, there appeared to be a recovery in the next two years, 537 and 538, with the real 'crash' taking place in 540–1. So 536 is a year of very widespread reduced growth, but it is notably separate from the real downturn which affects the oaks at AD 540, with a mean growth reduction of around 25 per cent. Overall, European oaks show a dramatic effect in AD 536, a brief recovery and a more profound growth reduction in 540, from which recovery is not complete until around 545. The Göttingen chronology represents oaks affected from 531; these were a group of riverside oaks from the north of Germany, not far from the North Sea coast. It seems likely that these trees were affected by some local effect possibly related to flooding or inundation. Although this may seem like a good reason for ignoring these trees, as we will see later this circumstantial evidence may fit a wider pattern.

Once it became apparent that European oaks and Fennoscandian pines were both affected in the 536–45 period, a wider search was made. Trees in other areas showed growth reductions at the same time. Ring widths for bristlecone pines and foxtail pines, both high altitude, temperature-sensitive species, from the western United States, showed growth downturns around AD 540. There seems no doubt that the decade-long downturn was widespread. Scuderi, studying foxtail pines, had compared his cold-year records with the volcanic record from the Greenland ice cores and had concluded that volcanoes were causing the cooling in most instances (results very consistent with the light-ring evidence for poor growth following volcanic eruptions). In the Irish oak work the volcano relationship had also come from comparisons with the ice-core records. So a lot of essentially independent evidence was pointing at the dust-veil causing the environmental effects around AD 540. Scuderi, following the Briffa approach, attempted a temperature reconstruction from his chronology and cited AD 535, 536 and 541 as his

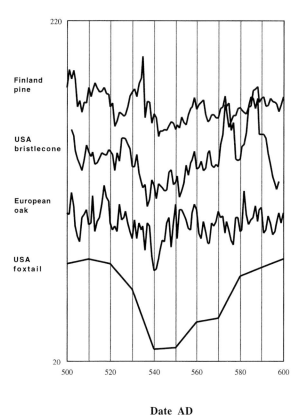

Chronologies which cross the sixth century AD showing the growth reduction centred on AD 540. The Finnish chronology was prepared by Pentti Zetterberg; the bristlecone pine chronology by Val LaMarche and Wes Ferguson; the Foxtail pine chronology by Louis Scuderi.

second, third and fourth coldest years in the last 2000 years.

Above I noted that 536 was the second coldest year in Fennoscandia; it was the third coldest in the Sierra Nevada. However, the other extreme years, with the exception of 541, do not agree. Although at face value 536 appears to be only 'the second or third coldest', in fact it is easily the most significantly cold year in the two records. This makes 536 a truly extraordinary year, certainly one of the coldest in the last two millennia with 541 hard on its heels.

Once we have a good reason to suspect a severe event 'around AD 540' many disparate pieces of evidence can be brought into play. There seems to be widespread tree-ring evidence for at least a hemispheric downturn and that a

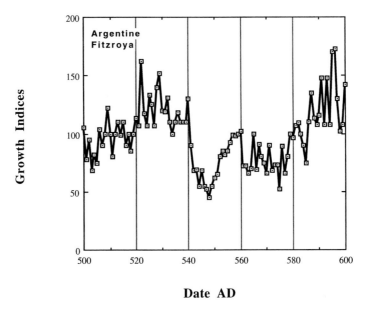

An Argentine Fitzroya chronology prepared by José Boninsegra and Richard Holmes. Showing dramatic growth reduction after AD 540. This data may imply a delayed response by some trees in the Southern hemisphere.

very significant dust-veil can affect the growth of trees (and possibly most other species) in a profoundly widespread fashion. The work of dendrochronologists tends to be local in character – base chronologies have to be built from coherent, local, groups of trees. Until recently chronologies were not available to check for widespread effects. Now that they are becoming available, it is possible to see these synchronous events in numerous tree-ring series for the first time. For example, it is now known that Pentti Zetterberg, working with Finnish pines has found a really dramatic event across AD 540. Following exceptionally wide growth in AD 535 (an interesting anomaly in itself given the thrust of this book) mean ring width in 536 drops by 67 per cent; by 542 growth is a mere 13 per cent of that in 535. In Douglass' work in the American Southwest (see Chapter 1) AD 536 was marked by a ring so stressed that it was specifically recorded as 'often microscopic and sometimes absent' by Douglass himself. Chronologies for Douglas fir and juniper from the same area told the same story. There is no doubt that AD 536, and the years thereafter, stand out as a highly unusual tree-ring event.

44 BC

Pang mentions 44 BC as a dust-veil event in his Chinese astronomical studies. In 44 BC we appear to have another dust-veil event similar in more or less every respect to those in 208 BC and AD 536; however, we have no available Irish tree-ring data. There is a break in the Irish oak chronology between 95 BC and 13 BC which was bridged, when we were building the chronology, by ring patterns from the Roman archaeological sites at Carlisle and London. The list of details associated with the year 44 BC speaks for itself:

c. 50 BC	Ice-core acidity peak, in all Greenland cores
43 BC	Frost ring event in bristlecone pines
44 BC	Following Caesar's death 'there were earthquakes and the obscuration of the sun's rays: for during all that year its orb rose pale and without radiance' (Plutarch)
44 BC	Chinese histories record a red daylight comet in May and June The comet's colour can be attributed to dust in the atmosphere
44–42 BC	Six consecutive grain harvests fail in China (over three years)
43 BC	Chinese records state: in April it snowed and frost killed the mulberries. The sun was pale blue and cast no shadows
43–42 BC	Chinese records hint at several distinct eruptions. By October 43 BC the sun seemed to have recovered, but in spring 42 BC the sun, moon and stars again appeared 'veiled and indistinct'.

Ice-core workers, in attempting to match historical records with acidity peaks, noted that the cores showed no record of a summer, that is, no summer-like change in chemical composition of the atmosphere, between the two acid peaks which, according to histories, were about a year apart in May 43 BC and March 42 BC. There seems little doubt that this episode in the 40s BC contains more than its fair share of dust-veil references. We could add in the information from Virgil, who states, after the death of Caesar (in 44 BC) 'How often we saw Etna flooding out from her burst furnaces, boiling over the Cyclopean fields, and whirling forth balls of flame and molten stones ...'

Virgil's testament, when added to the Chinese references, suggests, if the dates are correct, that there may have been recurring dust-veil phenomena spread over 44 to 42 BC. This ties in with evidence from Scuderi's foxtail pine chronology from the Sierra Nevada: 'a large decrease between 44 and 43 BC and continued decreased ring width values in both 42 and 41 BC ...'

Although we do not have Irish tree-ring records across 44 BC, other available information, including particularly LaMarche's 43 BC bristlecone frost-ring, suggests another significant event. As with the AD 540 event, where various strands of evidence suggest multiple occurrences in the period AD 536–545, there are hints that these particular events are not just single volcanic eruptions. One could reasonably ask if they are multiple events of some kind.

We can now see that each of the events, which showed up in the Irish oaks at 1628 BC, 1159 BC, 207 BC and AD 540, is backed up by at least some other tree-ring evidence for widespread effects. In addition, although we started this chapter with only four events, the similarities of 44 BC to the others suggests that it should be included, at least for discussion purposes. Having now specified our events in tree-ring and broad environmental terms, we can start to add in additional information from historical and archaeological sources. Though this information is not as well dated, it would not be stretching the imagination to see the possibilities of association.

HISTORICAL AND ARCHAEOLOGICAL EVIDENCE

THE SEVENTEENTH CENTURY BC

We have already seen how the collapse of the Xia dynasty in China, with its dust-veil type descriptions, and the implied withdrawal of the Mandate of Heaven, could plausibly be related to the volcanic dust-veil effects associated with 1628 BC. As LaMarche and Hirschboeck have already posed the question whether the 1628 BC event might be related to Santorini in the Aegean, it is possible that there were some effects on the Minoan and Egyptian civilizations at the same time, of which more later. However, a new piece of information from a distant informant, Leroy Ellenberger, concerned the Venus Tablets. Tree-ring work, combined with the ice-core acidity, allows the proposition of obscured skies in the window of 1630 to 1628 BC due to a volcanic eruption, possibly Santorini. Given that completely independent scientific suggestion, can we find any reference in ancient historical sources to anything relevant in this narrow date window?

One would imagine that the answer should be no, but surprisingly the opposite could be true. Scholars believe the Venus Tablets to be ancient records of observations of the planet Venus by Babylonian astronomers, in the second millennium BC, relating to the reign of King Ammizaduga, and covering many years. In year nine of the record there was a long interval when the Babylonian astronomers could not see the planet Venus: the text refers to a 'nine month and four day invisibility'. This is unusual because Venus is an extremely bright object and the skies over the region that comprised the Babylonian Empire are not noted for cloudiness. Ellenberger suggested that it might not be beyond the bounds of possibility that year nine of King Ammizaduga's reign was the year of a significant dust-veil.

Tree-rings and ice cores suggest that there should have been a dust-veil in 1628 or possibly 1629 BC; this suggestion does not rely on any ancient history. Ellenberger is saying there is a curious ancient Babylonian record of astronomers experiencing obscured vision of the planet Venus. What calendar year might the ninth year of Ammizaduga be? Astronomers have studied the entire record of Venus observations in these ancient annals and have tried to work out which period of years they relate to. Unfortunately they cannot fix on a single span of years because there appears to be some corruption of the texts. However, possible solutions have been proposed. The great retro-astronomer Huber felt that there were only four solutions which were more or less compatible with both history and astronomy. Huber, working before the proposals concerning 1628 BC, posited that year one of Ammizaduga began in 1701, 1645, 1637 or 1581 BC. By this calculation, the dates of year nine of Ammizaduga, in which is recorded *a nine-month four-day invisibility of Venus*, become 1693, 1637, 1629 or 1573 BC. Incredibly, having specified the date of a dust-veil from tree-rings, we find that there is a pre-existing suggestion of a possibility that something may have obscured the Babylonian skies in 1629 BC. It is astonishing that in the narrow specified date range of 1630–1628 BC it is possible to find even the remotest suggestion of a pre-existing reference to obscured skies. As Ellenberger pointed out, we can now hazard a guess that the first year of King Ammizaduga was indeed 1637 BC – with a one-in-four chance of being correct.

THE TWELFTH CENTURY BC

Sometime near or in the twelfth century BC, allowing for flexibility in archaeological and ancient historical evidence, the whole fabric of ancient society appears to have crumbled. Some have suggested that in most of Britain there was upland abandonment, particularly severe in Scotland, followed by an upsurge in the construction of defensive sites. Around the Mediterranean there was an endless list of movements and collapses. Most interesting was the demise of the Mycenaean civilization in Greece with the ensuing four-century 'Greek Dark Age' which descended on the Mediterranean region. Here was an extremely dramatic decline where people had already argued for some sort of environmental 'event' involving a prolonged and highly regionalized drought. Herodotus refers to a 'grim tribulation' which was said to have afflicted Lydia for 18 years, and finally forced the Etruscans to leave that country. In Barnett's contribution to *The Cambridge Ancient History*, it is taken as read that this event must have taken place some time *before* 1000 BC. With the tree-rings suggesting upheaval in the 1159–1141 BC period (which is about 18 years given the recovery in some trees in 1141 BC) was it possible that all these effects could be related? Could the volcano-related event in the mid-twelfth century have been involved in both the collapse of the Shang dynasty in China and of the Mycenaean civilization in the Mediterranean; might the latter be Herodotus' grim tribulation?

207 BC

As mentioned earlier, articles were written to publicize this developing story and to draw attention to the marker dates in the hope that others would be able to add information from their own special fields of study. The 207 BC event is an excellent example of the success of this approach. Included in my 'Do Irish Bog Oaks Date the Shang Dynasty?' article was an implied request for classical scholars to examine the period 208–204 BC. Almost immediately Phyllis Forsyth replied in an article in *The Ancient History Bulletin*. Apparently there were several relevant pieces of information in classical texts relating to this decade. Forsyth wrote:

> *Livy tells us that in the year 206 BC two suns were seen at Alba, and adds that light appeared in the night at Fregellae (28.11.3–4); for the year 204 BC he notes that a halo had encircled the sun … Appian, who mentions that certain direful prodigies sent by Jupiter had appeared at Rome in 204 BC.*

So there were a number of things seen in the sky in this immediate period. Forsyth goes on to mention Livy's comments on a major epidemic in and around Rome in 208 BC and another in 205 BC. The Romans consulted the Sibylline books and were told 'to bring the image of Cybele, the Magna Mater, to Rome from Asia Minor'. The goddess was brought back to Rome in the hope of saving the city – why? According to Livy, the decision to consult the books was specifically 'frequent showers of stones seen in 205 BC'. But strange occurrences may have started even earlier. Stothers and Rampino had noted Livy's 217 BC record that 'the sun's disc seemed to be diminished'. They also noted that Silius Italicus mentions glowing stones suddenly appearing from the south and falling near Rome, while Livy chronicles another shower of stones in 212 BC. These showers of stones, and the apparently innocuous reference to light appearing in the night are discussed later.

Overall, Forsyth's article added significantly to the suggestion that a dust-veil might have had environmental consequences in the period around 207 BC in yet another area. Apart from the portents, there were crop failures, famines and epidemics as well as drought. China and the Mediterranean were affected at the same time yet again.

IRISH ANNALS

We have now seen supporting evidence for environmental effects taking place at around the times of the 1628 BC, 1159 BC and 207 BC tree-ring events. One additional unexpected twist was provided by information contained in the ancient Irish king lists – the World Chronicle section of the Irish Annals.

Until recently, it has been generally accepted that all the early references, pre-AD 500, are mythological. However, as we have seen already, Warner feels that the information relating to the second-century BC Corlea trackway is too accurate to be coincidence and that there may be a grain of truth in these records. Taking these annals at face value, he looked for references to catastrophes. He found only a few severe events and published these together with what he believes are their 'dates' (we should remember that when finally compiled in the early seventeenth century AD, the prehistoric annals were given a chronology dated in years from the start of the world in '5200 BC'. Here are three of Warner's suggested 'catastrophes':

• AM 3580–3656 i.e. 1620–1544 'BC'
 Tigernmas died, with three-quarters of the men of Ireland.
 This reign was followed by seven years without a king.
• AM 4020–4169 i.e. 1180–1031 'BC'
plague … in which … perished … a countless number of the men of Ireland.
• AM 4991–4001 i.e. 209–199 'BC'
There was a great mortality of cattle in the reign of Bressal.

There are obvious problems with records of this sort. There were no written records in Ireland in the BC period. At best, some sort of oral tradition might have survived long enough to be written down by literate Christian scholars in the first millennium AD. To most scholars it is not clear how such an oral tradition could have been handed down in prehistoric times – a king list, which is how the information appears to be organized, implies a king. Unfortunately there is no evidence that early Irish society would have been structured in such a way as to allow a king list to be meaningful over long periods, and, as a result, most scholars reject these early records out of hand. (An alternative reason for ignoring the records is the assertion that the World Chronicle section of the Irish Annals is simply a fabrication of myth, fiction and biblical history produced specifically to provide a history for early Ireland.) However, they may contain some elements of truth. If this were the case, then we might expect that the most catastrophic events might well be those best remembered. After all, the Chinese, Egyptian and Hebrew histories are all based on king lists, so why should the Irish not have one?

From our point of view, here is a single source which might just, with only a little stretch of the imagination, mention three of our tree-ring events. It is an interesting issue. Intuitively, the worst events ought to be the ones which are best remembered, but is it all too much to believe? In a sense it does not matter. The Annals cannot be used to prove anything; they just add colour. What is slightly surprising is that two of the other events in the Irish Annals list take place at 2341 'BC' and AD 536-9. We will see more of the 2341 date later. For consistency let us deal with the AD 536 date first.

AD 536–545

Warner pointed out two rare and cryptic references in the Irish Annals to 'failure of bread' in AD 536 and AD 539. Christianity was just becoming established in Ireland in the fifth and sixth centuries, and few records exist for the time. Though these references are terse, their occurrence at all in the near-vacuum of this period of the Dark Ages is almost certainly significant. The failures are simultaneous with the severe famines recorded in China. The Justinian plague begins in AD 542 in the Mediterranean and spreads across Europe. Either this, or some other plague, is recorded as arriving in Ireland in AD 544–5 (suggesting that the annals are in fact not a bad record). All this, coupled with Stothers and Rampino's AD 536–537 'densest and most persistent dry fog on record', ties down the sixth century dust-veil and its global effects pretty tightly.

THE ANGLO-SAXON CHRONICLE

One of the few English documents relating to the Anglo-Saxons in the Dark Ages is the *Anglo-Saxon Chronicle*. The earlier portion of the chronicle was compiled several centuries after the events it describes; for the sixth century it is decidedly 'thin'. However, while some references exist for the early sixth century, there are none for the period AD 534 to 544, with the exception of solar eclipses recorded in AD 538 and AD 540:

> *This year [538], fourteen days before the kalends of March [15th Feb] the sun was eclipsed from early morning till nine in the forenoon … (and in 540) This year the sun was eclipsed on the 12th of the kalends of July [20th June] and the stars showed themselves fullnigh half an hour after nine in the forenoon.*

As both of these events sound like total eclipses seen from England (which would be unusual) – the accuracy of the references was checked. The eclipses did occur, as recorded, though they would not have appeared total to a viewer in England. They would have been total in the Near East or the Mediterranean and it is most likely that they were originally recorded in Byzantine annals. Why should two Byzantine eclipses be recorded in the *Anglo-Saxon Chronicle?* I would suggest that the most likely explanation for Byzantine eclipses in an English record is the following.

The compiler, several centuries after the events, is working from some patchy local records, possibly even an oral tradition. These records perhaps suggested 'a dim sun this year' or 'the sun gave no heat this year'. The compiler, seeing the detailed eclipse records in Byzantine annals, assumes that these adequately explain his local records, so copies them into the annals. This speculative interpretation does raise the possibility that there may have been two pre-existing references to something involving the sun in AD 538 and 540 in northern latitudes. But we know that a severe dust-veil was recorded in the Mediterranean area in AD 536. Could there have been more than one dust-veil between AD 536 and AD 540? Maybe even three? Yet again the very act of specifying these dates produces information which implies that something unusual was going on around the AD 540 tree-ring event.

There is more evidence relating to something happening around AD 540. Take for example the case of an unfinished, dug-out boat from Lough Neagh in the north of Ireland. Being oak, and containing a long ring record, this partly hollowed trunk was easily dated to AD 524 +/-18, allowing for missing sapwood. The tree was most likely to have been felled in the range AD 506 to 542. When the AD 536–45 environmental event became known, the dug-out offered some interesting possibilities. What is the use of an unfinished dug-out and why was it found preserved out in Lough Neagh? Was it possible that it was abandoned when the level of the lough rose suddenly at the AD 540 event? We had the advantage of other oaks preserved around Lough Neagh relating to the sixth century: three naturally-preserved trees which had presumably been growing close to the edge of the lough. When dated, two of them had estimated death dates which bracketed AD 540, while the only survivor saw a very dramatic reduction in ring width at exactly AD 540; the ring width not exceeding 0.4 mm for the next 25 years. These several strands of evidence would be consistent with a notable rise in Lough Neagh level. For such a large body of water (Lough Neagh is the largest in the British Isles) to rise significantly would imply either notably more water input due to increased precipitation or some tectonic alteration in drainage or water table.

Moving further afield, in Central America there is a Mayan 'hiatus' just around this time, 'when few dated works of art or buildings were made'; though subsequently the Maya thrived during their Late Classic period (AD 550–900). Interestingly, those studying the famous Nazca lines in southern Peru note that at some time in the mid-sixth century a great drought started, which lasted forty years. This drought, which may have been related to a change in the Humbolt Current in the Pacific Ocean, stands a good chance of having been triggered by the events around AD 540. In India the Gupta dynasty, which had been a period of cultural and artistic brilliance, came to an end c. 540. The dendrochronological successors of A.E. Douglass in the American Southwest have now dated hundreds of archaeological sites and phases; they see a notable flowering in building activity immediately after the decade of the 540s, a decade from which no datable timbers have been found. And so it goes on.

MORE UNIFYING FACTORS

BURGESS AND CATASTROPHISM

In the same way that Warner's list of catastrophes in the early Irish Annals serve to link the 1628 BC, 1159 BC, 207 BC and AD 540 events, so Colin Burgess, a noted catastrophist, sees parallels in the events of the sixth century AD and in the twelfth century BC. He believes that the known population collapses in the fourteenth century AD, associated with the Black Death, and in the sixth century AD, associated with the Justinian plague, might be mirrored by events in the twelfth century BC. He pointed out that the expanded population of the thirteenth century AD was ripe for reduction by disease, starvation and strife and wondered if overcrowding is actually a significant factor in stressing a population. On the other hand, an improved or stable climate could encourage the expansion of human populations. Any significant downturn in climate leading to crop failures, or merely to reduced yields, then leaves the human population vulnerable to starvation and disease. In extreme cases there could be near-total collapse. This would coincide with those earlier observations in the dry American Southwest, where reliable harvests allowed Anasazi populations to boom and pueblos to expand. Sudden reversals in those areas, with regularly failing harvests, led to starvation or abandonment.

The rate of population contraction would presumably depend on particular circumstances. However, Burgess puts in a nice twist. Human beings resist change – if a decline sets in gradually they adapt to it, trying to offset the change. In such a situation any sudden worsening, as might be induced by an abrupt dust-veil event, will tip the balance to the point where the system collapses. Overall the outcome of a dust-veil, volcanic or otherwise, may be critically dependent on the existing population status; a stable population may survive, a population which has already outstripped its resources may be liable to collapse.

Burgess argued that all the right conditions prevailed to make the events of the AD 540s a dry-run for the events of the Black Death. The Justinian plague arrived after AD 542 and 'appears to have been as savage and far reaching in its consequences as the Black Death'. Burgess also saw clues in the archaeological record relating to the later-second millennium BC of another population decline. Specifically, he saw, in the abandoned upland settlements, and in the development of defensible hill-top enclosures all the signs that somewhere near the end of the second millennium BC a deterioration in climate and a population collapse had taken place.

Yet again we see pre-existing suggestions from other workers that at around the time of the 1159 BC event, and specifically at AD 540, unpleasant things had happened to human populations. Burgess makes the following point about the Mediterranean area:

The breakdown of the existing order in the East Mediterranean c. 1250–1150 BC has long been a familiar concept. The Aegean world, Mycenae, the Hittite empire and the great Late Bronze Age cities of Cyprus and Syria all came to an inglorious end, and even Egypt was so exhausted by the struggle as to be finished as a world power …

Overall, it appears that by putting dust-veils into the twelfth century BC and the sixth century AD we may be providing an explanation, or mechanism, which can be added into the existing framework.

We can conclude this chapter by noting that from our original list of narrowest-ring/dust-veil events in the Irish tree-rings, the four at 1628 BC, 1159 BC, 207 BC and AD 540 are all found to be associated with significant information from other sources. In particular they all appear to have been traumatic for human populations. While the first two are so far back in time that no absolute links can be forged, in the case of the later events in the third century BC and the sixth century AD, there are direct one-to-one relationships between precisely dated historical information and the tree-ring dates. Since at 207 BC and AD 540 the tree-rings so obviously 'got it right', logic would suggest that in the fullness of time 1628 BC and 1159 BC should turn out to be the two most important dates in that millennium.

To summarize, the events, even quite early in the development of the story, looked like this:

The 1628 BC event

1645+/-20 BC	Ice acidity layer in Dye 3 core
1629 BC	Venus Tablets 1 in 4 chance sky obscured
1628 BC	European oaks show reduced growth
1627 BC	Bristlecone pine severe frost-ring event
1620–1544 'BC'	Irish king list records a 'catastrophe'
1600+/-30 BC	Chinese describe dust-veil phenomena
1600+/-30 BC	Chinese 'Mandate of Heaven' withdrawn = dynastic change, end of Xia

The 1159 BC event

1180–1031 'BC'	Irish king list records a 'catastrophe'
1159 BC	Irish oaks show reduced growth

1153 BC	Conventional date of Egyptian famine
1150+/-10 BC	Turkish enhanced growth anomaly
1120+/-50 BC	Ice acidity layer in Camp Century core
c. 3200 BP	Antarctic acidity layer
c. 1100 BC	Chinese describe dust-veil phenomena
c. 1100 BC	Chinese 'Mandate of Heaven' withdrawn = dynastic change, end of Shang
c. 12th BC	Suggested British upland abandonment
c. 12th BC	Widespread collapse of Mediterranean civilizations

The 208 BC event

210+/-30 BC	Ice acidity layer in Camp Century core
210–200 BC	Annals suggest Irish murrain of cattle
208 BC	Sky obscured, stars invisible from China
208–204 BC	Narrow rings in German oaks
207–204 BC	Severe famines in China
207 BC	Irish oaks show reduced growth
206 BC	Bristlecone pine frost-ring event
205 BC	Roman apparitions, epidemics and famine
204–202 BC	Chinese 'Mandate of Heaven' withdrawn = dynastic change, start of Han
c. 200 BC	Deposition phase German river-valley oaks
197+/-9 BC	Irish prehistoric bog oak chronologies end

The AD 536 event

AD 535, 536, 541	Scuderi's extreme cold years in Sierra Nevada
AD 536–537	Vulcanologists note severe European dry fog
AD 536	Extreme cold summer in Fennoscandia
AD 536	Irish Annals refer to 'failure of bread'
AD 536–538	Chinese famines
AD 536	Chinese note star Canopus not seen
AD 537	Mortality in Ireland and Britain
AD 538	Anomalous Anglo-Saxon 'eclipse' record
AD 539	Irish Annals refer to 'failure of bread'
AD 540	Anomalous Anglo-Saxon 'eclipse' record
AD 540+/-10	Dye 3 ice-core acidity peak (later moved)
AD 540–542	Irish oaks show notable reduced growth
AD 542	Justinian plague appears out of Egypt

CHAPTER 5

•

NOT ALL PLAIN
SAILING: TENSIONS IN
THE VOLCANO STORY

We can now look at some key issues concerning volcanoes, the 1628 BC event, and the AD 540 event, just to give a feel for the debates which arise about dating and environmental issues. These key events had been identified in the Irish oaks and linked to volcanoes by the ice acidities. A great deal of interesting information, some circumstantial, some robust, had tended to support the idea of widespread environmental downturns with human consequences. Now that we knew the dates of some major ancient eruptions, we were beginning to understand their apparent effects. Santorini in the Aegean might just be one of them.

However, it was not long before the problems emerged. The first signs of disagreement arose with respect to the duration of the effects in the oak tree-rings. While the bristlecone frost-rings occurred in a single year, for example, at 1627 BC and 206 BC, the effects in the oak varied from one year at the 207 BC event to the extreme 18 years following 1159 BC; the 1628 BC event lasted until around 1623 BC. The problem was that all recent studies on the effects of volcanoes tended to show that the effects lasted for only about three years. Why were these ancient events different? A number of explanations are possible.

The prehistoric Irish oaks had mostly grown on the surface of peat bogs, a situation which is marginal at best. Their dramatic growth downturns at the time of the dust-veil events would seem to relate to colder or wetter conditions. That explanation would be consistent with the cooling which is known to follow recent dust-veils, for example Tambora 1815 or Pinatubo 1991. Unfortunately, there are other ways of looking at the problem. Perhaps the effects were not simply cold and/or wet; it was possible that dry cold would be just as effective in deterring growth. Other workers, for example, Grattan and Gilbertson, postulated acid deposition as a likely vector, especially in the case of Icelandic eruptions close to Ireland. Furthermore, the duration of the effects in the trees might not be the same as the duration of any actual environmental downturn. Possibly, the trees needed time to recover from the effects of an abrupt environmental downturn which simply acted as a trigger. For example, a short period of cold or water-logging or drought might affect the tree for years afterwards, just as an instant defoliation involving the loss of branches might involve many years for the tree to recover. Overall it was difficult to say exactly what the ancient environmental conditions were like, and how long any downturns lasted, from the tree-rings alone.

To all that could be added a quite sobering fact. In almost no case in the distant past was there a proven relationship between a known volcano and its environmental effects. This stems directly from the standard geological approach of dating volcanoes by radiocarbon which is about the only method available. Most ancient volcanoes which have been dated have had one, or a few, radiocarbon determinations carried out on organic material – peat, trees, etc. – which had been buried or killed by the eruption under study. Radiocarbon dates have inherent errors and until recently most were quoted with errors of around +/-80 years: take as an example a typical radiocarbon date such as 2800+/-80 BP (Before Present). The error quoted with the date is really a statistical estimate of probability; there is a 68 per cent probability that the true radiocarbon age lies within +/-80 years of 2800 BP (this is known as the one standard deviation probability range). What they could just as easily have said is that there is a 95 per cent probability that the true date lies within +/-160 years of 2800 BP (the two standard deviation range) – a wide range in time. Moreover, in order to turn radiocarbon age ranges into calendar age ranges, the radiocarbon range has to be calibrated, that is, compared with the calibration curves worked out by dating known-age wood. It is safe to say that virtually no ancient volcanoes are dated to better than a range of a few *centuries*. Santorini, which had numerous radiocarbon dates applied to buried material from the town of Akrotiri, is still only dated to the range 1670–1530 CalBC by radiocarbon.

No ancient volcanoes, other than a sprinkling from the first millennium BC to first millennium AD in the Mediterranean, which are referred to by classical authors, are accurately dated (of which Vesuvius AD 79 is the best known). Since most environmental information prior to the tree-ring investigations came from pollen profiles, which are also dated by radiocarbon, not surprisingly volcanoes and effects seldom match. It is fair to say that vulcanologists do not know the actual environmental consequences of any ancient volcanic eruption – except for Toba in Sumatra which erupted 74,000 years ago and almost certainly helped the planet into the last Ice Age. But, as Mike Rampino points out, the Toba eruption was truly huge – its remaining caldera is 70 km (43 miles) across.

It is into this sea of uncertainty that we have launched some well-dated environmental effects which seem to be volcanic in origin. We cannot tell why these particular events – 1628 BC, 1159 BC, 207 BC and AD 540 – stand out so clearly. Were the ancient volcanoes whose effects show up in the tree-rings simply 'bigger'? Not as far as the volume estimates go. Did they produce more dust or acid? Not as far as we can see from the amount of acid in the Greenland ice layers. (They certainly did produce a lot of acid, as the Danish workers showed with the initial analysis of the Camp Century core, however, there are large acid spikes in more recent times with no equivalent environmental effects.) Were the effective ones sea-level volcanoes, loading the atmosphere with water vapour? This is possible, but the case is unproven. Were the volcanoes which stand out actually 'multiples', that is, several big volcanoes erupting within one or a few years? The problem with multiple eruptions is in some ways critical for understanding the dilemma faced by vulcanologists. Because they use radiocarbon, which smears out date ranges, vulcanologists cannot see ancient simultaneous volcanoes. On statistical grounds, multiples are bound to occur from time to time. So multiples are bound to happen but vulcanologists cannot discover if they have happened in the past! Irrespective of what vulcanologists do not know, it seems intuitively likely that large volcanic eruptions may occur in clusters either because of the associated tectonic effects – volcanoes are normally associated with earthquakes and widespread earthquakes could trigger other eruptions, especially along plate boundaries – or through extraterrestrial gravitational or bombardment effects. Overall, irrespective of the difficulties, from this list it is possible to imagine several mechanisms which might from time to time produce anomalously effective eruptions; multiples being a real potential hazard. In that vein, we should remember those references to several dust-veils in 44–42 BC and the several possible references relating to the period AD 536–40. It is also possible that these 'special' volcanoes stand out because they are superimposed on existing downturns – we will come back to this possibility later.

There is irony in the fact that vulcanologists cannot date anything accurately, in that some vulcanologists were quick to point out the weaknesses in the tree-ring case. Dave Pyle noted that dendrochronologists could not tell from the tree-rings which volcanoes caused the environmental effects we were observing. Others stated that the duration of the effects in the tree-rings were all wrong, that is, that volcano effects last only a few years. The simple answer is that vulcanologists do not know what effects ancient volcanoes had because they cannot date either the volcanoes or the effects! They are trapped into having to rely on the observations which exist for the handful of large volcanoes which are well-dated historically. Some vulcanologists and climatologists are imposing a simple model of volcanic effects, based on the examples of volcanoes which have erupted in the last few centuries, on to all past volcanic occurrences. They can only be wrong, if for no other reason than that the big recent volcanic eruptions have tended to occur singly: Tambora 1815, Cosigüina 1835, Krakatoa 1883, Katmai 1912, Agung 1963. This leads to the debate surrounding Santorini. This debate arises because some archaeological opinion cannot accept a date as early as 1628 BC for the eruption of Santorini. Such an early date clashes with their interpretation of pottery and other archaeological evidence linking to Egypt.

The whole 1628 BC issue began with Val LaMarche and Kathy Hirschboeck's suggestion that the frost-ring in the bristlecone pines at 1627 BC might be due to the eruption of Santorini. As soon as the suggestion was made people sought to indicate why it might be incorrect. But, for the reasons given above, no one could possibly prove them wrong; all anyone could do was to indicate alternative scenarios. One of the first criticisms levelled at LaMarche and Hirschboeck's suggestion was that the frost-ring effect in the high-elevation Californian bristlecone pines might be due to some local effect, for instance, an Alaskan volcano rather than Santorini. The observation of the reduced growth in Irish, English and German oaks at 1628 BC moved the debate on by reducing the likelihood of a local cause; clearly there were global aspects to 1628–27 BC. Sadly, Val LaMarche died in 1988, shortly before the Third Santorini Conference on Thera in 1989. I had published the Irish evidence in 1988 and was invited in his place. I arrived on Santorini prepared to discuss the issues of whether the eruption might have taken place in 1628 BC in an open-minded sort of way – after all it did not matter to me whether the date was 1628 BC or not, as it was patently LaMarche and Hirschboeck's date anyway.

What I was not prepared for was the level of anti-1628 BC sentiment which was apparent at the conference. While some of the more traditional archaeologists could have been expected to be 'anti', the sheer weight of scientific opinion ranged against 1628 BC was unexpected. Why? Several scientific camps were involved. First there were the Danish ice-core workers who had been pushing the 1645+/-20 BC date as 'different' from the tree-ring derived 1628 BC event. I suppose that was to be expected even though all logic (as we have already seen and will see again later) says that the two dates are the same. But there were vulcanologists present who clearly could not see the logic that 1645+/-20 had to be 1628 BC; as a result arguments raged about the date being 1645 BC rather than 1628 BC. There were also arguments about sulphur: the vulcanologists had decided that the amount of sulphur from Santorini was too little to account for the amount of sulphur observed in the Dye 3 ice-core at 1645+/-20 BC (which is 1628 BC). They said that Santorini would not show up in Greenland as acid, and, since sulphur is supposed to be the driving force for environmental effects, it should not show up in the trees either. One school of thought was saying that Santorini was an 'invisible' volcano: it would have produced no significant environmental effects. Another school of thought held that volcanoes were self-limiting – the eruption columns tend to collapse and the sulphate and dust is not injected high enough into the stratosphere to stay up for long; hence only short-term environmental effects should be expected. In fact it was clear that there was a strong lobby to play down the size and effects of Santorini. This was then coupled with the final complicating issue – other candidate eruptions. Several other volcanoes were introduced as possible candidates for the 1628 BC event – again an attempt to rule out Santorini.

Why? What was going on at this major, multi-disciplinary, international conference that so many people were there to argue that Santorini either had not, or need not, have erupted in 1628 BC? Few people seemed to be willing to give 1628 BC serious support. Though the conference was fantastic, set on the edge of the caldera, I left it with a sense that Val LaMarche and Kathy Hirschboeck's date had not got a very fair hearing.

Looking back, it is now possible to view the issues in a more measured way. The issues are tree-rings, radiocarbon dating, archaeological dating, volcanic sulphur and alternative candidate eruptions. Starting with the tree-rings, we can still be fairly certain that some sort of large environmentally-effective volcanic event took place in 1628 or 1629 BC; I feel sure no one in any of the represented disciplines would disagree with that statement. However, whether Santorini was involved, either on its own or as part of a multiple, is not proven. It has now been accepted by nearly all interested persons that radiocarbon cannot further the debate. The available radiocarbon evidence, though it can be interpreted to favour a late-seventeenth-century BC date for Santorini, can always be stretched to include the range 1670–1530 CalBC because of the shape of the radiocarbon calibration curve. So radiocarbon has moved to the sidelines.

Archaeological dating is interesting. Basically, two schools exist; for the sake of simplicity we could call one the 'conventional Peter Warren school' – which still favours an eruption date around 1500 BC – and the other the 'radical Sturt Manning school' which would interpret the archaeological evidence as being not inconsistent with the 1628 BC dating. The very fact that there are two archaeological schools implies that the archaeological evidence on its own cannot answer the question. Much of the argument about the dating has to do with people's faith in the Egyptian historical chronology and the security of archaeological contexts and relationships. This is well exemplified in the repeated claims by Manfred Bietak that finds from Tell el-Dab'a, Egypt, including Minoan-style wall paintings, water-borne pumice from Santorini and pottery from Cyprus, are sixteenth century BC on the basis of conventional Egyptian chronology. If Bietak is correct, Santorini cannot have erupted in 1628 BC, whereas, if Santorini did erupt in 1628 BC, there must be something wrong with the Egyptian chronology or Bietak's interpretation of the evidence. The sheer levels of disagreement within the archaeological camp(s), coupled with the uncertainty over the Egyptian chronology, dictate that a definitive dating for Santorini cannot come from archaeologists alone.

On the question of sulphur we have seen remarkable changes since 1989. At the time of the Santorini conference the amount of sulphur was believed to be the best measure of the likely environmental effects of an eruption. It was also noted just how little sulphur Santorini had produced, estimated as four million tons at the conference. This estimate was produced by analysing the amount of sulphur left in the erupted magma from the volcano. By the time the conference proceedings had been published, that estimate had increased to 17 million tons. What changed all arguments was the discovery, from satellite observation of the 1982 El Chichon and 1991 Pinatubo eruptions, that the amount of sulphur produced by a volcano can be vastly greater than the residues in the rock would indicate. Vulcanologists now realize that not only are they unable to date eruptions or their effects very well, they cannot tell how much sulphur they produce either.

The question of other candidate eruptions for 1628 BC is also interesting. It was always possible that some other volcano actually gave rise to the 1628 BC environmental effects. However, none of the other candidates is as well dated as Santorini itself. Similarly, estimates of how much sulphur the other candidates produced suffer from the same vagaries as the estimates for Santorini. In other words, one of several other volcanoes could have erupted in 1628 BC instead of Santorini, or, for all we know, as well as Santorini. Introducing other poorly dated candidate volcanoes, of unknown environmental effect, does not alter the story in any meaningful way. Santorini is still the only large candidate eruption which is definitely in the 1670–1530 BC range.

By the end of the 1989 conference it was thought that the Santorini issue could be resolved, perhaps by finding a tree killed by the eruption and dating that tree directly by dendrochronology – a very long shot – or by finding a carbonized tree killed by the eruption and dating it by a radiocarbon technique called 'high-precision wiggle-matching'. It could be resolved by finding environmental effects in tree-rings downwind of the volcano itself, or by finding chemically identifiable shards of volcanic glass (tephra) in the Greenland ice layer for 1645+/-20 BC.

One amusing sidelight on this issue was provided by The *Guinness Book of Records* which has for some years simply given the date for Santorini as 1628 BC, without comment. They might even be correct! On balance, Santorini probably did erupt in 1628 BC, but this still must be proven. We will be returning to this issue later from a rather different direction.

THE ICE-CORE ANOMALY AT AD 540

We have now seen that the key dates – 1628 BC, 1159 BC, 207 BC and AD 540 – are all connected with volcanic dust-veils. However, one of these events was 'strange'. When AD 540 was noted in the narrowest-ring index, this tied in well with a strong acidity signal which the Danes had found and initially dated at AD 540+/-10 in the Dye 3 ice-core. Stothers and Rampino had also noted a number of references to a 'dry fog' in the Mediterranean in AD 536. They quoted the sixth-century Byzantine author Procopius:

During this year a most dread portent took place. For the sun gave forth its light without brightness … and it seemed exceedingly like the sun in eclipse, for the beams it shed were not clear …

and John Lydus:

The sun became dim … for nearly the whole year … so that the fruits were killed at an unseasonable time.

Reports from Constantinople suggested climatic upset for more than a year and a late chronicler, Michael the Syrian, elaborated thus:

the sun became dark and its darkness lasted for eighteen months. Each day it shone for about four hours, and still this light was only a feeble shadow … the fruits did not ripen and the wine tasted like sour grapes.

So, around AD 536–40 there was evidence for a major volcanic event recorded in Greenland, while in the Mediterranean the sun was dim in AD 536–7. This episode is regarded as the most dense and persistent dry fog in recorded history. From the dimmed-sun records Stothers was able to estimate that for up to 18 months in AD 536–7 the sun must have appeared up to ten times fainter than usual. There are other reports; for example, a contemporary Italian record by Cassiodorus states:

The sun … seems to have lost its wonted light, and appears of a bluish colour. We marvel to see no shadows of our bodies at noon, to feel the mighty vigour of the sun's heat wasted into feebleness, and the phenomena which accompany an eclipse prolonged through almost a whole year. We have had ... a summer without heat ... the crops have been chilled by north winds ... the rain is denied ...

However, though the Irish trees did show a narrow ring in AD 536, the really narrow event – the *narrowest* rings – occurred in 540–1. Why was there a delay in the onset of the really extreme conditions? Questions like these raised the possibility of multiple eruptions: that is, was there one dust-veil in 536 and another a few year later? But the strangeness of the event was heightened considerably when it was found that the date of the Greenland acidity layer, in the Dye 3 core, which was given as 540+/-10 in 1980, had been changed to 516+/-4 by Claus Hammer in 1984. From the historical records it was clear that there was a major dry-fog event in AD 536, with tree-ring effects afterwards; this movement of the ice acidity layer to AD 516 cast serious doubt on the ice-core chronology in the sixth century AD. In the wider ice-core record around this critical time, the original Crête core stopped at AD 553+/-3 and the Camp Century core turned out to be unusable down to the first century AD. This means that, until recently, the ice-core information for the sixth century AD relied solely on the Dye 3 core. Moving the 540+/-10 acid layer by 24 years meant that there was no good evidence for a layer of volcanic acid at AD 540; but surely there must have been a volcano at 540, the tree-rings events are volcanic, are they not?

With this situation in mind, the results of the early 1990s GISP2 (American) and GRIP (Danish) cores from Summit, Greenland, were awaited with interest. Unfortunately, preliminary results from the GISP2 core indicated no significantly enhanced acidity in the annual layers attributed to the years around AD 536–40. Then in 1983 something happened which served to colour my judgement still further on the nature of the AD 540 phenomenon. In the summer of 1983 I called on Greg Zielinski at the University of New Hampshire. Greg was heavily involved in the analysis of the GISP2 core and showed me many of the available results which were astounding, to say the least. As noted earlier, individual annual layers could be resolved back to beyond 40,000 years. While there I gave a talk for the postgraduate students on the tree-ring/volcano story, ending up with the AD 540 event as outlined so far. In particular I discussed why the ice-core evidence was critical to establish if more than one volcano was involved. After the talk one of the postgraduates called up the analysis data for the sixth century AD on his computer; another student, Greg and myself were also in the room. 'That's funny, we have 14 metres of missing record,' said the postgrad. 'No, we do not,' said Greg. 'Yes we do,' said the postgrad. 'There are no analyses between AD 614 and 545.'

Having just given a talk stressing why the sixth century was interesting and how the ice-core evidence was critical to understanding what had actually happened around AD 540, I was witnessing the revelation that most of the record of the sixth century was missing; 14 m (46 ft) of core equal to about seventy annual layers. Moreover, it was apparent that the extent of the missing core had not been fully appreciated even by the ice-core workers themselves. The GISP2 core is a full 3 km (2 miles) in length, made up of 1500 consecutive 2-metre (6.5 ft) lengths … and the only significant bit that was lost was in the sixth century AD – 14 metres, just where the tree-rings indicated something interesting. As I was pondering this, the other student spoke up: 'Oh yes, I remember that, I was up on the ice at that time … Elvis was up on the ice, all sorts of stuff was going down, the core was trashed, motors [the drill is a self-contained, motor-driven, 2-metre coring unit dropped on a hawser] were burning out … there was carbon in the drill hole …'

There are times when real life out-does science fiction. It could be that just by ill luck the American team had run into problems at that point in the coring. It could be that the carbon had come from the burnt-out motor in the drill rig and that Elvis was indeed up on the ice-cap at that time. If it was not just coincidental ill luck then something might have affected the ice in the sixth century AD and the carbon in the drill hole might not be from the motor; what then? Greg and the students kindly checked the daily logs which confirmed that each of seven consecutive two-metre sections had come up 'trashed', that is, as shattered ice. The longest stretch of lost ice in more than 3000 metres (9842 ft) had indeed been lost in the sixth century AD. This missing 14-metre section, between c. AD 614 (+/-15) and c. AD 545 (+/-15), introduces a slight imponderable into the dating of the core below the missing section and it is not beyond the bounds of possibility that the existing GISP2 core does not cover the AD 536–45 period at all.

The coincidence of 'problems' with no less than three ice-core records in the sixth century – Crête stops at AD 553+/-5; Dye 3 has the AD 540 to 516 'redating' and GISP2 has a 'lost' section – is hard to swallow. There simply must be something going on, especially as the significance of the period had been stressed in advance. I had even been to a conference in Hawaii in 1992 to tell the vulcanologists and ice-core workers of the possibilities of multiple eruptions around AD 540 and to ask that special attention be paid to this period. (Incidentally, I discount another possibility, which is that the CIA have been systematically trashing the cores around AD 540 to cover up the existence of debris from a crashed UFO.)

However, fortunately, a fallback situation exists. The Danish GRIP core (also 3 km (2 miles) long and from a site just 30 km (19 miles) from the GISP2 location) may provide the answers when the results of its detailed analysis become available. The Danes appear not to have lost any of their core, so a continuous record across the sixth century does exist. So far only an electrical conductivity survey (used to pick up strong acid, that is, volcanic signals) has been carried out on this section, but, interestingly, they see no large acid signal across the AD 536–45 period. It looks increasingly as if a volcano (still less volcanoes) was not the cause of the AD 540 environmental event. This raises a lot of questions, and Härke has picked up on this issue in the context of those anomalous eclipse records in the *Anglo-Saxon Chronicle* in AD 538 and 540. He posits that:

> *the entire northern hemisphere was affected in the late 530s by a sudden climatic deterioration caused either by a major volcanic eruption (Baillie's suggestion) or by dust-veils from a cometary impact (Victor Clube's suggestion).*

If the ice-core evidence is correct and there is no significant acidity layer in the Greenland ice around AD 540 then Clube's suggestions will have to be taken seriously, and we would have to decide how one might separate ancient descriptions of the effects of volcanoes from those of cometary impacts. Bailey, Clube and Napier have already suggested that in their view the Earth was at increased risk of bombardment in the interval AD 400–600. There can be no doubt that some momentous happening took place in the early- to mid-sixth century AD, but we do not know definitively the cause (or causes). However, the sixth century is as yesterday in geological time; something which could happen then could happen now. It is important that this event be fully understood, whether it be volcanic or meteoric, or indeed something we have simply not thought of. We will see in later chapters that it is possible to put together a very interesting circumstantial case for what may actually have happened.

"If we are forced to choose – and we decidedly are not – is the evidence not better for the God of Moses than for the comet of Velikovsky?"

Carl Sagan, 1977

PART II

Up to this point I have been developing a story which is firmly rooted in direct observation – fact if you like. Chronologies were built, dates were produced for artefacts and environmental events, patterns of human activity began to emerge. Attempts to use the tree-ring records as proxies of past climatic downturn yielded the story of the various marker dates including those from 2345 BC to AD 540. Quite a lot of information has flowed in to suggest that there is something special about these dates. The following chapters represent a building story so fantastic in some ways as to be almost unbelievable. Why should so many disparate pieces of information appear to fall into place? Why are so many of the original marker dates continuing to attract attention? Can volcanoes really be such a dramatic force for change in past human societies? What is going on? Is it an artefact of something I am doing? There are many questions. What I was not prepared for was the next stage, when the trickles of reinforcing information turned into a deluge. Even if what follows is not the answer, or even near the answer, the very fact that it can be written in a logical fashion almost defies the imagination.

So from here on the reader is about to embark on a journey which will stretch credulity but which is entirely based on documentary sources and a few logical jumps. Having, over a number of years, become immersed in a wide range of pieces of information relating to the tree-ring events, it started to become apparent that other connections existed between the events; the original connection had seemed to suggest volcanic eruptions as the common cause. As we have just seen, doubt about the volcanic origin of the AD 540 event forced a change of direction and a new 'stream of consciousness' developed. None of what follows is made up. Much of the connective logic is supplied by me, but in most cases the steps are self evident. The secret, as I see it, is not to be put off by doubts about minor parts of the story, rather to watch the bigger picture unfold.

CHAPTER 6

•

PROBLEMS WITH DATING THE SHANG DYNASTY AND THE NEW KINGDOM

It would seem that from an almost standing start in the 1960s, where only ancient history and archaeology were available, we have moved on dramatically, with evidence from the tree-ring chronologies and the ice-cores providing a wholly new chronological yardstick for the period of civilization. We have looked at the progress which dendrochronology has made since 1980, at chronology construction, and at least the preliminary exploitation of the chronologies for environmental and other information. Almost for the first time a series of catastrophic environmental events have been identified – they can hardly be ignored. In this chapter it seems appropriate to see how the two dust-veil events at 1628 BC and 1159 BC can be accommodated in the pre-existing early historic frameworks of China and Egypt. We know already that all the ancient chronologies before the eighth century BC are flexibly dated. The question is whether their dating is sufficiently flexible to allow them to conform to the dated tree-ring and ice-core events. The way to do this is to propose, yet again, that the New Kingdom in Egypt and the Shang dynasty in China be forced to conform to the environmental events – to see what happens. When we attempt to do this it becomes apparent that there may be a bigger story lurking within the spacing of events in the second millennium BC.

We can start by looking again at the spaced events in the Irish oak record in the second millennium BC. The events defined as 1628–1623 BC and 1159–1141 BC are the only hard facts in the whole of this discussion, because the dates are based on dendrochronology. These dates, deriving as they do from tree-rings and ice-acidities, are completely independent of any archaeological or ancient historical evidence. Readers have seen already how the specification of the dates prompted Pang and his colleagues to make associations with their astronomical estimates for the dates of the start and the end of the Shang dynasty. The dates which they suggested, based on their independent, astronomical, retro-calculations (and associated with dust-veil-like descriptions) were:

End Xia/Start Shang	1600+/-30	i.e. 1630–1570 BC
End Shang/Start Zhou	1100+80/-60	i.e. 1180–1040 BC

This duration for the Shang is not far out of line with one set of traditional dates which are given by Chang as 1617 BC to 1122 BC. Traditionally, dating in China was believed to be calendrically exact back to 841 BC, though that is now helped by Pang's double sunrise reference in 899 BC which extended the precise chronology. The similarity between the date ranges for the start and end of the Shang dynasty and the ranges which Richard Warner came up with when he looked up the catastrophes (serious happenings) from the ancient Irish Annals (which no one believes) are striking. The catastrophes identified by Warner are assigned to broad dating-windows, and it does not really matter whether these Irish dates are contaminated with biblical history because by definition both are independent of records from China. So Warner provides from the Irish Annals:

A catastrophe 'dated' in the range 1620–1544 'BC'
A catastrophe 'dated' in the range 1180–1031 'BC'

Even more curious is the fact that early Chinese history notes, with respect to the very start of the Shang dynasty, 'the floods were followed by a severe drought that lasted *seven years* into the next, Shang, dynasty'. This observation takes on more significance when one considers that the Irish World Chronicle records similar phenomena at the death of Tigernmas, somewhere around 1600 'BC'. At that time, apart from 'lakes breaking out', we have the notable reference: 'This reign was followed by seven years without a king ...' Wet in both cases; seven years in both cases – a positively strange coincidence and apparently completely independent.

Turning to Egypt, the ancient history of Egypt is divided up into thirty-one dynasties which in turn are blocked into 'Kingdoms'. Modern sources give the following dates for these main dynastic episodes:

Old Kingdom	2575–2134 BC
Middle Kingdom	2040–1640 BC
New Kingdom	1550–1070 BC
Late Period	712–332 BC

Each of the Kingdoms is separated from the next by an 'Intermediate Period'. As in China, these represent the periods where doubt creeps into the chronologies. Just as in China where doubt arises between the end of the Shang dynasty and the precise dates after 841 BC, so in Egypt doubt creeps into the chronology between the end of the New Kingdom (the most glorious episode in Egyptian history) and the precise date 712 BC. In Egypt this Third Intermediate Period has many doubtful aspects and parallels the four-century-long Greek Dark Age in the Mediterranean region. Similarly, there is another period of doubt after the Middle Kingdom:

Second Intermediate period – (2IP) 1640–1550 BC
  Third Intermediate period – (3IP) 1070–712 BC.

In the Intermediate Periods there is doubt about the exact number of rulers, their reign lengths and issues such as simultaneous reigns. There is evidence that national unity may have broken down, with fragmented areas ruled by different kings. The very existence of Intermediate Periods suggests that the system has succumbed to stress of some kind, presumably brought on by such factors as famine or invasion. Unfortunately, historians tend to try to impose order upon available information which may be very incomplete. In the case of the Third Intermediate Period and the Greek Dark Ages some revisionist scholars have made repeated attempts to eradicate the chronological problems by eradicating the Dark Ages themselves. People such as Peter James and David Rohl would like to move 1200 BC down to 800 BC (or shorten the Greek Dark Age by several centuries) and totally eliminate the difficulties. Unfortunately this approach brings them into conflict with calibrated radiocarbon chronology, and indeed dendrochronology itself. Their attempts lack conviction because they have to suppress information in order to sustain their arguments. However, their extreme views on the Dark Ages serve to give some idea of just how difficult these periods are.

Irrespective of difficulties with Intermediate Periods, we can now see that, at around the times when we see two spaced environmental events in Irish tree-ring records, three areas of the world show very similar event spacing in their cultural histories:

China	1630–1570 BC	1180–1040 BC
Ireland	1620–1544 BC	1180–1031 BC
Egypt	1640–1550 BC	1070–712 BC
Tree-rings	1628–1623 BC	1159–1141 BC

If we return to the hypothesis that the environmental effects were caused by volcanic dust-veils, it appears that a reasonable case exists to suggest that the effects were global in nature. The question is whether this attractive proposition is real or whether it is an artefact, or a coincidence. My feeling is that we need to consider the obvious proposition, that the package of events represents cause and effect, that is, the catastrophic natural events recorded in the tree-rings *caused* (or were somehow involved with) the hiatus in the various records. They may have acted as triggers for the dynastic changes.

The concept of environmental trigger events, which initiate periods of instability, seems reasonable. Even at a simplistic level, the means of the first three start dates in the list above are 1630 BC and 1143 BC, highly coincident with the tree-ring dates. It may be that we are looking at the trigger events themselves. One way to assess the impact of this idea is to ask what difference these new tree-ring dates would make to the ancient chronologies. It is fairly evident that the event in the seventeenth century would make very little difference. The start of the Shang dynasty in China, and at least one modern suggestion of the start of the Hyksos period (the Second Intermediate Period) in Egypt, are both within a few decades of the 1628 BC tree-ring date. However, when we look at the end of the Shang dynasty and the start of the Third Intermediate period, there is a greater divergence. While the Shang date is wide enough to encompass any tree-ring estimate, the traditional date of the end of the Egyptian New Kingdom is around 70 years too late. This in turn raises the question of whether the Egyptian chronology is really as well dated as is usually supposed.

While not intending to discuss in detail the Egyptian chronology, I will make what I feel are some relevant comments. First, all Egyptologists admit that the New Kingdom is not precisely dated, that is, it is floating in time. Most estimates of the degree of float, with the exception of the extreme estimates of the revisionists (who would move the New Kingdom closer to the present by several centuries), range over only a few decades. Kenneth Kitchen, an acknowledged expert in the field, suggests that the errors vary 'from about 30 years in 2000 BC, through 20/10 years by 1500 BC, to 11 years in the thirteenth century BC'. The problem is that there is no definitive way to substantiate these error estimates because there are no fixed points to work from and no neighbouring civilizations better dated. It is widely recognized that Egypt is the best-dated historical chronology, which is why it is used as the yardstick for dating cultures such as the Minoan in the Aegean.

In order to supply some additional context we need to look at the issue of the date of the Santorini eruption again. The outstanding problem with Santorini is that some conventional archaeological opinion dates the event to *c.* 1500 BC, because of archaeological links to Egypt. But there is more than one way to think of that issue. If we could confirm the date of Santorini – say, for the sake of argument that it was 1628 BC – then we could use that information to judge the accuracy of Egyptian dating. From a scientific perspective, that is what should be done, and was the spirit of LaMarche and Hirschboeck's suggestion that Santorini might be around 1627 BC. They posed the question, 'what would happen to Aegean and Egyptian chronology if Santorini really did erupt in 1627 BC, or one or two years earlier?' Unfortunately, for Aegean archaeologists who have lived all their lives with the yardstick of the Egyptian chronology it is not easy to question the very cornerstone of their chronological framework. Not all archaeologists are so conservative, and Sturt Manning has worked hard to show that most archaeological evidence can be seen as compatible with a seventeenth-century date for Santorini, especially if the Egyptian chronology is viewed as something less than sacrosanct. Santorini should be used to test the Egyptian chronology, not the other way round.

It is possible to construct long sections of robust chronology where everything is in exact relative placement. Dendrochronologists did this extensively when they were building up the main sections of their chronologies. However, having a robust unit of chronology is not the same as having a precisely dated chronology. Take as an example the New Zealand *Phyllocladus trichomanoides* forest which was buried by the large Taupo eruption around AD 200. Jonathan Palmer and his colleagues have constructed a 426-year tree-ring chronology which ends at the year when the eruption took place. They can suggest that the season of the eruption, deduced from the incomplete final growth ring, was in late summer or early autumn. Unfortunately, the chronology is not tied to the present and is only dated by radiocarbon analysis. Currently the best that can be said is that the eruption took place in the late summer or early autumn of a year *somewhere between* AD 150 and AD 250.

The situation is similar for Egyptologists. They have a good understanding of the internal detail and the relationships of the pharaohs of the New Kingdom. But the New Kingdom is equivalent to a 500-year floating chronology. There are no definitive links to the 'real time' historical chronology after 700 BC; in fact the New Kingdom is separated from real time by the woolly Third Intermediate Period. So Egyptologists have had to try to tie down their chronology by astronomical retro-calculations, particularly relating to records of eclipses and the rising of the star Sothis. These attempts have not been successful.

When attempts are made to date Egyptian sites by radiocarbon, the limitations of that method again show themselves. The margin of doubt in the dating of the New Kingdom is less than a century and, until now, none of the radiocarbon work on Egyptian samples has allowed resolution of the issue to better than a century. The Egyptian chronology will remain floating until some good fixed point is introduced into the proceedings. A good astronomical fix in the reign of any one pharaoh in the New Kingdom would probably be sufficient, but so far has not been unequivocally available. Ironically, Santorini is one of the best options for that fixed point, once its date is finally agreed. As we will see, several options point to 1628 BC (or just possibly 1629 BC).

SANTORINI AND EGYPT

The sub-text of much of this chapter centres on the issue of cause and effect. If the close juxtaposition of the dates of the tree-ring-dated environmental event at 1628 BC with the onset of dynastic changes, and other upsets, is considered dispassionately, logic dictates that the environmental event caused the breakdown in the fabric of the Middle Kingdom. The unsettled Second Intermediate Period – the Hyksos Period – should therefore start at or just after 1628–1623 BC. Alternatively, the upset could mark the end of the Hyksos Period and the start of the New Kingdom. For this sort of environmental interference to be a realistic possibility, we would have to have some reason for believing that Egypt might be adversely affected at the time of large dust-veil events. Surprisingly, there is some relevant information.

Phyllis Forsyth, in her discussion of the reign of Cleopatra, notes that one famine occurred about 43–42 BC. Apparently, Cassius had requested aid from Cleopatra but she refused, saying that Egypt was in the grip of famine and pestilence. This is a documented case of serious happenings in Egypt at the time of a known volcanic dust-veil. Forsyth explains that the likely cause of Egyptian famines is any failure of the Nile floods, which can occur as a result of failure of the spring monsoons in Ethiopia, affecting the Blue Nile. Alternatively, Egyptian water supply can be affected by either a failure of rainfall in central Africa, affecting the White Nile, or reduced melt-water run-off from the Mountains of the Moon in Uganda, the latter affecting the Albert system of the Nile. So there are several mechanisms for upsetting the environment in Egypt, all involving occurrences much further south in Africa. As Forsyth puts it, the Nile system would be deprived of water from all its sources should the monsoons and rains of Africa be eliminated or reduced. Is there a possible mechanism for a major dust-veil to reduce rainfall in Africa? The basic answer is yes. Although not everyone would agree with his ideas, Paul Handler has proposed that dust-veils can significantly alter monsoon patterns by cooling the surface of the Pacific. In some ways we do not have to rely on outside mechanisms, but instead ask whether there is a tendency for

Egypt to be affected by the very events we are considering. The answer again seems to be yes. In AD 542 the Justinian plague arrives 'out of Egypt', effectively coinciding with the severe dry fog in AD 536–37 and the events from AD 536–45. It seems that Egypt, with its vulnerability to reduction in the Nile floods, as even Pliny makes clear, is in the front line when there is a major dust-veil. This might be the case particularly if the eruption, as in the case of Santorini, was relatively close to Egypt.

This leads obviously to speculation about whether any records exist of Egypt being affected by a dust-veil, or any related phenomena, in the mid-second millennium BC. If the Egyptians described the eruption of Santorini in a particular year of a particular pharaoh and if the date of Santorini was specified – whether to 1628 BC or to some other date – there would at last be a fixed point in the Egyptian early history. So, is there any appropriate record? *Two* possibilities have been found. The first is a known reference to 'a storm in Egypt during the reign of Ahmose'. Ahmose, the first pharaoh of the New Kingdom, is traditionally dated to the early to mid-sixteenth century BC; not all that far from 1628 BC and certainly within the calibrated radiocarbon range of the eruption at 1670–1530 CalBC. The storm record is on a stele from Thebes and, as Davis puts it, it relates to 'a destructive storm related to flooding'. Apparently this event has to be before Ahmose's year 22 and, as Davis says, 'this would place the event either between 1550 and 1528 BC or between 1539 and 1517 BC ... [which] ... would support the traditional chronology'. Unfortunately,, we don't know whether this is a Santorini-related volcanic storm or just a severe ordinary storm. The descriptive elements make it difficult to say what the original writers intended. Although terms such as 'tempest', 'darkness' and 'all that had existed had been annihilated' are used, there is no overt symptom which specifies a volcanic connection. There is no indication that it was a protracted dust-veil lasting months or years; there is no fall of dust or ash and no obvious reference to what might be acid damage. It would be special pleading to make the Ahmose storm into the aftermath of Santorini. Nevertheless, if the Ahmose storm does relate to the Santorini eruption, then either Santorini erupted in the range 1550–1517 BC on the traditional chronology, or, just as likely, Santorini erupted in 1628 BC and there is a problem with the traditional historical chronology of Egypt. We cannot check the validity of the Egyptian chronology by using that same chronology to date Santorini, which ultimately must be dated independently, without reference to Egypt. Still, at least there is a record of a storm in broadly the right vicinity.

A second 'record' does associate volcano-like happenings with Egypt, but it is of a highly controversial nature. As we will see later, several recent writers relate Santorini to the biblical Exodus. At this point I want to address the suggestions of the renegade scholar, Immanuel Velikovsky. An exploration of Velikovsky's works would take more than a book in itself. He was a catastrophist whose ideas were so extreme and so unscientific that he ran into a storm when he published them in the 1950s. His name has become synonymous in scientific circles with the 'lunatic fringe' and most scientists would not even mention his work for fear of becoming 'contaminated'. I mention him here because one part of his overall thesis appears to bear directly on our Santorini/Egypt question. Velikovsky believed that the biblical Exodus – the flight of the Israelites from Egypt – related to a particularly catastrophic time. Why, he asked, if the Israelites recorded this event, is it not mentioned in Egyptian history? He then proceeded to convince himself that it *is* mentioned. According to Velikovsky, the Exodus from Egypt was at a time of severe tectonic/volcanic activity. Moreover, the Exodus took place at the start of the Hyksos period – the Hyksos being effectively the interregnum between the Middle and New Kingdoms, that is, the Second Intermediate Period. If we look at a respectable modern source, for example Renfrew and Bahn, we find that the start of the Hyksos is given as *c.* 1640 BC. By suggesting tectonic/volcanic activity at the start of the Hyksos, as the Israelites left Egypt, Velikovsky might as well have been saying that Egypt was affected by relatively local tectonic/volcanic activity in the vicinity of 1640 BC. He did not state it like this; he wanted to shorten Egyptian chronology by centuries and harmonize it with the shorter Hebrew chronology. However, putting this latter nonsense aside, if we take his main points we see not just the volcanic link to Egypt but that link at the correct – Hyksos – period. For better or worse, there does seem to be a pre-existing suggestion of volcano-related

This nineteenth century engraving shows Moses with his rod parting the waters. In the background the artist indicates both the pillar of fire and, to the left, a cloud which could as easily be a dragon as an angel.

activity in Egypt at a time within about twelve years of 1628 BC.

Leaving Velikovsky for the moment, we should remind ourselves of the list of horrors which are associated with the departure of the Israelites from Egypt. These are, from various Old Testament descriptions:

Dust, ashes and profound darkness
Hail, vines, flax and barley destroyed by hail
Cattle killed by hail
Flocks killed by thunderbolts
Water poisoned and fish killed
Water breaking out of rocks
Parting of the 'reed' sea – tsunami-like.

This list contains many of the symptoms which might be associated with a major volcanic event. Unlike the storm of Ahmose, the Exodus does have dust and ash and poisoned water. Interestingly Usher, who attempted to put a timescale on the happenings in the Old Testament, suggested a date of 1491 'BC' for the Exodus, which is only 137 years out if Santorini did erupt in 1628 BC, and less if the more conservative sixteenth-century date for the eruption was to prove correct.

We have now seen how the evidence, albeit much of it circumstantial, is building up for the reality of those two environmental events in the mid-later second millennium BC. Much information points towards the consistent scenario of widespread effects on the ground affecting human populations in the seventeenth and twelfth centuries BC. In this chapter I have used only the information which was available up to 1995 in order to keep the arguments simple and to show how the evidence has built up. The remainder of the book builds on the foundations laid up to this point.

To conclude, there are two events at 1628 BC and 1159 BC. The former may be the date of the Santorini eruption and, by extension, could be the date of the biblical Exodus. The latter, which we can call the 'Hekla 3' event – for want of a better name –may be implicated in the demise of the Mycenaean civilisation and for all we know could have ushered in the start of the Greek Dark Age. At around the time of each event, the ruling dynasties in China and Egypt, both of which ruled with the Mandate of Heaven, may have been toppled when the Mandate was withdrawn.

CHAPTER 7

•

EXODUS AND THE
480-YEAR INTERVAL

N ew research and information has allowed increased confidence in
the reality of the events at 1628 and 1159 BC. All new information
appears to bolster the idea that the former may be the date of the
Santorini eruption and, by extension, could be the date of the biblical Exodus.
The latter date may have implications for the demise of the Mycenaean
civilization and for all we know could have ushered in the start of the Greek
Dark Age. In this chapter we will address four additional issues, namely new
tree-ring information, ice-core deductions, additional information on
Santorini, and a surprising contribution from biblical history.

NEW TREE-RINGS

Peter Kuniholm, working in the Department of Classics at Cornell University,
has been piecing together a long chronology using timbers from Anatolia.
This Mediterranean chronology building exercise is different from those of
northern Europe – the area does not provide large quantities of naturally
preserved timber; instead sampling depends on available archaeological
sources. Fortunately archaeological sites are plentiful and charred wood seems
to survive particularly well in this area. Fifteen years of intensive sampling has
allowed Kuniholm and his team to take the Aegean chronology to the point
where it is almost complete. Long chronology sections have been built and
detailed radiocarbon analysis, using a radiocarbon wiggle-matching
technique, has allowed those sections to be specified closely in time. The
longest chronology section now runs from the eighth century BC to the
twenty-third century BC, running right across the mid- to late second
millennium, and tied down to within about +/-25 years in real time.

Our interest in this chronology stems from Kuniholm's initial
observation that there was a notable growth anomaly in the twelfth century
BC. Originally this was among the only support for the 1159–1141 BC event
in the Irish oaks. As the sections of this long Aegean chronology were cross-
dated, and the chronology extended back in time, it became apparent that
there was an even more dramatic anomaly in the seventeenth century BC. In
this well-dated chronology, at around 1640 BC (+/-25), growth in a series of

trees from Anatolia suddenly increases on average by 240 per cent. This massive positive anomaly suggests that these trees, in an area where there is usually little summer growth because of the extremely dry conditions, suddenly put on summer growth, presumably due to a notable increase in available moisture. Such a major growth enhancement suggests a sudden environmental event, one which was 'negative' in the sense of cooler and or wetter conditions (even though it was positive in sense of tree growth).

Several things spring to mind when confronted with such an observation. One is that this anomaly coincides rather well with the previously observed negative effects in the Irish, English and German oaks (with their narrowest rings) and the bristlecone pines (with their frost-rings). Another is that Anatolia is 'downwind' from Santorini. If one wants a mechanism to explain the anomalously wide summer growth in arid Anatolia, what better than the five billion tons of magmatic water stated by the vulcanologists to have erupted from the Santorini volcano? These trees normally suffer from a lack of water, when one year – possibly 1628 BC – a volcano just a few hundred km upwind from where the trees grow just happens to spew out 5000 million tons of water. A growth enhancement might well be a logical possibility. Vulcanologists also recognize that the Santorini eruption may well have evaporated a huge mass of seawater; after all, Santorini was a sea-level volcano. After its magma chamber had emptied – that is, after about four days during which it threw out the equivalent of some 29 cubic km of ash and rock – the whole edifice collapsed, forming the caldera which is now a bay, 400 metres deep, in the centre of the island. Up to 5 billion tons of seawater may have been evaporated during the eruption. So apart from the water which actually came out of the volcano itself, there may well have been as much again evaporated. Most of this water would have been injected into the lower levels of the atmosphere and would have dropped out quickly as rain. Ash from the Santorini eruption was deposited in an easterly direction, that is, there are finds of ash in Turkey and the Nile delta. We can be pretty sure that the Anatolian trees were indeed downwind and would have been in line to receive unusual quantities of moisture directly from the eruption.

It is easy to see how the mind tries to draw these various observations together to create a hypothesis – maybe Santorini affected trees all the way from Turkey to California to Ireland to England to Germany. It is very unfortunate that we do not know the season of the year when the Santorini eruption took place. However, there is an additional twist to Kuniholm's chronology with its placement by Kromer's radiocarbon wiggle-match. I have already noted there is another anomaly in the twelfth century BC. It happens that these two anomalies start – a sudden increase in growth in both cases –

exactly 470 years apart. This has to be fantastic because, the spacing between the start of the two events in the Irish oaks at 1628 BC and 1159 BC is 469 years. The Irish negative anomalies, 469 years apart, were pointed out back in 1988 when that work was first published; now in independent tree-ring work in the Mediterranean, two anomalous growth events occur exactly 470 years apart, the earlier of which, moreover, is placed by wiggle-matching at 1641+70/-22 CalBC, to be specific. It would be perverse to imagine that these are not the same events showing up in the two chronologies, both in the mid- to late second millennium BC. Kuniholm and Kromer, in collaboration with Sturt Manning, have proposed that the two events in the Anatolian trees should be placed at 1628+/-1 BC and 1159+/-1 BC respectively – until proven otherwise.

This support for the original Irish observations is better than one could ever reasonably have hoped. In addition, the scale of the anomaly in Anatolia at 1628 BC, or just possibly 1629 BC, does nothing to weaken the case that it may have been Santorini which erupted in that year. In fact, if anything, it strengthens the case. Since LaMarche and Hirschboeck had very little to go on when they suggested that 1627 BC might be Santorini, it is amazing that first Irish, English and German trees back up their event – now Mediterranean area trees carry the possibilities right into the Santorini area.

NEW ICE-CORE DEDUCTIONS

Underpinning the tree-ring–volcano debate is the issue of the acid layers in the Greenland ice-cores. It was surprising that the ice-core workers had not been too worried about the lack of replication between their various records. For example, while they observed a major acid signal in the Dye 3 core at 1645+/-20 BC, there was apparently no equivalent signal in the Camp Century core; or again, the 1120 (almost certainly 1150) +/-30 BC event in the Camp Century core was not present in the Dye 3 record. Addressing this issue, I have pointed out that a quite strong circumstantial case exists that the cores could be replicated if we accepted that the pairs of acid layers at 1598+/-30 BC and 1388+/-30 BC in Camp Century were the same as 1645+/-20 BC and 1428+/-20 BC in Dye 3. All these dates could be read from the published Danish results. It was possible to suggest that these were the same layers and that they should actually date to around 1628 BC and c. 1415 BC respectively; the former, of course, being the Irish oak–bristlecone pine tree-ring date.

While this conclusion had been deduced from pre-1988 ice-core data, new information from Greenland began to emerge as the results of the coring in the early 1990s came on line. In the early 1990s two new cores were drilled at Summit in Greenland. Here the ice is three km thick and contains a record of snowfall which runs back for more than 120,000 years. In the new 3000-

metre GRIP core the Danes announced that they saw three notable acid layers at 2050 BC, 1645 BC and 50 BC (all +/- a few years).

This suggested very strongly that they were actually seeing the same events as those which caused LaMarche and Hirschboeck's frost rings at 2036 BC, 1627 BC and 43 BC. This infers just as strongly that the ice-core 1645 BC event really was the same thing as the 1628 BC tree-ring event. This was useful because it suggested that the previously proposed redating of the Camp Century and Dye 3 records was on the right lines. The other record was the American GISP2 core. It was not until 1994 that Greg Zielinski and co-workers carried out sulphate analysis on this core and produced a detailed record back to 8000 BC. Although this publication paid little heed to likely error limits on the ice-core dates, it was evident from related publications that the errors were probably of the order of +/-1 per cent to +/-2 per cent, that is, dating errors of around +/-30 to +/-40 years back in the second millennium BC. Could we see any of the key ice-acidity layers, equivalent to 1628 BC, 1415 BC and 1150 BC, which had been deduced from the pre-existing Camp Century, Dye 3 or GRIP records?

The answer *appears* to be yes. There are three significant acid layers at essentially the same spacing in the GISP2 core. These are spaced at 217:260 years. However, the layers gave a strong appearance of being displaced by about 40 years from the target dates, that is, at 1669 BC, 1452 BC and 1192 BC. Could the spaced events in GISP2 actually be the same as the spaced events in the earlier cores? Fortunately there is some supporting evidence. There were other layers where equivalents could be found in the different records. The more complex spacing picture looked like:

Previous cores	210 or 216:	176:	92 years
GISP2 core	210–215:	170–175:	92–94 years

If all this were correct, and it almost certainly is, it implies that in the ice-cores we really do have volcanic events (or at least events giving rise to acid layers) at spacings estimated in two different records at:

Camp Century	1599–1120 BC = 479 years
GISP2	1669–1192 BC = 477 years

Given the avowed flexibility in the ice-core records, and the fact that the ice-acidities are spread over several years, it would seem that we have here spacings which are identical. If we accept this logic we now have strong circumstantial evidence for similarly spaced events in Irish oaks, Anatolian trees, Camp Century ice core, GISP2 ice core, Chinese historical records,

Egyptian historical records and Irish historical (mythological) records.

All spaced at around 470–490 years and all in the mid- to late second millennium BC! Again we are forced back to noting that environmentally effective dust-veils could cause widespread synchronous events; so the scenario is actually plausible. However, though we can be pretty certain that some volcano (or volcanoes) erupted in 1628 BC or 1629, whether it was Santorini still represents a slight question. This seems the logical place to discuss the possibility that Santorini could be tied to the biblical Exodus.

THE BIBLICAL EXODUS

Many people seek answers from biblical sources, and we have already seen how Velikovsky saw them as highly relevant. We can now try to take a more objective view. The Old Testament is essentially a history of the Hebrew people, the Israelites. In many ways it is no different from the histories of early China or early Egypt, maybe even early Ireland; it is presumably built around an historical core which was originally part of an oral tradition for a long period before it was eventually written down. If we treat biblical history as another source of information derived from a population who lived downwind of the Santorini eruption, what can we deduce?

Anyone arguing about a big explosive volcanic eruption in the Aegean in the mid-second millennium BC would have to consider that the biblical Exodus might be describing the same event. A number of authors have suggested this, including Ian Wilson in 1985, Mike Rampino and his colleagues in 1988 and Hendrik Bruins and Johannes van der Plicht in 1996.

Despite this, it is not generally accepted that Santorini could be involved in the Exodus. The principal reason is chronological – for many years people have tended to 'date' Exodus very late: 'about 1250 BC' is constantly suggested. This is probably due to the various attempts to guess which Pharaoh was responsible for the persecution of the Hebrew people. It has always been widely reckoned that Rameses II was the 'villain', even though it is not in any way proven. Irrespective of proof, Rameses' dates are habitually linked to the Exodus. Rameses reigned, on the traditional Egyptian calendar, from c. 1290–1224 BC, therefore the Exodus must be thirteenth century BC. However, opening the *Expositor's Bible Commentary*, one can quickly find that this Rameses dating has no more justification than the next best alternative which 'would set the Exodus at c. 1446 BC [thus] making Thutmose III the Pharaoh of the Oppression'. So, although scholarly opinion is steeply divided on the likely date of the Exodus, both common possibilities, whether Rameses II or Thutmose III, are far too late for Santorini to be involved.

At this point it is important to note that biblical scholars have been debating the date of the Exodus for centuries and the best they can come up with is a choice of likely dates some two centuries apart. Since both proposed dates cannot be correct, one is justified in asking if either need be correct. Interestingly, as we have seen, the King James Bible (with traditional chronological annotation by Usher) gives a date of 1491 BC for the Exodus. We will return to this later.

The descriptions of what happened at the time of the Exodus read like many other ancient (and modern) descriptions of the aftermath of major environmentally effective, presumably volcanic, dust-veils. We have seen the Chinese descriptions of the environmental effects recorded at the beginning and end of the Shang dynasty, and those at 208 BC, at 44 BC and at AD 536:

> the earth emitted yellow fog ... the sun was dimmed ... three suns appeared ... frosts in July ... the five cereals withered ... therefore famine occurred' and again 'it rained dust at Bo. For 10 days it rained ashes, the rain was grey ... it snowed in July ... frosts killed the five cereals ...

These give us a fair idea of what 'remote viewers' (who probably did not even know what a volcano was) would tend to record when they experienced the effects of a large environmentally effective dust-veil, whether caused by a volcano (or several volcanoes) or some other agency such as a cometary impact or atmospheric loading from cosmic dust.

Now when we look at that package as a whole we can see reflections of the Chinese phenomena in descriptions from 'remote viewers' of the Indonesian eruption of Tambora in the early nineteenth century: a persistent 'dry fog' which dimmed the sun the year after Tambora erupted in 1815. The summer saw abnormal cold in regions bordering the north Atlantic, the 'Year Without a Summer'. Crops failed to ripen and there were famines and outbreaks of disease. Stars were abnormally dimmed and appeared tremulous. However, the Israelites might not have been so remote from Santorini. So we have to take account of what populations closer to Tambora experienced in 1815: thunderous detonations were heard more than 1000 km away. In some places within 600 km of Tambora the sky was pitch-black for one to two days and ash fell over a similar distance. Tsunami (seismic sea waves) were associated with Tambora even though it is not a sea-level volcano. With this knowledge of the experiences of other remote viewers, we have a better background to develop a feel for the Exodus story as preserved in early Hebrew records from the second millennium BC.

The Exodus includes dust, several days of darkness, hail, fish killed, un-drinkable water, sycamores destroyed by frost, vines destroyed by hail, cattle killed by hail, flocks killed by thunderbolts, plagues of flies, water breaking out of rocks, the earth opening, the sea parting as in a tsunami, and so on. In fact, all that is needed to make the event entirely due to a volcano is to move the ten plagues to follow the Exodus and the package would be almost exactly what one might expect of the aftermath of an environmentally effective eruption. Someone looking at the Exodus story and knowing about descriptions of other distant volcanic effects might offer the possibility that the Israelites escaped from Egypt under the cover of a major natural, possibly volcanic, event. Their wise men subsequently put the various remembered components of the event into the logical sequence preserved in the Old Testament.

In his book, *The Exodus Enigma*, Ian Wilson asked exactly this question and moreover asked it in the specific context of Santorini. He set out to show that the Exodus saga fitted extremely well with Santorini (though he assumed the traditional *c.* 1500 BC dating, which is not relevant here). One of the issues Wilson concentrated on was the 'pillar of cloud by day and fire by night'. He asked the question: could the eruption column of Santorini have been seen from Egypt? Allowing for the curvature of the earth, Wilson came up with the surprising fact that, even though Santorini is 800 km (500 miles) from the Nile delta, the eruption column only had to be 50 km (30 miles) high to be visible from the Nile delta! Indeed, there is no reason to suppose that the Santorini eruption column was limited to 50 km (30 miles): Santorini with its sea-level caldera may well have been an exceptionally explosive event, in which case it may have exceeded the estimates of modern-day modellers. Pinatubo in 1991 is reliably estimated to have had an eruption column 40 km (24 miles) high, even though it was not as big an eruption as Santorini, and was almost certainly less explosive. Vulcanologists theorize, but they do not know what big volcanoes can do in terms of eruption column. However, most vulcanologists would accept that Santorini would have had an eruption column at least 50 km (30 miles) high which is quite adequate for Wilson's theory.

So Ian Wilson had set an interesting hare running. To extend Wilson's ideas: if the erupting Santorini actually was the 'pillar of cloud by day and fire by night' then we should be able to go back to Exodus and look again at the detail of the story. If this scenario were correct, as the Israelites moved north the pillar would act as a reference-point broadly 'in front' of them to the north-west. Whereas, when they turned east across the reed sea it should be more or less 'behind' them. Thinking about this I referred to the relevant chapter of Exodus (13: 23): 'And the Lord went before them by day in a pillar of cloud, to lead them the way; and by night in a pillar of fire, to give them light: to go by day and night …'

Imagine this apparition on the horizon, a fixed point day and night; if it was Santorini it would have been an unprecedented phenomenon for those who witnessed it. However, after the Israelites have been instructed to turn across the sea, presumably indicating a turn to the east, it states clearly (Exodus 14: 19): 'And the angel of God which went before the camp of Israel, removed and went behind them; and the pillar of the cloud went from before their face, and stood behind them ...'

It would appear that here we have an eyewitness account, handed down from the middle of the second millennium BC, from someone who, from Egypt, saw on the north-west horizon the eruption column of Santorini. The column did not move, the Israelites changed direction. Vulcanologists estimate that it took about four days to empty the magma chamber at Santorini, that is, the column may have stayed up for about four days, just about the same length of time that it took the Israelites to leave Egypt and cross the reed sea.

Velikovsky had convinced himself that the Exodus took place just as the Hyksos were entering Egypt (to within a matter of weeks or so). Recent authors place the start of the Hyksos at c. 1640 BC, alarmingly close to the date of the volcanic event in the tree-ring and ice-core records. So what we might call marginal literature (Velikovsky) had already made connections between volcanic activity affecting Egypt and the Israelites at the time of the Hyksos, whereas we are discussing volcanic activity affecting the Aegean and presumably also Egypt at 1628 BC close to a time when the Hyksos, according to non-marginal literature, were entering Egypt c. 1640 BC. Are we being drawn down a fictitious path? Or are we gradually seeing a real story come together before our eyes? It certainly cannot be dismissed out of hand. As always, at this stage of an argument, one casts around for additional information; is there anything else which might add to this story?

FURTHER CONTRIBUTIONS FROM BIBLICAL HISTORY

David Rohl is a revisionist, that is, one of those writers who wish to prove that the conventional Egyptian historical chronology is too long by about 250 years. I believe the revisionists are wrong because calibrated radiocarbon dates broadly support the conventional Egyptian chronology. For the revisionists to be correct calibration and dendrochronology would have to be wrong and that is not possible, given the degree of tree-ring replication and the shape of tree-ring-based radiocarbon calibration curve itself. While he dismisses radiocarbon and dendrochronology, in his book *A Test of Time*, he mentions an important 480-year period in biblical history: 'According to 1 Kings 6:1–2, the Exodus from Egypt took place four hundred and eighty years before the construction of the First Temple of Jerusalem. The building of the first temple dedicated to Yahweh was begun in the fourth regnal year of King Solomon.'

As we have been discussing in this chapter and the last, 480 years is not just a random period in the context of the mid- to late second millennium BC. Rohl's comment triggered the realization that if the 470-year spacing was significant in dendrochronology and in the ice-cores, then it might be equally significant in biblical history. The spacing from the Exodus to the building of Solomon's Temple is not just 480 years, it is also the spacing between two of the most important events in early Hebrew history and perhaps the sort of spacing which just might be handed down correctly. If the 1628–1159 BC ideas are correct, and there were catastrophes at these times in Ireland and plausibly in both China and Egypt, should we not find some description of a catastrophe at around the time when Solomon builds the temple?

In the King James Bible the opening chapters of the first book of Kings are interesting, but nothing very catastrophic happens. By 1 Kings Chapter 8 we are getting well past the building of the Temple when verse 10 happens to mention that a 'cloud filled the house of the Lord'. In the margin is a reference to Psalm 18. Psalm 18 is about David (Solomon's predecessor) praising God for his manifold blessings in a period of distress. The later verses of the psalm open up a new set of possibilities because they sound distinctly catastrophic. Only the key words and phrases are listed here:

earth shook and trembled... foundations of the hills moved and were shaken... smoke... fire... coals... darkness... dark waters... thick clouds of the skies... hail stones and coals of fire... thundered in the heavens... hail stones and coals of fire, again... arrows... shot out lightenings... channels of waters were seen... the foundations of the world were discovered... at the blast of the breath of thy nostrils...

This Psalm is repeated almost word for word in 2 Samuel 22 and refers to events in David's reign, shortly before Solomon and the construction of the Temple. Reference to adjacent chapters produced the observation in Samuel 21: 1: 'There was a famine in the days of David, three years, year after year ...' and later 24: 15, 'So the Lord sent a pestilence upon Israel ... and there died of the people ... seventy thousand men.'

It will be apparent that some fairly profound happenings appear to have taken place towards the end of David's reign, involving famine, plague and Exodus-like catastrophic activity. What about dates? Previous scholars have done the work for us. Just as Usher provided the Exodus with the date 1491 'BC', so David's famine is dated 1021 'BC' and the pestilence 1017 'BC' with the catastrophic list somewhere in between. Thus the spacing between the catastrophic happenings associated with the Exodus and the start of the catastrophic happenings associated with David are, according to Usher, 1491 minus 1021 = 470 years.

Readers can decide for themselves if there is any significance to the observation that the Bible preserves a record of two catastrophic and highly significant events, with distinctly tectonic overtones, 470 years apart; while two tree-ring chronologies register abrupt environmental downturns, with strong links to volcanic activity, 469–470 years apart, both in the mid- to late second millennium BC.

This poses some interesting questions, not least about chronology. For example, if Santorini actually erupted in 1628 BC, and if the Exodus relates to Santorini, then it would make it likely that the Exodus took place in 1628 BC and the construction of Solomon's Temple started in 1149 BC. In fact, whether Santorini erupted in 1628 BC is in some ways irrelevant to the argument. The spacing and character of the two events is such that by logic the Exodus–David episode should fall from 1628 to 1158 (or from 1629 to 1159) BC simply on the basis that the Bible and the tree-rings could well be recording the same environmental events. Following that logic – that we can suggest the date of the Exodus–David events in a single jump from the spaced Irish and Anatolian tree-ring events – then, since the pillar in the Exodus, by logic, is likely also to be Santorini, we can now be fairly certain that Santorini erupted in 1628 BC.

The fact that this simple statement has profound implications for the chronology of the Old Testament, and indeed for Egypt, seems inevitable. It does not matter if the new 470-year placement of Exodus–David disagrees with conventional wisdom on where Moses and David come in historical time. All that matters is that Hebrew history preserves a memory of two traumatic events 470 years apart.

CHAPTER 8

◆

THE
EXODUS/SANTORINI
SCENARIO:
INDEPENDENT TESTING

We have seen how a scenario has gradually developed with respect to Santorini and the Exodus. However, there is a problem with much of this scenario. Archaeologists had tried to date Santorini using classical linkages through artefacts to Egypt and the conventional Egyptian chronology; the more traditional of them arriving at dates around 1500 BC. In addition, there are traditional estimates that the Exodus may date around either 1250 BC, because of the idea that Rameses II was the most likely pharaoh to have ground down the Israelites, or around 1450 BC if one preferred Thutmose III. These four very different chronological estimates – 1628 BC, *c.* 1500 BC, *c.* 1450 BC and *c.* 1250 BC – of course make it hard for anyone to make sense of the Exodus–Santorini link.

It is difficult to untangle Exodus–Santorini arguments and seek significance. For example, Santorini was invoked by the ice-core workers as the likely cause of their 1390+/-30 BC acid layer when they published Camp Century in 1980; by 1987 they had switched to the 1645+/-20 BC layer in Dye 3 in tune with LaMarche and Hirschboeck's suggested 1627 BC dating. But LaMarche and Hirschboeck were strongly influenced by the calibrated radiocarbon evidence for a possible seventeenth-century date for the eruption. In 1988 Baillie and Munro followed LaMarche's suggestion, again suggesting Santorini as being seventeenth century. Similarly, Sturt Manning has tended towards the seventeenth-century scenario in his reinterpretation of much Aegean chronology, which again is influenced heavily by radiocarbon evidence. Basically, all of the Santorini suggestions involving the seventeenth century take some account of the radiocarbon evidence from Akrotiri.

Everyone has come into the Santorini debate, and indeed the Exodus debate, with his or her judgement coloured to some extent. It seems reasonable to step back and ask if there is any independent route to arriving at 'Santorini and the Exodus in the seventeenth century BC', without using either prior radiocarbon evidence or prior archaeological evidence. What follows is based on my analysis of the problem. Where to start? We could list a series of facts relating to the debate, then attempt a segregation into independent routes:

(1) Santorini erupted somewhere in the range 1670–1530 CalBC on the basis of radiocarbon evidence.

(2) LaMarche and Hirschboeck saw what they believed to be a volcano-related event in 1627 BC in their upper tree-line, bristlecone frost-ring record. They suggested Santorini as the cause simply because Santorini was known to be in the sixteenth to seventeenth century BC bracket on archaeological and radiocarbon evidence. Also, in 1984, it was the only large volcano known to have erupted in the mid-second millennium BC.

(3) Irish oak narrowest-ring events suggested that there were volcano-related environmental occurrences in 1628 BC and 1159 BC. Santorini was cited purely due to its prior citation by LaMarche and Hirschboeck, though Irish oaks cannot definitively identify Santorini; however, there is a strong circumstantial case that the Irish narrowest-ring events are related to volcanoes because of the spacing of the events and the similar spacing of the acid layers in the Greenland ice.

(4) The ice-core workers came up with two relevant ice-acidities: 1120+/-50 BC in Camp Century and, later, 1645+/-20 BC in Dye 3. Although virtually certain to be related to the 1628 BC and 1159 BC events in the Irish and Anatolian tree-ring records, they are not (yet) positively identified to particular volcanoes. The 1645+/-20 BC acidity is not directly related to the Santorini eruption, although the acidity is strongly related to the 1628–1627 BC tree-ring effects.

(5) Kuniholm, Kromer and Manning have two anomalous tree-ring events in the seventeenth and twelfth centuries BC, exactly 470 years apart – the same spacing as in the Irish oak case.

(6) Pang and his co-workers have determined that the Chinese Shang dynasty is approximately 496 years long and starts and ends with descriptions which sound very like dust-veil events: so major events of this kind are sometimes recorded as stress events in human history.

(7) There is similar spacing between the Egyptian Second and Third Intermediate periods.

(8) There is less well-authenticated (i.e. probably derivative) spacing of catastrophic events in the prehistoric 'World Chronicle' section of the Irish Annals.

(9) We know that the King James Bible, based on early Hebrew

history/mythology, with Usher's interpolated dates, has two 'events' (those of Exodus and later David) which read like tectonic-related environmental events, both involving famine and plague, spaced (by Usher, if not the original writers) 470 years apart.

What is independent from this list? On consideration, item 1, the radiocarbon evidence, is independent of all the rest. Archaeologists would have obtained radiocarbon age estimates on buried material from Akrotiri even if there had been no other dating evidence. Items 2–9 can be thought of as completely separate from the radiocarbon evidence and thus do not depend on the radiocarbon evidence. Can an independent suggestion of a seventeenth-century BC date for Santorini be generated from items 2–9?

The bristlecone-pine evidence is totally independent of any other evidence. The 1627 BC frost-ring event was identified as possibly volcanic purely on the basis of modern nineteenth- and twentieth-century parallels. Even if LaMarche and Hirschboeck had never heard of Santorini they would have proposed a major volcano in 1627–1629 BC. The Irish oak evidence could have been found purely as a response to LaMarche and Hirschboeck's specification of the 1627 BC frost-ring event. Sooner or later someone would have looked to see if the Irish trees showed any effects at this specified date. So the Irish oak evidence for volcanoes at 1628 BC and 1159 BC does not have to rely on radiocarbon evidence.

All the tree-ring and ice-core evidence is completely independent of radiocarbon and, indeed, completely independent of Chinese or Egyptian chronology. The 'Exodus to David' event-spacing is also independent of all other considerations and has been in print with Usher's suggested dates since the seventeenth century. It should be noted that, for various reasons, people studying the interval between Exodus and Solomon's temple have commonly pointed out that the specified '480 years from the Exodus to the building of Solomon's temple' is a number which probably has no real significance, that is, it is the product of 12 x 40, both components of which are themselves mystical numbers; thus 480 is probably an invention of mystical significance. In my view, people have tried to explain away the 480-year spacing for no particularly good reason. The *470*-year spacing is not affected by such arguments, as it is not a mystical number. Instead, we have independent tree-ring (469-year) and biblical (470-year) spacings. If we make the connection 'tree-ring-469-year-spacing *to* 470-year-biblical-spacing' we find ourselves lining up the events:

1628 BC		1159 BC
tree-ring event	469 yr.	tree-ring event
Exodus event	470 yr.	David event

This matrix could have been produced as a basis for discussion without any recourse to radiocarbon dating evidence. (I am not going to discuss the problems which would be raised by this matrix; suffice to say that conventional wisdom would see David in the tenth century BC, and moving him to the twelfth century would cause ripples in several academic disciplines ...)

But, and this is a key point, we have already seen that the Exodus gives a very good impression of being a detailed description of a volcanic event, *and* that Santorini was a major volcano within line of sight of the Nile delta. This package of association – tree-ring spacing, biblical spacing, Exodus and Santorini – would have allowed the postulation that Santorini may have erupted in 1628 BC without any involvement of radiocarbon or Egyptian history. So the 'matrix for discussion' could be expanded to include Santorini.

1628 BC		1159 BC
tree-ring event	469 yr.	tree-ring event
Exodus event	470 yr.	David event
Santorini		

Once we have arrived at this possible Santorini = 1628 BC scenario, the independent radiocarbon evidence can 'test' the scenario. The radiocarbon evidence provides a range which brackets the proposed 1628 BC date. Thus the calibrated radiocarbon dates for Santorini are *not inconsistent* with the suggestion that Santorini erupted in 1628 BC, a suggestion which I maintain could have been generated independently. Perhaps more importantly, this whole scenario is completely independent of Egypt or Egyptian/Aegean archaeological dating. If I were an Egyptologist I would be interested in this 'tree-ring spacing, biblical spacing, Exodus and Santorini – not inconsistent with radiocarbon' scenario. What are the chances that such a chain of evidence could exist by accident?

Although a lot has been written in chapters 3–7 about tree-rings and human civilizations responding to volcanic dust-veils, there is an inevitable tension in this whole story, relating to the fact that vulcanologists and climatologists do not think volcanoes can cause such dramatic effects. Arguments regularly encountered are: dust washes out quickly from the atmosphere; residence times in the stratosphere are short; modern eruptions have only had effects for up to three years; the column heights of eruptions are self-limiting, and so on. While I am not convinced that volcanoes are as 'safe' as many other workers seem to believe, I am forced to recognize vulcanologists' arguments. However, we are left with some apparently dramatic ancient events such as 1628 BC, 1159 BC and AD 540 which, although they seem to be related to 'dust-veils', should not be directly due to 'ordinary' volcanoes. So, why do these events stand out? Why are there so few of them? What is special about these particular events which seem to occur at, or close to, crucial points in Chinese, Hebrew, and maybe even Egyptian, history? To some extent, these same questions were always there in the volcano story.

One possibility is what might be called the 'nightmare scenario'. The story may hold together fairly well with volcanoes as the main agency for the dust-veil events, but is it possible that there is something else in the equation? If we stand back for a minute, we can remind ourselves that the reason why we know volcanoes are involved relates to the presence of acid layers in Greenland. The events have, with the exception of AD 540, volcanic associations. But is it possible that the volcanoes are a red herring? Could the volcanoes be a *secondary* effect rather than the prime mover? Could something else, something less visible, be the real cause?

This query has always been lurking in the volcano story: volcanoes erupt somewhere around the world every year. Why would a mere handful, over several millennia, stand out as 'different'. The ones we are considering do not seem to be all that much 'bigger'. There is no good evidence for 'multiples', that is, several erupting at once (though we have seen that a possible reason for this could be the use of radiocarbon to date volcanoes, with resulting 'smearing' of dates through time). Is there another class of phenomena which could act as a better prime mover? An obvious aspect for consideration would be something extra-terrestrial; perhaps cometary fragments; perhaps interstellar or cometary dust. Could our earlier marker events actually be the result of extra-terrestrial activity of some kind, as hinted at around AD 540? Is there even a shred of evidence to make us consider such a suggestion seriously? Well, again, yes, there is.

EXTRATERRESTRIAL ASPECTS

The first slightly worrying observation came about as the details of the various 1628 BC, 1159 BC, 207 BC, 44 BC and AD 540 events came together. In 44 BC, at the time of Caesar's death, a daylight comet was seen. Then Phyllis Forsyth noted those 'stones falling from the sky' around 207 BC, and we have already mentioned the possibility of AD 540 being an impact event of some kind, falling as it does in Bailey, Clube and Napier's period of increased cosmic risk, coupled with the absence of a definite volcanic-acid signal. This hint of a recurring pattern forced me to ask if 'things appearing in the sky or falling from the sky' might be the missing common factor. There appeared to be no evidence for anything cometary at the earlier dates 1628 BC and 1159 BC. Imagine my surprise when, while reading Carl Sagan and Ann Druyan's book *Comet*, I find this statement:

This connection of comets and misfortune is made in the earliest surviving reference to a comet, a single Chinese sentence from the fifteenth century BC. 'When Chieh executed his faithful counsellors, a comet appeared'... and just a few lines later: 'When King Wu-wang waged a punitive war against King Chòu, a comet appeared with its tail pointing towards the people of Yin ...'

The very first records of comets were at the start and end of the Shang dynasty. Because, of course, King Chieh was the last emperor of the Xia dynasty, when the earth emitted yellow fog, and there were summer frosts etc., while King Chòu was the last of the Shang where we had dust raining for ten days, etc. The only strange thing about these quotes from Sagan and Druyan is their apparently completely erroneous fifteenth-century date for Chieh.

Why would the Chinese record these two particular comets? They are cited by Sagan and Druyan as the 'first' and 'second' references to comets in ancient history. People were not regularly mentioning comets, so these references are significant by any standards. It has already been suggested that the start and end of the Shang dynasty should be in some way related to the 1628 BC and 1159 BC environmental events in the tree-ring records. Not only volcanoes can have global effects, so can comets. With these observations from Sagan and Druyan we now have:

1628 BC	possible cometary association; end of the Xia dynasty
1159 BC	possible cometary association; end of the Shang dynasty
207 BC	stones from the sky/apparitions; end of the Ch'in dynasty
44 BC	red daylight comet
AD 540	possible impact scenario

Is there a cosmic element to these events which show up so widely, which appear at first sight to be volcanic, but which volcanologists and climatologists say are inconsistent with normal volcanic effects? Could it be that impacts or the loading of the atmosphere with cometary dust might be the prime movers?

OLD TESTAMENT ASPECTS

We have seen above that it is possible to make use of the '470-year' biblical interval between Exodus and the trauma at the time of David. While reading through the other relevant books which deal with this time I found a version of the story in 1 Chronicles 21: 14, 16:

So the Lord sent pestilence upon Israel; and there fell in Israel seventy thousand men ... And David lifted up his eyes and saw the angel of the Lord

stand between the earth and the heaven, having a drawn sword in his hand
stretched out over Jerusalem ...

Is this a reference to a comet at the time of the second spaced event in
the later second millennium BC? Subsequently I discovered that a number of
other authors, including David Levy (the co-discoverer of the comet
Shoemaker/Levy 9), have taken this description to be a *direct* reference to a
comet. Can we begin to see a pattern here? If we lay out the various strands
the story begins to look like this:

1628 BC		1159 BC
dust-veil		dust-veil
tree-ring event	469 yr.	tree-ring event
Exodus event: Santorini?	470 yr.	David event: comet?
Shang dynasty start: comet?	496? yr.	Shang dynasty end: comet?

Looking at this table, one obvious thing is missing; a comet at the time
of the Exodus. Should we ask if Santorini was triggered by a comet? After all,
anything is possible in the past, given how little we know. We have to ask if
there is any mention of a comet just at or before the Exodus story. We have
already seen that the Angel of the Lord, regarded as a comet when he appears
to David, was also present at the Exodus: 'the angel of God, who had been
travelling in front of Israel's army, withdrew and went behind them. The pillar
of cloud also moved from in front and stood behind them ...' More cometary
imagery around the time of the Exodus appears if we examine the story.
Referring to Exodus 4: 2–4:

And the Lord said unto him [Moses], What is that in thine hand? And he
said, *a rod. And he said, cast it on the ground. And he cast it on the ground, and*
it became a serpent: and Moses fled from before it. And the Lord said unto Moses,
Put forth thine hand, and take it by the tail. And he put forth his hand, and
caught it, and it became a rod in his hand ...

Could this serpent be the imagery of a comet? A serpent or a dragon is
virtually a euphemism for a bolide, a fireball leaving a trail through the
heavens. One biblical commentary give an exegesis of the 'rod' issue as
follows, reinforcing the unusual nature of the serpent: Aaron's staff (it was the
same as Moses' staff or the staff of God) when cast down became a *tannin*
('great serpent', 'dragon', or 'crocodile'). The word *tannin* is usually used for
larger reptiles such as crocodiles, or a sea monster or even Leviathan. Is there
just the faintest hint in all this that, in the run-up to the Exodus, with its

'pillar of cloud by day and of fire by night', which might just be the Santorini eruption, there is indeed the imagery of a comet or bolide?

A nineteenth-century Hebrew encyclopaedia had no direct entry for 'comet', but instead a cross-reference to 'astronomy'. Under 'astronomy' it is stated '*The comet, because of its tail, is called kokbade-shabbit (rod star)*'. Rod star! Moses threw his *rod* to the ground where it became a *serpent*, and then the Lord told him to pick it up *by the tail*. It appears that the Exodus is an original text laced through with cometary/fireball imagery. It may not be without significance that the association is preserved in the name of the Hebrew god Yahweh. Although normally explained as 'I am' or 'I am that I am', an ancient belief was that Yahweh was derived from the Egyptian for 'one moon'. But there are other suggested explanations:

(1) 'To fall' and originally designating some sacred object such as a stone, or an aerolite, which was believed to have fallen from heaven
(2) 'To blow' a name for the god of wind and storm
(3) 'He who causes to fall' the rain and the thunderbolt
(4) 'The storm god' and in other forms Shaddai 'To lay waste', 'The destroyer', 'The devastator'.

It is possible, by following a logical set of questions, to end up with the scenario that not only were there catastrophic events, 470 years apart, in ancient Hebrew texts, but also those catastrophic events had cometary associations. Perhaps the Exodus really was associated with both a volcano and a comet. Dewey Beegle, a professor of Old Testament theology, discussed the manifestations of both royalty and deity, that is, descriptive terms related to gods and kings, says:

> *Variations of this dual identity of royalty and deity have been found all the way from Greece to India. Two specific words used in Babylonia are helpful in understanding the idea ... Melammu is a dazzling halo or luminous cloud surrounding anything divine ... the related term puluhtu designates anything which inspires fear and awe, and at times it refers to a garment of flame surrounding a god or king ...*

In such a context the Angel of the Lord, who appears in the sky with a bright halo and a flaming garment, would inspire fear and awe. Those sound like cometary aspects. In the New Testament another Angel of the Lord, Gabriel, announces the births of John the Baptist and Jesus Christ. Christ's birth was announced by a star that stood still over Bethlehem. Does that mean that Gabriel also has a cometary aspect? Gabriel has another association which is also telling: 'in the Book of Enoch, part of the pseudepigrapha, he is one of the seven archangels ... Later Christian tradition made him the trumpeter of the Last Judgement.' The trumpeter of the Last Judgement! The Last Judgement, as we will see later, has both catastrophic and cometary aspects.

It is interesting when independent observers come up with similar scenarios using independent evidence. In the next chapter I want to explore two apparently independent suggestions that extraterrestrial factors may have been involved in both the twelfth-century BC and sixth-century AD events. However, before moving on to that it must be said that this whole scenario could come to nothing. I have already pointed out that there are serious differences of opinion on the detail of the end of the Shang dynasty and its length, so the comets at the start and end of that dynasty are not a known number of years apart. Similarly, we only have to turn away from the standard Bible to Josephus and we find that the '480 years from the Exodus to the building of the temple' can become 'five hundred and ninety two' years. These points highlight the difficulty of working with ancient records; they are inherently flexible and subject to interpretation. However, these records do open up some interesting possibilities.

Here is another quote used in Sagan and Druyan, this time from Hyginus, *c.* 35 BC:

> *But after the conquest of Troy and the annihilation of its descendants ... overwhelmed by pain she separated from her sisters and settled in the circle named arctic, and over long periods she would be seen lamenting, her hair streaming. That brought her the name of comet.*

The fall of Troy is traditionally in the twelfth century BC, where this chapter places David's possible brush with a 'comet', not far from where the Shang dynasty ends with a comet. Are all these references to the same comet, to returns of the same comet, or to a period of notable comet activity? If all three of these early references really are twelfth century BC, it was obviously an active time. Even more can be added in. Sagan and Druyan also tell us that there is an unambiguous Babylonian reference to a comet (or comets, as there are both favourable and unfavourable omens) in the twelfth century BC during the reign of Nebuchadnezzar I. What is perhaps most surprising about Sagan and Druyan's comment is the offhand manner in which they note that the twelfth-century descriptions are of 'a comet that rivalled the sun in brightness'. They then make the deduction that such a comet, to look like this, 'must have come very close to the Earth'. One is left wondering just exactly what did happen in the twelfth century BC, when dynasties changed due to the withdrawal of the Mandate of Heaven, and when a four-century-long Dark Age began.

Another detail is supplied by the Sacred Books, translated from the Chinese by James Legge. At the time of T'ang's conquest of King Chieh, that is at the Xia/Shang transition (possibly 1628 BC, but let us just say seventeenth century BC):

> *the king of Xia [Chieh] extinguished his virtue, and played the tyrant … suffering from his cruel injuries, and unable to endure the worm-wood and poison, you protested with one accord your innocence to the spirits of heaven and earth. The way of heaven is to bless the good and make the bad miserable. It sent down calamities on [the house of] Xia, to make manifest its guilt. Therefore I, the little child [T'ang], charged with the decree of Heaven and its bright terrors, did not dare to forgive …*

In this interesting quote from T'ang, there are two allusions. The first is to wormwood and poison, the second to Heaven sending down calamities and bright terrors. This chapter has raised the possibility of a comet being around at the time of the Exodus and the start of the Shang dynasty. Now we have at the start of the Shang a mention of 'worm-wood and poison'. Wormwood is artemesia, a bitter weed of cultivation. Why might it be mentioned repeatedly at times of extraterrestrial bombardment and dimming of the sun? Valerie Hall supplied a persuasive answer. Artemesia is a frost-resistant weed; if crops are decimated at a time of atmospheric loading with reduced sunlight and climatic upset, weeds may be all there is to eat. 'When the people are tired of wormwood and poison': their crops have failed. Let us refresh our memories on Revelation chapter 8:

> *And the third angel sounded, and there fell a great star from Heaven, burning as it were a lamp, and it fell upon the third part of the rivers, and upon the fountains of waters.*
>
> *And the name of the star is called Wormwood: and the third part of the waters became wormwood; and many men died of the waters, because they were made bitter.*

So we have in Chinese ancient records, from the start of the Shang dynasty, heaven sending down calamities and 'bright terrors' in the context of 'wormwood and poison'. In the Near East we have what others thought of as wormwood and poison. The book of Revelation associates these with a great star falling and people dying from poisoned waters (calamities). Revelation goes on to mention the after-effects of seeing the falling star :

The strange similarity between the circa 1600 BC Chinese reference to 'Heaven's bright terrors' at the end of the Xia Dynasty and the 'star called Wormwood' in the book of Revelation hints that both are impact related.

A comparison of a Medieval illustration of a comet having notable effects on the Earth with Durer's Angel in the ninth print from the Apocalypse. Durer, a master of allegory, seems to have understood that Angels could be comets.

The sun, the moon and the stars are all darkened... and I saw a star fall from heaven onto the earth ... and there arose a smoke out of the pit, as the smoke of a great furnace; and the sun and the air were darkened by reason of the smoke of the pit.

Having arrived at the tentative conclusion that a comet was involved at the fall of the Xia and the start of the Shang dynasties, what are the chances of being able to find T'ang's statement about wormwood, poison and calamity, and having it so clearly explained by the Book of Revelation unless there is something to it? These connections can be further reinforced. For the Passover, the culmination of the Exodus plagues, on the very night when the Angel of the Lord is to 'pass over', the people are instructed to eat bitter herbs. Thus we have:

Chieh: comet, wormwood, poison
Revelation: falling star, Wormwood, poison
Exodus: comet(?), bitter herbs, poisoned waters (first plague).

There is almost a three-way connection with, in every case, meteoric or impact imagery:

Chieh: heaven sends it bright terrors
Revelation: a star falls from heaven
Exodus: terrible hail from heaven (seventh plague).

The detail does not let us down. In each of these cases we can add in another specific similarity:

Chieh: the sun was dimmed
Revelation: the sun was darkened
Exodus: the plague of darkness (ninth plague).

When an uncontrolled nuclear disaster occurred at Chernobyl – meaning 'wormwood' – in 1986, many people were reminded of Revelation and wondered if it was a sign of the coming of the end of the world. They need not have worried: the sign, when it comes, will most likely be from above, not from below.

CHAPTER 9

◆

INDEPENDENT SUGGESTIONS OF EXTRATERRESTRIAL EFFECTS

The story developed in the last few chapters has been built up by following observations which suggested links between events in tree-ring sequences, ice-core records and ancient history. The initial suggestion, given the Greenland ice-acidities, was that large volcanoes, or episodes of volcanic activity, had given rise to hemispheric effects at 1628 BC, 1159 BC, 207 BC, 44 BC and AD 540. However, given the apparent severity of these episodes, there either was something unusual about these particular volcanoes, or else the volcanoes may have been secondary effects. This led to the noting of the various cometary and related extraterrestrial possibilities.

The explosion of cometary fragments in the atmosphere, or the loading of the atmosphere with cometary dust/debris in the past is inherently difficult to prove. At Tunguska on 30 June 1908, a lump of cometary debris, possibly 40 m (130 ft) across, exploded about 10 km (6 miles) above Siberia with a force estimated at between 12 and 30 megatons; but we only know this because of surviving accounts of something travelling across the sky and exploding with a huge fireball, great noise and earthquakes. The accounts were enough for Leonid Kulik to search out and investigate the site of the devastation caused by the airburst. Without the accounts, and Kulik's observation of the flattened forest, within a century the event would have been difficult to interpret and might have escaped detection altogether. All we would have had to go on would have been the fact that, on 30 June 1908, people in Europe experienced an abnormally bright night, and seismographs recorded a shock wave. Without the fuller picture the largest impact of the twentieth century on this planet, to date, as far as we know, might well have been missed by scientists.

As we go back in time with poorer record-keeping and less literacy it becomes very difficult to prove any impact without a crater. Since most ancient impacts involving cometary fragments will have been airbursts, and

The flattened and burnt forest resulting from the circa 20 megaton airburst of a 40 metre cometary fragment (or an equivalently sized asteroid) at Tunguska on 30 June 1908.

since a majority of these will have been over the sea, it is apparent that proof may not be easily forthcoming. So what might we expect in ancient records? There might be records noting 'an arrow of fire', 'fire from heaven', 'lightning', 'tremendous thunder', 'earthquakes', 'dragons in the sky'. Or there might be a record of a 'dim sun' or other abnormal atmospheric phenomena. However, each of the phenomena could be interpreted as earthbound storms or tectonic or atmospheric effects. Even unusual records of phenomena such as 'fire from heaven' can be dismissed as uneducated descriptions of aurora or just lightning.

We can identify environmental effects but we cannot easily distinguish the cause. In reality, the best hope would be to find some physical or chemical tracer in the preserved snowfall in Greenland or elsewhere – a direct whiff of something extraterrestrial like the iridium layer at the demise of the dinosaurs 65 million years ago. Unfortunately, impacts the size of Tunguska don't seem to leave detectable traces in distant ice layers; ice-core workers have analysed ice from 1908 and come up with nothing so far. It seems that if Tunguska had happened in any previous century there would not be a trace of its existence!

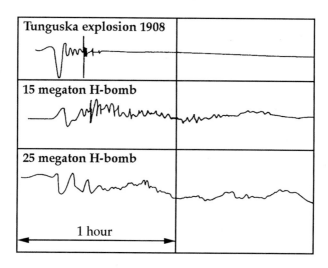

Victor Clube and Bill Napier used this evidence of recorded pressure waves associated with the Tungaska impact to estimate that the force of the 30 June 1908 airburst was equivalent to something like a 20 megaton bomb.

But astrophysicists are beginning to realize that impacts in the past should have been quite common. Some astrophysicists such as Victor Clube and Duncan Steel posit the idea that multiple Tunguskas or 'cosmic swarms' might have been (and will be again) serious hazards to civilization. They are beginning to think that odd impacts happen quite frequently and that we should have had a fairly big one, or a swarm of smaller ones, in the last 5000 years, that is, within the time span of civilization. However, as far as physical traces go, the impact evidence may not now be evident. Archaeologists and ancient historians have a problem on their hands – there may have been a major vector for human change which is to all intents invisible.

This is probably the place to mention some of the latest findings by astrophysicists. From infra-sound evidence – listening for large explosions in the atmosphere – it is now known that on average each year there is one impact by an object up to 6 m (19 ft) in diameter; giving rise to an explosion of about 15 kilotons, *and,* on average, about ten impacts of objects around 2 m (6 ft) in diameter; giving rise to roughly 1-kiloton explosions. These explosions take place high in the atmosphere and the only human records relate to bright flashes of unknown (till now) origin. It is this information on the small 'tail' of the distribution of impactors which tells the astrophysicists, when combined with the estimates of a Tunguska class of impact every century or half century, that larger impactors of up to several hundred metres across, or clusters of Tunguska-class impactors, must arrive on timescales of thousands of years. In the last 5000 years the earth must have been seriously impacted at least once, probably several times.

Anyone wanting to pose the question, 'Have human populations been disrupted by comet-related impacts in the past?', must cast around for circumstantial support to get the hypothesis off the ground, that is, evidence which, while not proving the hypothesis, does nothing to undermine it. In science support can come in some unexpected ways and one of these is independent suggestion. I have always been struck by the particular power of two *independent* workers arriving at the same hypothesis based on different lines of evidence. In this chapter we will look at two examples of apparently independent suggestions relating to comets. These relate to the so-called AD 540 and 1159 BC events previously discussed. The information comes principally from Don Carleton at Bristol and Bob Kobres at Georgia.

DID A COMET HIT THE CELTIC SEA IN AD 540?

In 1994 I published an article on the AD 540 event in the journal *The Holocene* under the title 'Dendrochronology raises questions about the nature of the AD 536 dust-veil event'. In that article I laid out the story much as related in this book. The premise of my argument was that the environmental event was real and that the ice-core evidence had weakened to the point where the event was evidently not volcanic in origin (though there is good evidence for a widespread environmental event around AD 540, there is currently no good evidence for a large volcanic eruption at or around AD 536–45). At the end of the article I asked how, in the absence of volcanic acid in Greenland, the effects of a large eruption could be distinguished from the effects of a medium-sized asteroid (or 'comet', 'cometary fragment(s)' or 'cosmic swarms') striking one of the world's oceans? I asked this partly to stake a claim on the event – as far as I know I had mentioned the possibility of an impact first – and partly to put pressure on the ice-core workers to undertake a detailed chemical analysis across the sixth century AD.

So there I was in 1993 with the *Holocene* article written and accepted for publication; my claim on a previously unsuspected sixth-century impact event was in. Imagine my surprise when one day the following phone conversation took place: 'Yes, I am the Mike Baillie who studies tree rings.' The caller was Don Carleton from Bristol who had been given my name by our information officer. 'What can I do for you?' I asked. 'Well,' came the reply, 'I wanted to know if you have anything catastrophic at AD 540?' 'Ah,' I replied, 'obviously you have been reading something I wrote.' 'No,' came the reply, 'I have not read anything you have written.' 'In that case,' I ventured, 'exactly what is your thesis?' The reply was electrifying: 'Well, I think that a comet impacted the Celtic sea in AD 540.' What, I asked myself, were the chances of an independent worker, who had not read anything I had written, arriving at such a scenario?

I have since met and corresponded with Don and it seems appropriate to paraphrase the logic of his position to show that his direction of enquiry was indeed completely different from mine. He had set out to write a history of the Bristol area, which led to an interest in the battle of Badon Hill, the supposed site of King Arthur's victory over the Saxons in the early sixth century. This in turn led to an interest in sixth-century history and a growing realization that something untoward had happened around AD 540. I had arrived at the suggestion of an impact at AD 540 through tree-rings, ice-core evidence, historical descriptions of dry fogs, Chinese records and the eventual weakening of the ice-core evidence for volcanic activity at the time. Don arrived at a suggestion of an impact at AD 540 from his studies of Arthurian legends, Dark Age histories, Welsh poetry mentioning inundations, Gildas giving warnings, peculiar tales from the Byzantine historian Procopius and from reading Clube and Napier. These routes are so close to being independent that one has to ask if the resulting hypotheses just represent a bizarre coincidence or whether there really might be something more to it?

SAINT PATRICK

In the course of learning about Carleton's Celtic sea comet ideas, I was becoming more and more aware of just how much information is available, and how much of it, despite its circumstantial nature, points to an impact scenario in this c. AD 540 period. This became apparent to me when I began to write an article for Volume 13 of the journal *Emania*, which the editor, Jim Mallory, had decided would be devoted to the 'origins of the Early Christian period in Ireland'. The article started as a half-page note and took on such a life of its own that it ended up spanning twelve pages. Basically, I started by asking why we know so little about one of the most important personalities in Irish history. Patrick is traditionally placed in the later fifth century; was it possible that we have inherited a genuinely impoverished record for the period before AD 600 because of the impact of events in the first half of the sixth century? Liam de Paor had already summarized the nature of the problem of the fifth century in Ireland, that is, that no actual manuscript of any kind written in that century now survives, and there is hardly a single Irish artefact in a museum or a single monument in the field of which an archaeologist could say with full confidence that it was made in the fifth century. Liam de Paor goes on to declare his sympathy with the idea that 'so far as Irish history is concerned, it [the fifth century] is a lost century.' This is very much in keeping with the situation in Britain, where King Arthur occupies a position

While modern tradition has St Patrick driving snakes out of Ireland, this early nineteenth-century engraving by Martyn has Patrick in his St Michael guise pinning a fiery dragon to the ground with his cross-headed staff. Coupled with his dream of 'Satan falling on me like a great rock' and the miracle that 'on the day of his death no night fell...' Patrick has more than his fair share of impact imagery.

more or less comparable to that of Patrick in Ireland. Very little is really known about Arthur except that one traditional date for his death just happens to be AD 542. In the last decade or so the doubts about Arthur's life and death have given way to a more general attitude that he may never have existed at all, and may, in fact, be a purely mythological figure.

In a similar way, Patrick can become fairly shadowy. The date of Patrick's arrival in Ireland is traditionally given as AD 432 but can be summarily dismissed as 'a [later] pious fiction' by de Paor, while the date of his death varies between AD 461 and AD 492–3. If we were to add in the doubts raised by discussions of whether there was more than one Patrick it becomes clear that much of what we think we know about Patrick may also be largely mythological.

When annalists, perhaps in the seventh or eighth century, began to keep contemporary records of important events, they felt a need to provide some historical background to their own existence. De Paor suggests that the people who began keeping annals wanted to supply an earlier history of Ireland up to the point where they themselves started. In order to create this history it was necessary for them to gather together all the records which were available, reliable or otherwise, and cobble them into a chronological order. Once they had done that, they set it out in annalistic form, just as if there had been chroniclers in Ireland, for centuries before them, carefully noting the chief events of each year – but of course, there had not.

What do we know for certain about this Dark Age period? We know that everything about this period in Ireland *was actually recorded later*, either from documents of which no originals survive or from oral traditions. The records have indeed passed through some sort of barrier or filter. Richard Warner sees this filter in cultural terms: in his view, relatively suddenly, during the sixth century AD, a new material culture suddenly emerged in Ireland, one which clearly had strong intrusive elements. Defensive settlements appear, both secular and religious, including ringforts, artificial islands called crannogs and defended monasteries. Warner also points out that the reduced growth event around AD 540 fits neatly with his ideas. Contemporary annals draw attention to the great famine of the 530s and 540s, and provide an explanation for both the cultural change and for the fact that the Christian traditions of pre-550 Ireland (such as those of Patrick) so completely fail to cross the divide. From this compilation it was possible to see that there was nothing very original about postulating a barrier or filter in the sixth century AD. Our environmental event around AD 540 merely provides a more refined focus for the barrier which others had already recognized.

From a scientific viewpoint, however, the really important issue is what *caused* the AD 540 environmental event? Although my original *Holocene* article casually referred to the possibility of a 'medium sized asteroid striking one of the world's oceans', I had had time to think more about this issue and to discuss it with others. The more I considered the issue, the more obvious it became that cometary debris, and atmospheric detonations, were more likely than the arrival of a single massive solid body. Cometary debris exploding in the atmosphere or impacting on oceans could provide the dry fog or dust-veil associated with the early records. This veil would then give rise to the environmental effects on tree-growth, famines, etc. In the absence of other evidence simple logic raised the possibility that a shower of cometary debris might have caused the environmental downturn while leaving no traces on the ground.

AD 540 was the sort of event that Victor Clube and Bill Napier proposed in 1990 in their book *The Cosmic Winter*. They had elaborated a scenario as follows. Twice a year, in June and November, the Earth passes through an annular cloud of meteoric dust – particles in this cloud, striking the upper atmosphere, give rise to the Taurid meteor showers. The annulus of dust is relatively coherent which means that it cannot be very old. So the Taurids are a clue that in the past 20,000 years or so a giant comet broke up in the solar system. Within this residual annulus of dust there are solid objects. Clube and Napier's hypothesis is that from time to time, in passing through the Taurid meteor shower, the Earth encounters some of these solid fragments and they point to two impact events: one certain, the Tunguska event of 1908, mentioned above, and one possible: Gervase of Canterbury appears to record a more-or-less first-hand account of a major impact on the moon on 25 June AD 1178 which could fit with the existence of the recent Giordano Bruno crater. If this latter case is correct, it suggests a 100,000 megaton impact caused by a body hitting the moon at 36 N and 105 E within the last thousand years. Clube and Napier go on to elaborate their 'cosmic swarm' scenario where, in a short period from months to years the Earth encounters a range of impacts; these impacts may be of objects composed of ice or stone and all mixes in between. They then go on to estimate that running into a 'cosmic swarm' of smaller objects can actually be *expected* to have occurred, and they make the following statement:

Overall, it seems likely that during a period of a few thousand years, there is an expectation of an impact, possibly occurring as part of a swarm of material, sufficiently powerful to plunge us into a Dark Age ...

Indeed they are even more specific:

If large boulders do form in swarms, then during close encounters with the comet or its degassed remnant there is a risk of occasional bombardment on a scale comparable with that of a nuclear war ... The occurrence of Tunguska-like swarms in recorded history is therefore expected ... Thus we expect a Dark Age within the last two thousand years ...

They review the evidence and, in collaboration with Mark Bailey, go on to suggest:

...it seems probable that the least biased measure of relative meteor activity during the Dark Age is now provided by the recorded incidence of meteor showers ... There have probably been at least two significant surges in meteor shower activity [in the last two millennia] namely AD 400–600 and AD 800–1000 ...

Here we have independent workers, who specialise in comets and comet hazards, saying that significant events are indeed likely and that one period of risk may have been AD 400–600. Why had they made this suggestion? In their view the cometary debris from the original giant comet produced numerous separate comets and these in turn have tended to break up. They cite one example relating to the earlier history of comet Biela which finally broke up in 1845:

...the incidence of its showers in particular has been traced back at least to the early part of the sixth century AD ... during the early stages of this body's fragmentation, possibly in the fourth and fifth century ... it is conceivable that the earth experienced some quite major bombardments, with effects on the ground similar to that of the ... Tunguska event.

We can add Clube, Napier and Bailey's suggested AD 400–600 hazard period in with Carleton's suggested AD 540 impact. Unfortunately these two lines of reasoning are not independent. As mentioned above, Carleton knew about Clube and Napier's ideas and used them to some extent in his arguments. However, at least the tree-ring–ice-core logic is independent of the whole Carleton–Clube scenario.

A whole raft of information is pointing towards something interesting happening in the sixth century. While there is no definitive proof of an impact, there is a strong circumstantial case to be answered. Despite the general lack of good documentation for the fifth and early sixth centuries it might be possible to move the debate forward using the *odd* snippets of evidence which seem to abound for the period. It seemed reasonable to look through any literature from, or about, the sixth century to see if there was anything which might help us understand what may have happened. The picture broadens out in some really quite surprising ways.

(1) Clube and Napier quote Klinkerfues:

In this year [524 after the Birth of Christ], though, there occurred also much running of the stars from evening quite to daybreak, so that everybody was frightened, and we know of no such event besides ... for 20 days there appeared a comet, and after some time there occurred a running of the stars from evening till early, so that people said that all the stars were falling ...

(2) There are many earthquakes recorded 'at Constantinople and vicinity' between AD 525 and AD 557 implying an episode of tectonic activity. In this vein, the most extraordinary description exists of the earthquake at Antioch in AD 526. Malalas talks of it as 'the fifth calamity from the wrath of God':

...those caught in the earth beneath the buildings were incinerated and sparks of fire appeared out of the air and burned everyone they struck like lightening. The surface of the earth boiled and foundations of buildings were struck by thunderbolts thrown up by the earthquakes and were burned to ashes by fire ... it was a tremendous and incredible marvel with fire belching out rain, rain falling from tremendous furnaces, flames dissolving into showers ... as a result Antioch became desolate ... in this terror up to 250,000 people perished ...

(3) In a discussion which clearly links early Chinese references to 'dragon fights in rivers or in the air' with calamities ranging from 'foreboding inundations, disorder, war, nay even the dynasty's fall' to, in one case, fireballs the size of houses falling from the sky, de Visser mentions:

In the sixth month of the fifth year of the P'u t'ung era (AD 524) dragons fought in the pond of the King of K'uh o (?). They went westward as far as Kien ling ch'ing. In the places they passed all the trees were broken. The divination was the same as in the second year of the T'ien kien era (AD 503), namely that their passing Kien ling and the trees being broken indicated that there would be calamity of war for the dynasty ...

(4) In the Annals of Ireland for the year AD 525, a gloss mentions that the literal translation of a comment, taken to refer to St Brigit, actually means 'fiery dart'. Richard Warner's writes: 'All the annals place the death of Brigit at about AD 525 but her first "life" was not written till more than a century after this date. Recent analysis of this "life" suggests a totally mythological person.' Is there any reason for placing the death of Brigit at 525? As early as the ninth century scholars commented that Brigit was an ancient goddess whose prime characteristic was her connection with fire:

a house within which she is staying flames up to heaven, cow dung blazes before her ... a fiery pillar rises over her head; sun rays support her wet cloak ... She has ... a perpetual ashless fire watched by twenty nuns ...

Finally, one of the medieval explanations for the name of Brigit was that it derived from Breó Saigit – 'arrow of fire'. In short, if the true Brigit could not have had any death-date, least of all one in AD 525, why is she credited with dying in AD 525? Perhaps a memorable event, in which heavenly fire played a part, took place in about 525, and that, because of her associations with heavenly fire, Brigit became attached to that event. What better reason to explain a major astronomical event than the 'death' of the goddess of fire; and what better way of preventing a recurrence than by keeping her sacred flame alive?

(5) In AD 530 many 'large shooting stars' were seen from China. This can be combined with references to a 'great meteor shower' in AD 531 in the Mediterranean area, and with 'showers of stars' on China in AD 532. The 532 shower is apparently also referred to by Theophanes, while John Malalas records that in AD 531–2 there was a great shower of stars from dusk to dawn 'so that everyone was astounded'. Obviously without the actual dates of the showers it is impossible to say just how many there were, though, irrespective

of this, there is the impression of considerable activity. To this can be added sightings of comets in AD 533 and AD 535, while in AD 538–9 Zacharias of Mithylene notes:

> *In the eleventh year of Justinian, which is the year eight hundred and fifty of the Greeks [AD 538–9], in the month of December, a great and terrible comet appeared in the sky at evening-time for one hundred days (elsewhere, several days) ...*

Taking all of these occurences together, suddenly we have a whole range of earthquake and comet/meteor phenomena recorded, not at AD 536–45 but in the broader period AD 524–40. In this case, while there are tectonic aspects to the descriptions, there are also clear hints that some of the sky debris may have made its way to Earth, a running of the stars, dragons wrestling in ponds – death of a fire goddess. Notably, all these are recorded in different parts of the world. Irrespective of what happened around AD 540, there seemed to be an active sky around a decade earlier. Just to show that some of the other records at the time are accurate, Halley's comet is recorded correctly in both China and Byzantium in AD 530. In the latter case it is recorded as 'a tremendous great star in the western region, sending a white beam upwards; its surface emitted flashes of lightening ... it continued shining for 20 days ...'

Is there anything else between AD 530 and AD 536? While researching this episode, David Keys talked to various Chinese scholars who informed him that in AD 534 the Chinese emperor ordered the abandonment of the imperial capital, Loyang; this was followed by the political collapse of northern China in AD 535–45 and an unexplained descent into economic and social chaos by southern China in the 540s after 200 years of economic progress.

At first sight this appears to be just another indication that something had happened in the AD 530s. But why would a capital be abandoned? One possibility might be that the court astronomers informed the emperor that there was something dangerous in the sky; perhaps an impact seemed imminent.

This record of Chinese abandonment struck a chord. In Britain there is only one writer of the mid-sixth century AD, Gildas, who is generally accepted as having been writing about this period as a contemporary. Gildas gave what have been taken as apocalyptic *warnings*, and, because he was warning in the tone that 'these things will happen again' it seems likely that the warnings related to things in the sky. Writing not far from AD 540, he uses phrases such as:

...fire of righteous vengeance ... blazed from sea to sea ... and ... Once lit it did not lie down, When it had wasted town and country in that area, it burnt up almost the whole surface of the island, until its red and savage tongue licked the western ocean ...

Though he may have been talking about Saxon hordes, what is clear is that, on opposite sides of the world, matters were afoot involving warnings or predictions which could suggest objects in the sky. To these can be added the Mediterranean eclipses in English chronicles, etc., but one more such item will suffice. Malalas records that in AD 541–2:

...in the fifth indiction the following incident took place. A woman living near what is known as the Golden Gate went into ecstasy one night and spoke a lot of nonsense [sic], so that the people of Constantinople ... took her to the Church of St Diomedes, for she was saying that in three days' time the sea would rise and take everybody. Everyone went in processions of prayer and chanted 'Lord have mercy', for reports were circulating that many cities have been swallowed up ...

This entry is glossed by another passage, probably from the original Malalas:

...in this year the sea advanced on Thrace by four miles and covered it in the territories of Odyssos and Dionysopolis and also Aphrodison. Many were drowned in the waters. By God's command the sea then retreated to its own place ...

In the context of looking for natural explanations for the widespread environmental downturn the evidence could support two hypotheses. The first is that this wider period, representing broadly the first half of the sixth century AD, was one of increased tectonic activity – a context within which the occurrence of either a single massive volcanic eruption or a series of eruptions might seem at home (though we might expect a significant ice-acidity signal which seems to be singularly missing). However, a second hypothesis must be at least as tenable: might we expect to see increased tectonic activity in the event of the Earth suffering bombardment by cometary fragments? This is where the inundation at Thrace might give a hint. An inundation could be due to a tsunami, which could be triggered either by tectonic movement or by an impact; indeed I have noted earlier a possible rise at this time in the level of Lough Neagh where the unfinished dug-out boat mentioned in chapter 4 was found.

It can be very difficult to begin to separate terrestrial-bound events from events induced by an extra-terrestrial agency. Several of the items above hold hints of what may be extra-terrestrial activity but prove nothing. In order to obtain proof we must await the analysis of the new ice-cores, though even then nothing may be forthcoming and we may be left wondering how we would ever prove an extra-terrestrial impact at a particular date in the past. Irrespective of any other considerations there seems to be little doubt that the early sixth century AD was a period when the sky contained its share of portents. There seem to have been comets, meteors, earthquakes, dimmed skies and inundations and, following the famines of the late 530s, plague arrived in Europe in the window AD 542–5.

Imagine people already unnerved by the appearance of meteor showers and comets, subjected to the severe dry fog of AD 536, the famines of the following years and, finally, decimated by the wave of plague after AD 542. There may have been some earthquakes thrown in as well. Was it the events of the early sixth century, and particularly c. AD 540, which assisted in the acceptance of Christianity in places such as Ireland? Was it in fact their similarity to the catastrophic aspects of the Exodus story? Some interesting parallels can be drawn. Early Christians certainly knew all about Moses, the plagues of Egypt and the Exodus. Many of the Exodus features may have assumed a living reality to populations around AD 540. The following list is not exhaustive, merely illustrative:

Exodus factors	Sixth century phenomena	Years
murrain of beasts	Columba sees black cloud pestilential rain/murrain	Sixth century
Boils and blains	And eruptions in men	
Fire along the ground	Malalas' description of Antioch earthquake	526
Hail brake every tree	Tree growth widely affected	536–45
Crops smitten	'Failure of bread', widespread famines	536–9
Frost	frost-rings/coldest years in tree-ring records	535–6 540–1
Plague of darkness	dry fog/dust-veil	536
Pestilence	Justinian plague	542
Water out of cloven rock	Lake level rise	c. 540
parting of the reed sea	Inundations	541

If instead of Exodus we were to consider the not dissimilar imagery of Revelation, the 'stones from Heaven' could be meteor showers falling in 524–40, and 'Wormwood' may be chronicling the effect of impacts. Overall, Christianity may have supplied the imagery to accompany a range of phenomena ascribed to the period around AD 540. People like Patrick or Gildas or their companions may have been seen to be promulgating a religion whose cosmic imagery had a contemporary relevance. Let us imagine that Christianity was, in fact, not all that well established in Ireland before AD 540 – a scenario which is entirely possible given the paucity of records – and well established after 540. When de Paor's Irish annalists 'wanted to record the history of Ireland up to the point where they started' they gave Patrick the credit for the wholesale Christianization of the country. The reality may as easily have been that Patrick and other early Christians merely sowed the seeds of conversion and that the symptoms of a profound environmental event did the rest.

Our consideration of an environmental event around AD 540 has led to an excursion into volcanic winters or even cosmic catastrophes. It is extremely difficult to tease out the exact details of any event this far back in time and even more difficult to prove any case – a lesson to all archaeologists and palaeoenvironmentalists studying events in the more distant past. Out of these deliberations, however, came a possible catastrophic scenario drawn from a variety of sources.

In the early sixth century circumstances may have graphically demonstrated the power of the Old Testament God of the Christians, who may not have been slow to use the circumstances to the benefit of their religion. In this vein it may not be coincidence that, as Verdet notes:

...in Auxerre, France, in AD 538 the Catholic hierarchy, as part of a drive to remove other systems of belief which could challenge its own authority, condemned those who made fountains, woods and stones the object of cults ...

Thus, a new look at the possible package of natural phenomena of the period suggests that the phenomena themselves may have helped to create a Christian society. Finally, and still in the same vein, one has to adduce one further piece of 'evidence'. This chapter has shown that there is a strong circumstantial case to support the possibility of cosmic bombardment in the sixth century, in line with Clube, Napier and Bailey seeing AD 400–600 as a period of increased meteor activity with risks from cosmic swarms. Interestingly, De Paor includes in his volume stories of miraculous happenings from Muirchu's *Life of St Patrick*, one of which is related to the day of Patrick's death, which is termed the 'Twelve days without night':

For on that day of his death no night fell ... evening did not send the darkness which carries the stars. The people of Ulaid say that to the end of the year in which he departed, the darkness of the nights was never as great as before ...

In itself such a phenomenon would be regarded as typical of the kinds of happening associated with saints. However, in the context of this discussion on increased meteor activity, this assertion is more interesting. Numerous writers, including Baxter and Atkins, have pointed out that on the night of 30 June 1908:

...the sky throughout Europe was strangely bright, Throughout the United Kingdom ... it was possible to play cricket and read newspapers by the glow from the night sky. Photographs were taken at midnight or later, with exposures of about a minute ...

30 June 1908, was the date of the Tunguska impact event and the bright sky was due to the injection of debris into the upper atmosphere. In fact, in both cases – the death of Patrick and the year 1908 – it is stated that the nights were less dark for months (1908) and for the rest of the year (Patrick). Although none of this information proves anything it can be said, yet again, that this tradition, associated with the death of Patrick, is not inconsistent with a hypothesis of earthly bombardment in the period from AD 400 to 600. Patrick is most famous for driving the snakes – serpents – out of Ireland (which is odd as Ireland had no snakes). As we have seen already, and will see again later, serpents and dragons relate to fireballs from space.

This 'bright night' miraculous occurrence is not the only tradition linked to Patrick which has an impact 'ring' to it. The seventh-century bishop Tírechán writes about Patrick and Tara, the ancient capital of Ireland:

And all saw the druid being lifted up through the darkness of night almost to the sky, and when he came down again, his body, frozen with hailstones and snow mixed with sparks of fire, fell to the ground in the sight of all; and [the druid's] stone is in the south-eastern part of Tara to the present day, and I have seen it with my own eyes ...

In this single statement we have the juxtaposition of effectively all the elements – hail, snow, fire and stone – normally associated with the makeup of comets. The sixth century is rife with hints that Clube, Napier and Bailey's thesis is on the right lines, that is, there seem to have been many occurrences consistent with bombardment, but no definitive eyewitness descriptions.

DRAGONS IN THE SKY

In the Chinese records probably the most relevant piece of information is of 'dragons wrestling in ponds'. It is quite clear that these 'dragons' refer to fireball-like phenomena. The simplest analogy is with Tunguska, where John Baxter and Thomas Atkins record:

> *...a heavenly body of fiery appearance cut across the sky from south to north ... where the flying object touched the horizon a huge flame shot up ... [the object] ... followed a south to north passage, and its burning trail streamed southwards' [when it fell] a huge cloud of black smoke was formed and a crash as if from gunfire was heard. All the buildings shook and at the same time a forked tongue of flame broke through the cloud...*

An incoming cometary fragment is witnessed in the twentieth century as a fiery object with a burning trail streaming behind it, passing with a roaring noise. It 'lands' (in this case exploding in the atmosphere) with a huge fiery explosion and an associated black smoke-cloud, giving rise to shock waves and tremors of earthquake proportions. At impact it flattens a huge area of forest. If we go back to our ancient descriptions of Chinese 'dragons' recorded by de Vissèr, and combine elements from three sixth-century dragon sightings, we have:

> *...in the second year of the T'ien kien era (AD 503) there were dragons fighting in a pool in Northern Liang province. They squirted fog over a distance of some miles ... In the sixth month of (AD 524) dragons fought in the pond of the King of K'uh o (?). They went westward as far as Kien ling ch'ing. In the places they passed all the trees were broken. The divination was the same as in (AD 503), namely that their passing Kien ling and the trees being broken indicated that there would be calamity of war for the dynasty ...*

De Vissèr goes on to cite a later example:

> *In the fifth month of the year yih-wei (probably AD 1295) on a place near the lake at I hing, all of a sudden there were two dragons which twisted around each other and fighting both fell into the lake ... In a short space of time a heavy wind came riding on the water which reached a height of more than 10 feet. Then there fell from the sky more than ten fire balls, having the size of houses of ten divisions. The two dragons immediately ascended (to the sky) for heaven, afraid that they might cause calamity, sent out sacred fire to drive them away ...*

It is this description and the attached information that tells us that dragons are bolides. We know from Tunguska that a fiery object with a trail (cometary debris or a 'dragon') disappears in a fireball with an associated smoke cloud. Also, 'where the flying object touched the horizon a huge flame shot up ... and at the same time a forked tongue of flame broke through the cloud'. This is the 'dragon' ascending to the sky. But de Vissèr's text makes it even more explicit:

Suppose that heaven had been remiss, for a moment, then within a hundred miles everything would have been turned into gigantic torrents. When I recently passed by boat the Peachgarden of Teh Tsing, those paddy fields were all scorched and black, some tens of acres in all ... [we] asked those villagers for the reason. They said: 'Yesterday noon there was a big dragon which fell from the sky. Immediately he was burned by terrestrial fire and flew away. For what the dragons fear is fire.

So ancient observers, in China at least, rationalized the arrival of 'dragons', and the fact that they never actually found one, by assuming that the fireball was terrestrial fire which drove the dragon away. The pillar of fire at Tunguska would have been the dragon ascending. The burnt fields and the broken trees in the Chinese version are exactly paralleled by the flattened and burnt forest at Tunguska.

The dragon imagery is not confined to China. The Russian astronomer Krinov writes that the oldest recording of a meteorite fall in Russian annals is in AD 1091: 'In this summer Vsevolod, who was trapping animals near Vyshegorod ... saw a large serpent falling from the clouds; all people were frightened. All of this time the earth was rattling.' There is no doubt that serpents and dragons are seen flying across the sky. But, for completeness, let us look again at the AD 1295 example from China. Krinov notes a well-attested impact at Velikii Usting in Russia in AD 1296 with great clouds, ceaseless lightening, the ground swaying, clouds of fire and great heat. So this Chinese event has a wider contemporary context. That context can be widened still further. Believe it or not, the Irish annals record the following: 'AD 1294 Lightening and meteors destroyed the blades of corn.'

It certainly sounds as if 1294–6 was a lively period for celestial activity (perhaps we should take another look some time at the major AD 1297 sequoia fire, mentioned in Chapter 1). Periodic events occur involving a range of phenomena from meteor showers up to Tunguska size (or bigger) impacts. By looking at these as a class of observations, it is fairly clear that the references to 'dragons wrestling in ponds' in the sixth century are actually descriptions of Tunguska-type impacts. However, if our list of similarities between the Exodus phenomena and those of the sixth century is realistic, we begin to see that the cometary scenario associated with the Exodus in the last chapter is reinforced by the comparison. We have arrived at a point, by another route, which would allow an independent suggestion that the Exodus may have had a cometary dimension.

PHAËTHON AND 1159 BC

In the case of the 1159 BC tree-ring event it is clear that there is evidence in the ice-cores for a large acidity signal at a date consistent with the mid-twelfth century BC, it has been common to refer to this as the 'Hekla 3' event for the simple reason that the calibrated radiocarbon evidence for this Icelandic eruption would allow it to have happened in the twelfth century BC. However, we cannot be certain that Hekla 3 erupted at exactly this time, and there are several lines of vulcanological and environmental evidence which suggest that this particular eruption, on its own, should not have had global effects. This uncertainty means that even from the first suggestions of the 1159 BC event there have been grounds for nurturing the opinion that it might be a multiple event of some sort. Just to give an example, in Ireland we see trees showing defoliation effects in 1159 and in 1153. The entire 1159–1141 BC event clearly falls into two sections in the tree-ring record, with the 1150s 'bad' and the 1140s 'worse'. From the start we had to have an open mind on the cause or causes of the event; then as already noted, Sagan and Druyan's comment about the comet at the demise of the last Shang king, Chòu, raised another spectre. Although it is a weak case, as with the AD 540 event, the possibility of an extraterrestrial involvement in the mid-twelfth century BC could not be ruled out.

In an article entitled 'The Path of a Comet and Phaëton's Ride', Bob Kobres propounds the theory that, in the middle of the twelfth century BC, the Earth had a close encounter with Encke's comet and that not only are descriptions preserved in ancient literature but there may well have been notable effects 'on the ground'. Who was Phaëthon? In Greek legend, Phaëthon (or Phaëton), the son of Apollo (Phoebus) and Clymene, asks to be allowed for one day to drive the chariot of the sun, in order to prove to disbelievers that he is the son of the sun. Despite Phoebus' misgivings (indeed warnings of the difficulties), Phaëthon sets off with the sun's rays on his head and his father's warnings ringing in his ears. He is told that he must control the chariot firmly, follow the tracks, and not to go too high or low so as not to burn either the heavens or the earth. Phaëthon loses control. The horses rush headlong and leave the road, hurling the chariot over pathless places 'now up in high heaven, now down almost to the earth'. The myth indicates an out-of-control sun-like object; but it is the effects on Earth which make the most interesting reading. The following is from Thomas Bulfinch's *Myth and*

Legend. First the moon notes her brother's chariot (containing the son of the sun) is running beneath her own, that is, implying between the earth and the moon. The effect of this close passage to the earth is dramatic:

> *The clouds begin to smoke and the mountain tops take fire; the fields are parched with heat, the plants wither, the trees with their leafy branches burn, the harvest is ablaze! But these are small things [sic]. Great cities perished, with their walls and towers; whole nations with their people were consumed to ashes! The forest-clad mountains burned …*

In the myth, Phaëthon sees the world on fire, and even feels the heat. The other symptoms are quite interesting. There is pitch-black smoke, and the air is like the smoke of a furnace filled with burning ashes; descriptions with a distinctly Exodus ring to them. There are also what sound like either drought or tectonic effects; the Nile dries up and:

> *The earth cracked open, and through the chinks light broke into Tartarus (the abyss under the earth) … Where before was water, it became a dry plain; and the mountains that lie beneath the waves lifted up their heads and became islands.*

The Earth calls on Jupiter to do something. Jupiter strikes Phaëthon with a thunderbolt and 'Phaëthon, with his hair on fire, fell headlong, like a shooting star which marks the heavens with its brightness as it falls.' We are left wondering what the stimulus for this tale might have been. Kobres has formulated a possible interpretation for this story.

The twentieth-century recognition of the impact origin of Meteor Crater, when combined with Tunguska, allowed a Jesuit scholar Franz Xaver Kugler to make the assertion in 1927 that some similar impact event might have given rise to the ancient fire-from-above legends such as Phaëthon's ride. However, for some reason (or reasons, including the Second World War and Velikovsky), although there were good grounds for academia to take a serious look at ancient fire-from-above stories, nothing much happened. Kobres set out to research these stories. He points out that if the Earth has a close brush with an active comet it might look, to an Earth observer, very like the descriptions in Phaëthon's ride. A comet in an Encke-type orbit making a close approach to Earth will have a 'tail' pointing away from the sun and effectively towards Earth. So Kobres envisages a scenario where, to a Mediterranean observer, the comet (with its tail shortened by perspective, pointing upwards) appears to rise before the sun – if it were close enough and bright enough it would look like the sun. For several hours the sun would then follow the comet until the comet appears to stop and then drop back,

Earth enters the cometary tail and, as the comet reaches perigee, the risk of impacting large pieces of cometary debris increases.

Kobres has described the close encounter to make it as reminiscent as possible of the Phaëthon legend, this does not negate his hypothesis. Rather, it shows that a real phenomenon could conceivably have been behind the myth: 'Phaëthon, with his hair on fire, fell headlong, like a shooting star which marks the heavens with its brightness as it falls'. But Kobres goes further and notes that observers in different parts of the world, witnessing such an encounter, would see it from different perspectives and would describe it differently. He illustrates how stories from Central America, the Middle East, China and Siberia all seem to hint at a common theme. Such a story is difficult to control, in that the legends have poor time constraint, or have to be worked at quite hard to make any connection; but one of them is interesting in this regard. Kobres has unearthed some relevant Chinese legends which apparently relate to Wu Wang (the Zhou king who defeats king Chòu, the last Shang king, in the later twelfth century BC). Thus in this case there is a definite link to the twelfth century BC, and we have already seen that there was a comet sighting at the end of the Shang dynasty. He interprets these legends as a description of the Phaëthon incident as it might have been seen from China.

The problem here is to try to establish if Kobres' route to a mid-twelfth century BC cometary scenario is independent, which proves to be somewhat difficult. Both of us use Chinese references to a comet at the time of Wu Wang and, worse still (from an independence viewpoint), Kobres actually cites the Irish 1159 BC tree-ring event as the key to fixing the date of the proposed cometary encounter. So, although the issue is interesting in providing a hint of things which might have happened, it cannot be used as strictly independent evidence to bolster the cometary idea. I cannot use as support for cometary involvement in the 1159 BC tree-ring event evidence which itself uses the 1159 BC tree-ring event – therein lies circularity. However, Kobres did not know about the explicit reference to the comet at the time of Troy, which is right in this twelfth-century range. With that piece of information, he need not have used the Irish tree-ring date and he could have produced a very plausible and largely independent hypothesis of cometary effects in the twelfth century BC, which would have fitted remarkably well with Sagan and Druyan's point about Babylonian texts describing a bright comet which must have been close to the Earth.

By this stage it should be evident that the main story devolves down to links between the catastrophic environmental events at 1628 BC, 1159 BC and AD 540 – the dates indicated by extreme reduced growth in some oaks. It appears that it is possible to use existing ancient literature to forge broad links between catastrophic historical events in the seventeenth century BC, twelfth century BC and sixth century AD. The important point is whether the trees and the humans were recording the *same* events.

CHAPTER 10

◆

OTHER ENVIRONMENTAL EFFECTS

Up to this point we have been following a distinct thread leading from building tree-ring chronologies to inferring what seem to be large-scale environmental events. Suggestions of volcanoes blend subtly into suggestions of cometary bombardment. Although the case is circumstantial, so much material points in the direction of bombardment that it is difficult to ignore the possibility. If the Earth has been bombarded in recent millennia, then up to now the events have been essentially invisible. If there are major gaps in our knowledge of what can happen to populations on this planet, it beholds us, as Victor Clube would say, to open our eyes. This chapter follows a stream of consciousness which takes on a life of its own, each issue leading to another. Connections are set out though not everyone may agree with them. Hopefully, irrespective of any other considerations, the information is of interest in itself.

In 1993 I was giving a lecture at the University of Laval out-station on Hudson Bay. As part of the talk I pointed out that in a European oak master chronology, averaging many chronologies from Ireland to Poland, a dramatic growth reduction emerges – very similar to that at AD 540 – in AD 1740–1. This growth reduction coincided with the largest temperature reduction in Manley's Central England temperature record, which extends from 1659 to the present. I suggested that such events require explanation. Observations of this kind, in precisely dated tree-ring records, raise questions about the limits of natural variation in Holocene climate, and 1740 is very recent indeed; perhaps we should learn more about the cause of that event.

Subsequently, Bruce Campbell pointed out that the date I had selected for illustrative purposes, the AD 1740 tree-ring event, actually represented a key date in Irish and northern European history. The clearly catastrophic character of the early 1740s has been discussed by Drake and Post. Up until the eighteenth century, population growth in Europe was episodic, with periods of growth and occasional demographic crises. A typical crisis would tend to cancel out previous growth. Just such a growth-reversing crisis occurred in much of western and northern Europe during the early 1740s. Comments about it are quite stark:

> *The early 1740s marked the last period when famine and a concomitant surge in the number of deaths reduced the population growth generated by the excess of births over deaths in years of good harvests ... The mortality crisis of the early 1740s ... produced the last grievous rise in the death rates of northern and western Europe ...*

It seems that in December 1739 a severe frost set in which lasted for seven weeks, triggering hardship, famine and vulnerability to disease in 1740 and the following years. It is clear from the tone of the statements above that nothing quite like this event has recurred on anything like the same scale in the succeeding 250 years. It is worth noting a few of the claims made for the winter of 1740. The following were pointed out by Peter Francis, who located them in *The British Chronologist*, published in 1789. First, an extract from a letter dated 1 January 1740 from an English gentleman in Leyden, Holland:

> *My wine is tolerably strong, yet the whole freezes into a solid mass ... boiling strong punch, put into a bowl, presents us with ice in eight minutes; my barber coming yesterday to shave me, put a little hot water into his basin below stairs, and in the time he was coming up to my chamber it began to freeze.*

The same gentleman reports that a friend took a bottle of water from a pump which was not frozen, but, 'going directly to pour some into a glass, it was immediately ice: but what is more surprising, part of the stream from the bottle to the glass froze, and stood up in the tumbler like an icicle.'

As the gentleman says, the like was never known in these climates. I would not have thought it was technically possible to freeze boiling punch in eight minutes. Other unusual phenomena included the freezing of Lough Neagh in Ireland, with people able to cross 20 miles on the ice (though apparently some people were drowned when the ice broke). The potato crop in Ireland was decimated where it was stored in the ground.

Here was a situation where, yet again, northern European oak trees and human populations had suffered at the same time. However, it turned out that virtually no one had ever heard of this crisis: 300,000 people died in a couple of years in eighteenth-century Ireland (as some records indicate) and no one remembered. Why would this happen? On the one hand, it is possible that the more famous famine of the 1840s wiped out the memory of the earlier event, though perhaps the memory was never very strong anyway. Catastrophic losses of people in pre-industrial times were so commonplace that probably there was not much interest outside Ireland. To show how usual mortality was in those times, in the last decade of the seventeenth century approximately half the population of Scotland is supposed to have perished through famine. But it could be that other events served to divert attention from the 1740 famines. One can think of Culloden and the '1745' Rebellion in Scotland, a good distraction in itself within the British Isles. But perhaps more influential in European terms was the infamous Lisbon earthquake of 1 November 1755. This event was so traumatic partly because it raised questions of a religious nature and in some ways drew a line under much that had gone before.

On 1 November 1755, on a bright All Saint's morning in Lisbon, church bells summoned large numbers of the faithful to High Mass. During the services, at about 9.45 am, the city was struck by a series of tremors which collapsed buildings, started fires and caused seismic seawaves. In all, tens of thousands of people died. Many others world-wide, including Voltaire, thought that this was somewhat unsporting behaviour and started asking some serious questions of their belief system. However, we are not here to discuss religion, rather to think about the nature of catastrophic events.

The Lisbon earthquake is interesting for a number of reasons. For example, it was not alone: that same morning there were two other earthquakes with epicentres in North Africa, and in the week following there were up to thirty aftershocks, with other reported shocks from a wide area occurring for months afterwards. But perhaps more interesting were the distant effects on that 1 November itself. Fishermen, standing in a German lake that day, suddenly found themselves drenched to chest height. In Ireland the effects were also recorded:

The most remarkable earthquake which destroyed a large portion of the city of Lisbon was felt sensibly at Cork, and in the south of Ireland, particularly along the Shannon, on Saturday, the first of November, the sea rose in an extraordinary manner in the bay of Kinsale, thirteen feet higher than usual. Great agitation of the sea at Portsmouth, and in the lakes of Holland, Sweden and Norway.

This movement of water, induced by the tectonic action, was widespread. Water in wells across Europe, from Ireland to Scandinavia, rose and fell several times, as our German fishermen had observed. Lakes, even large water bodies like Loch Lomond in Scotland, were observed to rise more than two feet, then drop to the lowest level in living memory, repeating the effect a number of times. This movement of water bodies, termed *seiches*, may help to explain those references in the early Irish Annals to 'lakes breaking out'. This is a near-perfect description for a lake which would suddenly overflow its banks – one could imagine the event would be remembered as 'the year the lakes broke out'. In fact, there are many other recorded effects from 1 November 1755, such as coastal inundations, distant tsunami and even an Irish castle falling down, but it is the lake phenomena which are the most telling. Would this sort of action disturb the sedimentary record in the lake beds? Might some deposits be homogenized while others slump? Might rivers be diverted, lake exits blocked or uplifted? Would the water table after the event necessarily be the same as before? Overall, once the issue is raised it behoves palaeoecologists to reassess the integrity of many of the lake levels and deposits which they habitually use when attempting to reconstruct past lake and rainfall conditions; maybe the record is more disturbed than we normally assume. What seems certain is that there has not been such a widespread northern European earthquake since 1755, just as there has not been a year as cold and dry as 1740 since.

Observations like these serve to remind us just how little we know about even relatively recent times. But they also serve as a springboard to look at other phenomena which have been almost completely ignored by those studying the more distant past.

2345 BC AND THE HEKLA 4 ERUPTION

This particular environmental event took place at a time which must be very close to the beginning of the Bronze Age in Ireland, and appears to be associated with the, so-called, Hekla 4 volcanic eruption in Iceland. The environmental event appears as an extremely narrow band of rings, beginning in 2354 BC and reaching lowest growth – the narrowest rings – at 2345 BC. It is apparent that trees in Lancashire also show reduced growth at the same time, reinforcing the view that this is a fairly widespread downturn. While the event was prominent in the ring-width patterns, with extremely narrow rings, it was a surprise to discover a highly unusual growth defect in one of the samples from the fenlands just to the south of Lough Neagh (Lough Neagh is one of the largest freshwater lakes in Europe, with a surface area of around 380 km^2 (150 miles^2). The sample shows a change in the character of growth, from normal ring porous to essentially diffuse porous, that is, the normally clear rings become almost invisible. This is an anomaly which lasts for about a decade and which could be consistent with the tree being inundated; possibly the level of Lough Neagh may have risen for a period. There is thus clear evidence for an environmental event affecting oak growth generally and trees near Lough Neagh specifically. However, the evidence in this case is not limited to the oaks themselves.

Tephrochronology involves the identification and dating of microscopic volcanic glass shards and their use as marker horizons in ancient deposits.

Recent work by Valerie Hall and Jon Pilcher has indicated that Hekla 4 tephra, which can be specifically identified to that Icelandic volcano on chemical grounds, is found in numerous Irish and Scottish peat bogs at 2310+/-20 CalBC. The dating exercise, carried out by Gerry McCormac, used a series of high-precision radiocarbon measurements on stratified peats across the Hekla 4 layer and it is likely that the date given above is correct in absolute terms to within a half century. The implication may well be that the narrow growth rings and associated tree-ring effects after 2354 BC are directly due to the environmental effects of Hekla 4.

This raises interesting questions. Because the radiocarbon dates associated with this event would be almost indistinguishable from radiocarbon dates for the earliest section of the Beaker period, it is possible to ask if the broader Hekla 4 event was in any way related to the arrival of the first metal-users in Ireland.

Richard Warner, in his study of the ancient Irish Annals, sees the 2354 –2345 BC event as very close to one of only four major disasters recorded in the World Chronicle section of the Annals. One of these references bears the date AM 2820 – year of the world or *anno mundi* 2820 (which Warner interprets as 2380 'BC') and states: 'Nine thousand ... died in one week. Ireland was thirty years waste' (i.e. down to 2350 'BC'). Although Warner draws attention to the human aspect of catastrophe in the Annals, things are even more curious: the Annals go on to say that in 'about AM 2859 and after' (i.e. '2341 BC' and after) 'lakes erupted'. We know that these ancient Annals have no basis in fact – or do they? (I should mention here that there are numerous such references which serve to make their occurrences less than significant. However, in this case the proximity to a real event has to be interesting.)

We have dated the inundation of oaks at the south of Lough Neagh (in Co. Armagh) in the period 2354 BC to 2345 BC; an earlier scholar with Armagh connections, namely Bishop Usher, worked out the date of the biblical Flood to be 2349 BC (see the King James Bible). Several things could be said about these coincidences, two of which seem appropriate. The first is a question: did the scholars who worked up the early section of the Irish Annals in fact use the same biblical sources as Usher to derive their chronology? Is it possible that the various scholars came into direct contact some time in the early seventeenth century? It appears that while Usher was working on the biblical chronology in Armagh, O'Cleary was compiling the ancient Irish sources in Donegal. They may even have borrowed books from each other. Inevitably this suggests that the prehistoric section of the Annals are probably as compromised as critics suggest. Though this in itself is an interesting point: when two king list-based histories meet, which one is compromised? After all, the 'lakes breaking out' has a distinctly Irish ring to it – it may even be original. As has been observed many times, when coincidences start happening they can take on a life of their own, as is the case with 2345 BC. Having been intrigued by the Irish lakes breaking out, and astonished to find Usher's date for the Flood, imagine the mild surprise when reading James Legge's translation of the early history of China – the *Shoo King*. Although no one would now agree with his dates, nevertheless he pointed out, in the nineteenth century, that the earliest historical character in China is king Yao, whose start date is 2357 'BC'. Yao's major attribute relates to the terrible inundations which took place during his reign. How is it possible that there are no less than three pre-existing suggestions of 'floods' within a few years of our postulated raised lake levels in 2354–2345 BC?

Although this is an intriguing blend of scientific observation and ancient historical information, the weakness of the chronology underpinning the ancient histories reduces this whole episode to merely 'interesting'. However, if we return to the tree-ring event, the likely rise in the level of Lough Neagh and the dated Hekla 4 tephra, these components are certainly compatible. The Lisbon earthquake tells us that at times of distant tectonic movement lakes in Ireland can indeed 'break out'. We can certainly imagine that at the time of the Hekla 4 eruption in Iceland there may well have been tectonic effects and they may well have been observed in Ireland as *seiches* or even as temporary changes in water level. We can begin to imagine the occurrences which may have confronted ancient populations living in earthquake- and volcano-free Ireland or Britain. Quite possibly, after a long period of normality, suddenly the earth shakes and lakes overflow their banks; people may be swept away by tsunami. Black clouds appear from the west with terrible storms and rain that poisons – Hekla has erupted explosively only 1300 km (800 miles) to the north-west. Who knows what conditions were actually like or whether these local effects were only part of a much wider phenomenon? The only outrageous aspect about these suggestions is the idea that the ancient annals could have preserved such an accurate estimate of the date! However, there may be a wider context for this whole event. Moe Mandelkehr, who has written extensively on the global goings-on around 2300 BC, has looked at the archaeological, climatological and geological evidence for 'An Earthwide Event at 2300 BC'. He states:

The archaeological evidence sets forth two significant phenomena that took place at about 2300 BC. First a large number of sites were destroyed by earthquake and conflagration, over a large land area encompassing all of the known advanced cultures at that time. Second, cultural changes occurred, not only in the areas of destroyed sites, but over the entire Earth.

Perhaps there was a cataclysmic event at this time of which Hekla 4 is just a symptom, rather than the cause.

OCEAN OUTGASSING

Once familiar with the package of events associated with the Lisbon earthquake, we find that other previously unrelated phenomena start to make some sense; the reference to 'lakes breaking out' was one. Another relates to ocean outgassing. One day in 1994 Peter Francis arrived in my room to ask if I had seen 'that programme about the Bermuda Triangle, last night'. I had seen the start of the programme but had deliberately switched it off with an 'Oh no, not the Bermuda Triangle again.' 'Ah well,' he said, 'you missed something interesting.' Peter, as a geologist, explained that someone had a new theory about the Bermuda Triangle, that is, if a pocket of gas was released from the seabed on the continental shelf, for whatever reason, a ship passing over the spot would suddenly find itself dropping like a stone, gas being not nearly as buoyant as water. Moreover, if there was methane in the gas mix strange 'lights' might appear at the same time. This would indeed explain the mysterious lights and the disappearance of ships and even aircraft, the very symptoms which had produced the Triangle phenomenon in the first place.

Peter's geology and his experience in the oil industry meant that he knew a bit about this undersea outgassing concept. Outgassing is a necessary consequence of the existence, in many deep-sea deposits, of what are commonly called clathrates or gas hydrates besides pockets of free gas trapped beneath the clathrate layers. At certain conditions of temperature and pressure (cold conditions coupled with high pressures) water molecules form themselves into a 'grid' within which methane gas, or other equivalently sized molecules, can be fitted (methane, CH_4, is natural gas as burnt in millions of homes; other molecules would be hydrogen sulphide, H_2S, and ammonia, NH_3). One cubic centimetre of gas hydrate can contain 180 cubic centimetres of methane gas. Geologists have now noted that there is a widespread occurrence of a layer of gas hydrate beneath some hundreds of metres of ocean deposit. This layer shows up on seismic survey traces where the hydrate layer acts as a bottom simulating reflector or BSR. As already noted, it is frequently observed that free gas exists below the BSR, waiting to 'get out', so to speak. It would seem that there is actual potential for release into the atmosphere of large quantities of gas from the ocean floor; all we may need is some tectonic movement as a trigger.

Now, of course, hearing this from Peter I said, 'I can give you an independent example of outgassing', and quoted him an example from the day of the Lisbon earthquake. It is really quite extraordinary just how much information David Niddrie accumulated when he was putting together his book on earthquakes in 1961. For example, on 1 November 1755, a British ship was crossing the Atlantic. The captain felt a strange agitation as if the ship had been jerked and suspended by a string from the masthead. He dashed up on deck and observed 'within a league three craggy pointed rocks throwing up water of various colours resembling liquid fire. This phenomenon ended in about two minutes with a black cloud which ascended very quickly.'

What could the captain have been describing? Did an underwater volcano erupt that afternoon somewhere close to the Azores? Possibly, but there could be another explanation. Perhaps the captain was witnessing an actual outgassing event directly associated with the tectonic activity, an actual disturbance of a gas hydrate layer or gas pocket.

This historical record, whether or not it relates to outgassing, does raise questions about the concept of outgassing. We already know that such things can happen concerning lakes: in 1986 a crater lake in Cameroon, Lake Nyos, belched out a cloud of hydrogen sulphide gas which sat close to the ground and ran downhill for some 15 kilometres. It poisoned/asphyxiated thousands of people and animals. But have such things happened in the past? On what scale might they have occurred? What might their effects have been? Can we imagine a situation where a major outgassing occurs close to an inhabited coast and gas blows onshore. What might have happened to human populations in such areas? Are there any cases in the historical or archaeological record where areas have been suddenly abandoned? Let us look at the possibilities.

When it comes to considering coastal outgassing, the likelihood would appear to be that clouds of methane might blow onshore. The methane might occur as itself or burn to CO_2 or it might be associated with that dread of oil workers, hydrogen sulphide (H_2S). As noted in the Cameroon case, if the gas concentration is sufficient people will be poisoned or suffocate. Any combination is presumably possible. While all are dangerous, in some ways, H_2S is the most interesting. It is the traditional 'rotten eggs' smell beloved of 'stink-bombing' youngsters. At lowish concentrations, a few parts per million (ppm), it poisons slowly and smells horrible; however, at stronger concentrations, above about 150 ppm, the smell is deadened and the gas is deadly in minutes. Above 800 ppm death is sudden.

Imagine a cloud of H_2S or a mixture of these gases blowing onshore. What surviving description might there be? Or perhaps there is no description, simply an area 'where people die'. As it happens, some historical records may be relevant. For example, there is a record of just such an occurrence in the 1920s off the African coast. An entire fishing fleet was killed by H_2S outgassing from the sea around them. Reconstruction of the event suggested that everyone had jumped into the sea and were either poisoned or drowned; the boats were empty. We know that it was H_2S because, apart from being poisonous, it is highly corrosive and the paint was stripped off the metal boats.

Browsing through ancient descriptions of earthquakes, it is easy to find a couple of other possible outgassings. In AD 526, there was a terrible earthquake at Antioch where ancient sources refer to fire coming down from the sky like rain, or fire issuing from the earth and more coming down from the heavens 'like a shower of sparks'. This raises the question of how an eyewitness would differentiate between fire actually falling from the sky, say as part of a meteor shower, and a curtain of ignited gas coming from the earth or sea. But one source adds a further detail which appears to point directly towards outgassing. John of Ephesus wrote that in addition to the fire, 'Moist dust bubbled up from the depths of the earth, and the sea gave off a great stench; and the dust could be seen bubbling up in the water as it threw up sea shells ...'

In another description of this earthquake there is talk of liquid mud (sea sand as it were) boiling and bubbling up from the nether regions. There was 'a rank stench of the sea, and water seemed to flow out, just as if sea water were coming up with the hot mud'. Is this a direct description of an outgassing associated with the great earthquake? It certainly would appear to be. The contemporary estimate by John Malalas puts the death toll at Antioch at about 250,000 persons.

Moving up to the fourteenth century, at the time of the Black Death we again find references to fire from heaven. In this case they refer to the East near Greater India, and to Turkey. One source specifically states that 'fire falling from heaven consumed the land of the Turks for 16 days.' This latter statement fits well with one of Ziegler's references to events on neighbouring Cyprus, where in 1347:

> *While the plague was just beginning a particularly severe earthquake came to complete the work of destruction. A tidal wave swept over large parts of the island ... A pestiferous wind spread so poisonous an odour that many ... fell down suddenly and expired in dreadful agonies ...*

Such references give an indication of what could be poisonous or flammable gas associated specifically with earthquakes. But do we believe these early writers? I am tending towards giving ancient writers the benefit of the doubt. Until proven otherwise, quite often they were being as objective as they could be, given their lack of scientific knowledge. Rosemary Horrox has translated a German scholar writing in the generation after the Black Death. He was someone bright enough to have been educated to write – for all we know he may have been a genius. He has considered the various arguments relating to the cause of the plague, including sin and God sending tribulations, and planetary conjunctions. He decides he does not like any of these: 'There is a fourth opinion,' he says, 'which I consider more likely than the others.' He describes in some detail his belief that the cause of the Black Death was the 'corrupt and poisonous earthy exhalation' which came from the earthquake which occurred on St Paul's day in the year 1347. This quite specific suggestion could have been put by an investigative scientist. He thought the pestilence was actually a poison cloud from an earthquake on a specific day, 25 January 1347. For all we know, he could have been right.

Some clues are subtle, in that the original writers may not have realised their significance. These are the best ones; they contain information which would have been meaningless at the time but which we can interpret now. The best example is from Italy at the time of the Black Death. It was recorded that 'The wine in the casks had become turbid (muddy).' We know now that for wine in casks to become turbid, a gas would have to be involved which could travel through the cask walls. It can be argued quite convincingly that the small hydrogen sulphide molecule would exactly fit the bill – not only could it get into the casks, but it is exactly the right chemical to make the wine turbid! The turbid wine is the nearest thing we have to a 'smoking gun' for an outgassing event in the Mediterranean in 1347; that and the description from Cyprus. With the exception of Lake Nyos in 1986, none of these episodes is a proven example of catastrophic outgassing. However, the events are otherwise poorly explained. We will see in the next chapter how the recognition that outgassing exists, even as a theoretical possibility, allows us to play around with the idea of a 'wasteland'.

CHAPTER 11

•

THE WASTELAND
CONCEPT

In the last chapter we discussed the spectre of some sort of ocean outgassing which could have had catastrophic consequences for people in the past. Quite a good circumstantial case can be built up from documentary references, while from a scientific viewpoint we know that the amount of radiocarbon in the atmosphere is sometimes diluted by old carbon which had to have come from somewhere; methane from gas hydrates, or even free gas, from layers trapped by gas hydrates in the ocean floor, could be the answer. Observations for the second quarter of the fourteenth century AD reveal that the radiocarbon ages of consecutive wood samples get older, rather than younger, which hints at significant atmospheric dilution – possibly an outgassing, just around the time of the Black Death. What other information do we have from the distant past? If such an outgassing event had happened in a coastal area and the gas had come onshore, what might we expect in the records? We might find archaeological evidence for sudden abandonment and, because of the unknown cause, quite possibly a superstitious dread of such areas. Could we find such descriptions?

Don Carleton, when putting together his AD 540 package, mentioned one possibly relevant piece. The Byzantine historian Procopius, writing in the mid-sixth century, mentions what appears to be an abandoned and deadly west of Britain; it seems that he is writing from second-hand accounts:

Now in this island of Brittia the men of ancient times built a long wall, cutting off a large part of it; and the climate and the soil and everything else is not alike on the two sides of it. For to the east of the wall there is salubrious air, changing with the seasons, being moderately warm in summer and cool in winter … but on the west side everything is the reverse of this, so that it is actually impossible for a man to survive there even a half-hour, but countless snakes and every other kind of wild creature occupy this area as their own. And strangest of all, the inhabitants say that if any man crosses the wall and goes to the other side, he dies straightaway, being quite unable to support the pestilential air of that region, and wild animals likewise, which go there are instantly met and taken by death.

In itself this is quite a strange piece of descriptive (not to mention contradictory) writing. Some have insisted that he meant Hadrian's Wall and that he was describing the separation of Scotland and England. Let us instead take the description at face value and imagine that somewhere in the west of Britain there was an area where in the sixth century it was 'actually impossible for a man to survive there even a half-hour'. What might Procopius have been referring to? Clearly pestilential air that kills straight away; not only humans, but animals as well. This is strangely reminiscent of another reference to the fourteenth-century Black Death, by Gregoras relating to events in the Aegean islands, and repeated by Ziegler:

> then it attacked the Rhodians as well as the Cypriots and those colonising other islands ... The calamity did not destroy men only but many animals ... dogs, horses, and all the species of birds, even the rats ...

The Procopius story provides a circumstantial fit of something unpleasant involving a 'wasteland' not too far removed from the AD 540 event, and apparently sited in Britain. Is there anything else that can be tied in with this either temporally or geographically? Another famous Dark Age person who experienced a wasteland is, surprisingly, Saint Patrick who we have already seen is associated with phenomena reminiscent of impact events, and who traditionally lived in the fifth century AD.

The reason most often given for believing that Patrick actually existed is the 'fact' that we have two pieces of writing 'by his own hand'. A recent writer writes of Patrick's *Confession*:

> There is no doubt as to its authenticity. Over the years scholars have disputed just about every aspect of the story of Saint Patrick, but no one has ever credibly argued that his Confession was faked. It is too clumsy, too vague and too idiosyncratic to be the work of a forger.

The tone of that statement would give most readers grounds for doubt. Any doubt would be compounded by the confused nature of the following extract, which seems relevant here. It is important to remember that it may relate to somewhere in the fifth or sixth centuries, because we cannot be absolutely sure of either Patrick's existence or his dates, and we can be certain that the earliest copy of the text was originally written down much later, probably in the seventh century. This text tells us that Patrick set sail on a ship from Ireland. After three days they reached land, and for twenty-eight days they travelled through deserted country lacking food and overcome with hunger. Eventually prayer brings relief, though Patrick has a strange dream that same night wherein he is violently assailed by Satan, 'who falls upon me like a huge rock, and I could not stir a limb'. In the same letter the duration of their journey through the deserted landscape is repeated, though in a sufficiently confused manner to suggest that it is not a narrative text:

Also on our way God gave us food and fire and dry weather every day, until on the tenth day, we met people. As I said above, we travelled twenty eight days through deserted country, and the night we met people we had no food left.

Conventional wisdom suggests that this whole letter is simply an admonition that without God's grace a wasteland results. However, the confused presentation sounds more akin to the descriptions included, for example, in much Arthurian literature. Such literature seems to be constructed around later writings based on garbled, half-remembered oral history. Irrespective of the interpretation, the imagery is interesting. With Patrick, the span of 28 days is repeated twice, so that the concept of a large wasteland, where you can wander for a month without seeing a soul, seems to be clearly intended. We can also ask why he uses the very specific image of Satan falling upon him like a huge rock. We have already seen that Saint Patrick has strange cometary associations, in the form of bright nights and serpents. We will see later that such an image may have more context than was thought previously.

In a sense, the detailed interpretations of the stories of Procopius and Patrick simply do not matter. However, in the sixth century we have a catastrophic event widely recorded in tree-rings, with its consequences for human populations recorded widely in human history. To that can be added the concept of 'wasteland' from two separate fifth–sixth century sources, Procopius and Patrick, both possibly relating to Britain. And we can elaborate on this general theme. Around this period some Welsh poetry talks about an unexpected inundation of Gwyddno's land. Apparently there was a sudden rush of wind; there was a noise like shrieks and lamentations and many casualties. There was an *offensive* smell and Gwyddno's horses died from drinking poisoned water.

In these three sources we have a circumstantial case that would support the notion of something laying waste to a section of Britain in or around the early sixth century AD. Nothing in the story is inconsistent with an outgassing event triggered by either something tectonic or an impact. This is an unproved case, but interesting. Who would want to lay odds on whether Gwyddno's offensive smell is a better clue than Satan falling like a huge rock?

ARTHURIAN LEGEND

Arthur, king of the Britons, is a figure of immense literary importance. The tales and figures associated with him – Merlin, the Holy Grail, the various knights of the round table, the lady in the lake, the sword in the stone – means that Arthur represents a key personality in British, if not European history/mythology. Is it significant that one of the suggested death dates for this quasi-mythological figure is AD 539 (others are 537 and 542)? Is it coincidence that the most famous Briton of the first millennium AD, whether mythical or not, dies within the tree-ring 'window' of AD 536–45.

My consideration of the Arthurian story was prompted by a letter in late 1989 from Peter Pritchard, which pointed out how well the AD 540 event fitted with the concept of the 'Waste Land' in the Grail legend. As Pritchard put it, the basic concept is of a stricken king whose infertility and uncured condition spreads to the whole kingdom. Eventually the land is desolate with nothing left alive and it is doomed to stay in this condition unless the king can be cured. Pritchard had picked up on my event–famine–plague AD 536–45 scenario, recognizing that the world-wide quality of the AD 540 event coincided well with the world-wide source of the Arthurian cycle. Many writers have tried to make Arthur into an historical figure. While this can be an interesting pursuit for literary historians, so flexible is everything about these Dark Age traditions that it seems best to just sift through the Arthurian literature for information. Images and figures include: the wounded king, the wasteland, the Grail, red and white dragons, Merlin, the Dolorous Blow, The Dragon Star, etc. Mainstream Arthurian or Grail or Merlin writings speak of: 'a cessation of worship,' or ' a cessation which in folk belief might be sufficient to account for any subsequent drought which might affect the land.'

To the image of 'subsequent drought,' we can add:
'...the combination of subterranean fire and darkness that covers the land and the flight of people reminds us of younger Pliny's account of the eruption of Vesuvius and its consequences ...

From 'subterranean fire and darkness' we turn to a Welsh tradition: 'where a magic mist falls over the land, the seven catriffs of Dyffid become barren and desolate ...' and then a Scottish tradition: '...envisages a struggle for succession ... Arthur has no heir ... Arthur gets death as a reward ... and in the aftermath the Britons are punished with swift and dreadful disaster.'

In other words, people writing about the Arthurian period habitually use phrases which smack of catastrophic happenings. We know there was a natural environmental downturn of unknown origin which started in AD 536 with a 'dry fog' or 'dust-veil' or 'dim sun,' causing reduced tree growth, famines and plague; all in the window from AD 536 to 545. Plague reached Britain and

Ireland at this time. But, we also know that traditionally Arthur is supposed to have died in AD 539 and above we have statements such as 'Arthur gets death … and in the aftermath the Britons are punished with swift and dreadful disaster'. Such a neat fit might imply that the traditional Arthurian tales are rooted (whether Arthur is real or mythological) in the episode already specified as AD 536–45, that is, in some ways these mythological stories give us as good an idea of what was going on as actual history.

If the Arthurian tales really are rooted at this time, can we use details from these stories to give us clues to the *nature* of the event, and perhaps to the *cause*. While there is no doubt about the environmental event, there is total doubt about the causal agent. So what does Arthurian legend tell us? As we have seen, there are the allusions to poisoned air, drought, subterranean fire, etc. But there are also numerous references to dragons and a Dragon Star, to the image of the sword, and to such occurrences as the 'Dolorous Stroke' or Dolorous Blow. It appears there is a long-established association of dragons and swords with Arthurian legend, presumably relating to the late fifth and early sixth centuries AD. We already know that Merlin is the wizard figure associated with Arthur, and Merlin has dragon associations. Arthur's father of course is Uther Pen*dragon*. Geoffrey of Monmouth tells the story of the 'Dragon Star', where Merlin interprets celestial movements as the heavenly approval of Uther and his son Arthur. As David Day puts it: 'The appearance of the hero is foreshadowed like that of Christ by a bright star, which in this case is obviously a twin tailed comet.' In Geoffrey's text:

> the star is of great magnitude and brilliance, with a single beam shining from it. At the end of this beam was a ball of fire, spread out in the shape of a dragon. From the dragon's mouth stretched forth two rays of light … the second … split up into seven smaller shafts of light. The star appeared three times, and all who saw it were struck with fear and wonder.

This group of myths associated with Arthur, who supposedly dies in AD 539, has overt comet, dragon and wasteland imagery. So from Arthurian legend alone we could put together a picture which fits remarkably well with the implied picture from tree-rings and from conventional history. We are still left with the question of what physical phenomenon caused all of this? Was it a volcano? Was it a 'cosmic swarm' of impacts? Was it an ocean outgassing event triggered by tectonic effects, or indeed triggered by impacts? Taking the Arthurian mythology at face value it has to be said that there seems to have been a comet lurking somewhere in the background, or just possibly in the foreground.

It is easy to see the circumstantial nature of much of this story, but is it possible to be objective? One aspect of the sixth-century story is the apparently recurring motif of dragons and ponds. In the last chapter we saw how Chinese records talk of 'dragons wrestling in ponds, and where they passed the trees were broken'. I demonstrated that the Chinese seemed to be talking specifically about impact events. It was quite surprising therefore to find that very similar imagery relates to the Old English poem *Beowulf,* where the hero wrestles with horrible monsters in a lake not once but twice, and dies fighting a fiery dragon.

A savage monster, Grendel, comes to the hall of Hrothgar, king of the Danes, to kill and eat the warriors. On one particular night, the monster has killed one warrior and devoured him when he runs into Beowulf, who 'sat up and stayed Grendel's outstretched arm'. Beowulf holds Grendel fast and the monster realizes 'that never had he met any man in the regions of the earth, in the whole world, with so strong a grip'. The wrestling goes on and eventually Beowulf tears off the monster's arm and shoulder. The monster heads for the marshes, fatally wounded. The people assemble and look in wonder at 'the tracks of the monster' where he had 'made for the lake of water-demons – leaving tracks of life blood'. At the lake 'the water boiled because of the blood; and fearful swirling waves reared up, mingled with hot blood.'

Subsequently Grendel's monstrous mother sets out to avenge her son's death. Again she comes to the hall and kills one of the warriors and makes off for the moors. In a repetition of the monster-lake imagery:

They followed the tracks along forest paths ... the lake lay beneath blood stained and turbulent ... the water boiled with blood, with hot gore ... then they saw many serpents in the water, strange sea dragons swimming in the lake, and also water demons ...

Other images also appear, for example, when wrestling with Grendel's mother, Beowulf hurls away his sword:
'...the warrior hurled Hrunting away, the damascened sword with serpent patterns on its hilt, tempered and steel edged, it lay useless on the earth.'

The Beowulf story is thought to contain the image of a serpent-decorated sword cast down, just as in Arthurian legend a dying, dragon-crested Arthur orders that Excalibur be cast into the lake. The name 'Excalibur' is believed to be derived from 'Caliburn', in turn derived from the Irish Caladbolg, meaning 'flashing sword'. Hence the description, a possible sword image, of comet Halley in AD 530:
'... a tremendous great star in the western region, sending a white beam upwards; its surface emitted flashes of lightning.'

And, of course, Beowulf wrenched off the arm and shoulder of the monster Grendel while a hand and an arm appear from the lake to reclaim Excalibur. The act of throwing down a (flashing) sword may fit with the general theme of cometary imagery.

An enormous amount of scholarly writing has been devoted to Beowulf: its meaning, its context, its derivation and its date. Many readers may be thinking, is Beowulf not ninth or tenth century? Although the poem may have been composed, and ultimately written down later, its setting and thus its imagery and symbols are early sixth century. Some Beowulf scholars have actually suggested a chronology of events relating to the poem, their suggestions being totally independent of the tree-ring phenomena which indicate AD 536–45. According to Fr. Klaeber, Beowulf may have been born around AD 495; in 515 he visits the Danes and kills Grendel and Grendel's mother; in 521 he assists in an (historically known) expedition against the Franks and after 533 becomes king. Subsequently (fifty years later in the poem, though Klaeber suggests that this is merely a poetic formula meaning 'some time later') he dies fighting a fiery dragon.

How do we handle information like this? My feeling is that it is significant when independent sources tell similar stories. When those stories carry similar dates, suggested by independent workers, it becomes hard to believe that they are not causally related in some way. For example, Klaeber was only suggesting dates based on some of the historical context referred to in Beowulf, but nevertheless he does, for whatever reason, place the incident of Beowulf wrestling Grendel in AD 515. Now Chambers reminds us that Grendel had been haunting the hall and slaying warriors for twelve years before Beowulf put an end to his activities. Twelve years before 515 is 503, which is the year when:

in the second year of the T'ien kien era (AD 503) there were dragons fighting in a pool in Northern Liang province. They squirted fog over a distance of some miles ... the trees being broken ...

Taking Klaeber's suggestion at face value, we might even suggest that the monster Grendel first makes his appearance in the very year that Chinese sources record an impact event. By tradition, Arthur may have died in AD 539. Halley was in AD 530 with another spectacular comet in 538–9. It has been suggested that Beowulf has a clear early sixth-century context and dies fighting a fiery dragon sometime after AD 533. The Chinese dragons are early sixth century. We could add in the miracle attributed to St Columba, again in the (admittedly later) sixth century, where he drives away a monster in Loch Ness; a 'dragon in a pond' if ever there was one. We have already discussed the wasteland image to demonstrate the consequences in Britain.

Overall, the imagery is strikingly similar and well constrained in time. The Beowulf poem goes on to honour its hero by comparing his deed to Sigemund's exploits in killing a dragon. In this case the serpent burns in its own flames. For comparison, the Chinese texts say that when a 'dragon falls to earth it is burned by terrestrial fire and flies away'; what better way of describing an impact fireball with the causal dragon disappearing in its own fireball – a serpent burning in its own flames.

A logical explanation of these images would be comets in the sky and meteors or fireballs raining down. Fireballs with their smoky trails look like dragons. The tectonic effects of their explosions in the atmosphere cause earthquakes. Earthquakes in turn cause tsunami, and can cause major effects on distant lakes. At the time of the Lisbon earthquake on 1 November 1755:

the waters of Loch Ness became violently agitated, a series of waves rolled along the Loch towards the upper end and dashed for 200 yards up the course of the Oich, five feet above the usual level of that stream. The pulsations of the water lasted for about an hour, and after a huge wave had been dashed against the NW bank, the surface resumed its wonted calm.

Bailey, Clube and Napier may well be on the right track: the earth may have been visited by something approaching a cosmic swarm in the sixth century. The next question relates to AD 536–45: was that a culmination? If, as Don Carleton suggests, a comet struck the Celtic ocean, could we add in outgassing from the continental shelf? Ellis Davidson, in *Gods and Myth of Northern Europe*, discussed the Beowulf dragon:

then did the visitant spit forth embers, and burn up the bright dwellings; the flaming ray wrought mischief to men, for the enemy flying through the air would leave nothing alive ... he encompassed the people of the land with burning, with fire and flame ...

Many of these motifs – dragons, swords etc. – have a long history. Perhaps what we are seeing in the sixth century is a reaction to contemporary incidents which rekindle memories of these ancient myths, causing new legends to be created. However, much scholarly interpretation of Beowulf takes a simpler line. It is widely held that the core of the story is the security of the warrior group ensconced in their cosy hall. Grendel is simply an outsider who cannot be trusted, often nothing more than 'the unknown'. Writers who have deduced this explanation of the poem's meaning were very close to the truth; their mistake was to confer human attributes to Grendel.

When it is postulated, as here, that Grendel is part of a bombardment of cometary fragments then everything fits. Fireballs come largely unannounced, they are not to be trusted, they do come from the unknown and 'kill everyone in the hall', they can come repeatedly. For anyone with lingering doubts, one of the key mysteries of Beowulf is why Grendel is not described in detail. Need I go on?

THE BLACK DEATH OF AD 1347

We will now look again at the run-up to the Black Death which arrived in Europe in 1347. What, we might ask, was the cause of the great earthquake that was felt throughout England in AD 1320? Writers in the past have been rather dismissive of the phenomena which fourteenth-century writers, albeit retrospectively, regarded as portents of the mid-century catastrophe. Earthquakes are not uncommon, however, this 1320 earthquake occurs just where oak tree-ring records from widely separated areas in northern Europe begin to record an environmental event. This event spans the two decades before the arrival of the Black Death. Without labouring the issue, and noting that Ziegler gives the observations little weight, nevertheless in a few pages he recounts the following phenomena recorded around the time of the Black Death: droughts, floods, numerous earthquakes, locusts, subterranean thunder, unheard-of tempests, lightening, sheets of fire, hail-stones of marvellous size, fire from heaven, stinking smoke, corrupted atmosphere, a vast rain of fire, masses of smoke. He discounts reports of 'a black comet seen before the arrival of the epidemic' but still records the warnings: heavy mists and clouds, falling stars, blasts of hot wind, a column of fire, a ball of fire, a violent earth tremor in Italy, a crescendo of calamity, involving earthquakes, shortly before the plague arrived.

The 'black comet' is an interesting concept, though not well documented. In a French record translated by Horrox, apparently in August 1348 a large bright star was seen 'in the west over Paris' late in the day but before the sun set:

'It was not as high in the heavens as the rest of the stars, on the contrary, it seemed rather near.' From a scientific viewpoint the rest of the description is interesting. The writer makes it plain that some time elapses, for as the sun sets the star appears to stay in one place and then 'once night had fallen' this large, and by implication, unusual star 'sent out many separate beams of light, and after shooting out rays eastward over Paris it vanished totally: there one minute, gone the next.'

The writer is at pains to give the impression that the star was visible for an extended period, from the sun still being up until after night had fallen – 30 minutes? An hour? How long? The star seemed rather near and then appeared to self-destruct in a pyrotechnic display. Even the writer considered the possibility of a comet, but in a tone which leaves the question open. It might have been a comet but it might have been something else, 'perhaps something condensed from some sort of exhalations which then returned to vapour ...' Was he guessing the existence of ball lightning or was he watching some low-angle bolide?

From an independent source we read of a plague in Dublin in 1331 which was accompanied by a notable whale stranding, a phenomenon which Ziegler parallels in his list of portents. It is possible to find even clearer descriptions: Rosemary Horrox translated the following document from the Paris medical faculty which was written in October 1348 while the plague was raging. Although it talks of planetary conjunctions and eclipses, it also refers to 'a deadly corruption of the air around us':

We believe that the present epidemic or plague has arisen from air corrupt in its substance ... Also the sky has looked yellow and the air reddish because of the burnt vapours ... and in particular the powerful earthquakes, have done universal harm and left a trail of corruption. There have been masses of dead fish, animals and other things along the sea shore, and in many places trees covered in dust ... and all these things seem to have come from the corruption of the air and earth ...

The significance of this relates to the hints it contains of other similar happenings at other times when the faint whiff of comets and catastrophes are in the air. Sagan and Druyan in their book *Comet* mention the Chinese assertion (within a long list of unpleasantness associated with comets) that 'When comets appear, whales die.' We have already seen that there appears to be some association between cometary activity at the Exodus and at the end of the Chinese Xia dynasty. Well, here is another possible Old Testament–Chinese connection. Psalm 74 states:

Thou didst divide the sea by thy strength.
Thou brakest the heads of the dragons (or whales) in the waters
Thou brakest the head of Leviathan in pieces

or again in Isaiah 27: 'In that day the Lord with his sure, and great, and strong sword shall punish leviathan the piercing serpent, even leviathan that crooked serpent; and he shall slay the Dragon that is in the sea.'

The imagery is continuously repeated: serpents, dragons, swords, lakes, ponds, oceans. Breaking the head of Leviathan: would that class as a 'dolorous blow'? It would be logical that impacts over or on the ocean might give rise to the death of whales. Statistically there will always be more impacts over the oceans than over the continents, thus, 'When comets appear, whales die.' If we look again at the references to 'whale strandings' in AD 1331 and those 'masses of dead fish, animals and other things along the sea shore' in AD 1348., perhaps these may be due to tectonic effects or outgassings or impacts.

It seems reasonable to begin to suspect that there are a number of possibly related phenomena about which we do not know enough. Several of these phenomena could have affected past human populations in a strongly negative way. There may have been impacts by comet fragments or cosmic swarms; there may have been significant global cooling as a result of atmospheric loading due to either cosmic or cometary dust, or there may have been outgassing events triggered by either terrestrial tectonic movements or by impacts. This is a wide spectrum of hazards; yet we have almost no specific evidence that any of the changes in the traditional archaeological or historical records were caused by any of these mechanisms. Trees affected in the sixth century and in the fourteenth century, just when the two major plagues of the last two millennia occur, indicate an environmental dimension to the plagues yet we do not know the causes of the environmental downturns. But circumstantially we have a very good idea of the cause of the sixth-century environmental event: impacts.

However, as soon as we try to invoke impacts, we are confronted with the fact that other than Tunguska (and a few poorly dated craters, such as those at Warbar, in the Arabian desert, and those on the Argentinian pampas) we have little direct evidence that any major impact events have happened in the last 5,000 years. In particular, there is no general awareness of any ancient human populations being affected by impact events. Ask archaeologists or historians if they know of a population movement or a cultural collapse induced by debris from space and you are likely to be met with anything from blank stares to derision. The ideas of catastrophism and environmental determinism have been so thoroughly marginalized that it is almost impossible to have an informed conversation on the topic of bombardment from space. Yet astrophysicists make a very plausible case that the Earth should have been affected during the last few millennia. They also make it clear that even within the last decade, we have had close fly-bys with pieces of space debris (either asteroidal or cometary) of a size range possibly consistent with the collapse of civilization, had we been less lucky – sometimes only hours have separated us from catastrophe. Even more bizarre, those same dismissive archaeologists and historians, asked if there have been collapses of civilizations or population movements in recent millennia, will happily answer in the affirmative. In the great whodunnit of history astrophysicists have the 'gun' and archaeologists–historians have the 'corpse', but no one suspects a 'shooting'.

Is it possible that we have simply been ignoring a quite significant suite of hazards? Historians and sceptical archaeologists adopt the line that if such things had happened they would have been recorded. This, I believe, is a fallacy. Impacts, and indeed outgassings, are phenomena which militate against direct eyewitness accounts – witness a 20-megaton airburst (or a significant outgassing) at close range and it is unlikely that you will be writing your experience down for posterity. Most relevant ancient descriptions, if they exist at all, will be secondary, or distant, in nature; each can subsequently be explained away and ignored or misattributed.

Apart from such secondary descriptions, which are inherently difficult to interpret, strange information can be consigned to the dustbin as being literally mythical; but is it all? As I have pointed out, the coincidence of myths makes them harder to ignore. 'Dragons in ponds' recorded in China *and* Britain at the same time demand some explanation. If both Chinese and Hebrew texts talk about whales dying in association with cometary imagery it is necessary to ask what possible causal mechanism might be involved. It is necessary to be more open-minded on the possibilities of impacts; impacts could form a remarkably plausible basis to explain a wide spectrum of these largely ignored ancient tales.

LAKE NYOS REVISITED

We can now return to the 1986 Lake Nyos outgassing and see what we can learn of relevance to this chapter. In 1986 there were many aspects of the outgassing which were puzzling. Scientists were confronted with apparently conflicting evidence. Seventeen hundred people were dead from an undoubted gas release from the crater lake. However, although survivors talked of a 'rotten egg' smell during the incident, analysis of the lake water showed almost no hydrogen sulphide present. So it was assumed that the asphyxiation was due purely to inert carbon dioxide gas. Moreover, it was not clear just how carbon dioxide could build up in large enough quantities in the bed of the lake. As a result, the scientists decided that the surviving witnesses had been 'hallucinating', or that there was some problem with the translation of the witness statements; put simply, they did not believe the eyewitnesses.

Rogers and Yevi have published recent findings on the Nyos outgassing. A layer of gas hydrate had built up at the bottom of the 208 m (680 ft) deep lake. This gas hydrate layer was saturated with hydrogen sulphide. The hydrate layer acted like a cap on the lakebed and accumulating carbon dioxide venting from the crater built up below it. At some stage, presumably due to this carbon dioxide pressure, the cap broke loose and started to rise to the surface. The rising layer of course reduced the pressure on the CO_2 saturated water beneath (like opening the top on a bottle of carbonated water) so that CO_2 bubbled out and accelerated the cap to the surface. The power of that acceleration is marked by the fact that a wave rose 75 m (250 ft) up one wall of the crater! Either on the way up, or when it arrived at the surface, the hydrate was converted to gas and a heavy mass of toxic hydrogen sulphide gas swept down a valley for 15 km (9 miles). The gas was so powerful that it uprooted some trees in its way and was estimated to have formed a cloud some 30 to 60 m (90 to 200 ft) in depth. This cloud chemically burned and poisoned its way down the valley, killing people and cattle. Hydrogen sulphide was found in the body tissues of victims and burns were found on bodies due to sulphuric acid associated with the hydrogen sulphide.

This new hydrate explanation reveals why there were large quantities of hydrogen sulphide present in the bed of the lake, the hydrate had actually scavenged H_2S from the water, which is why there was so little left in the lake water for the scientists to find. It explains the violence of the outgassing and how the gas had built up, and, most importantly, it confirms the eyewitness accounts of a rotten-egg smell – which, we should note, had not been believed! This last point is perhaps the most devastating: the witnesses had not been believed, but it looks as though they may have been *absolutely correct.* That has to remind us of comments around the time of the Black Death. These strange pieces of information were not easily explicable and were written off as retrospective attempts by a traumatized population to try to explain the horrors of the plague. Ziegler might just as well have said that people were hallucinating or that there was a problem in translating what they meant. My attitude is to take the opposite course. I think that the Lake Nyos experience tells us that eyewitness accounts should be taken more seriously; it is not that they are always right, just that sometimes they may be. If half of the information from ancient history, recorded in the last few chapters, is true, ancient writers were doing the best they could to describe things they did not understand.

CHAPTER 12

♦

VELIKOVSKY REVISITED

Everything in the foregoing text has come about as a direct result of observing events in tree-ring records and attempting to find explanations for the physical causes. The initial hypothesis was inevitably volcano-related because of the similar spacings between the tree-ring events on the one hand, and the acid layers in the Greenland ice record on the other. This volcanic scenario was pushed to its chronological limits and then gradually opened out in order to look at other phenomena. It became more and more apparent that there might be something else occurring – to do with comets, or just possibly ocean outgassing. There is a very strong circumstantial case that comets could have been involved in at least some of the environmental events we have noted, especially those at 1628 BC, 1159 BC and AD 540. It is also apparent that there is no physical mystery about comets, or indeed, asteroids.

There are two types of physical body which can hit the Earth, namely, comets and asteroids. In the past ancient people had seen and recorded comets; the bright gaseous plume which is illuminated by the sun was often described as a bow, or sword, or arm in the sky. There are no obvious records of asteroids, small dark bodies which are effectively invisible without a telescope, and not that easy to spot even with large telescopes. Astronomers have devoted quite a lot of time to asteroids because, from a hazard point of view, the most interesting ones are locked into orbits in the inner solar system. But perhaps the interest is actually stimulated by the fact that most of the early ones were discovered by accident and some are in Earth-crossing orbits. As we will see, quite a lot is now known about asteroids. Comets were known about because they were often seen, but their composition and origins were a mystery until recent decades. It is now known that the comets we see originate from what is effectively a shell of comets called the Oort Cloud which sits far out on the fringes of the solar system. From time to time gravitational effects from passing stars, or changes in our sun's position relative to the galactic plane, displace comets from the Oort Cloud into the solar system; some of these comets penetrate the inner solar system where we reside. As already noted, objects moving inside the inner solar system represent a definite hazard to inhabitants of this planet. Looked at simplistically, we are trapped in the middle of a target, orbiting close to the bullseye (the Sun) and from time to time objects are fired towards the centre of the target. Then, just to make the game more interesting, there is a deflector (in this case the giant planet Jupiter) whose gravitational field is sufficiently strong that it mops up most of the incoming missiles and either captures them or fires most of them back, away from the target. Unfortunately, the deflector is not 100 per cent successful and it actually encourages some material towards the target; worse still, it sometimes breaks the missile up and fires a scatter of debris inwards to the target. Though the reality is much more complicated than this simple model, the model is sufficient to get the feel of the problem, which can be stated as follows. For some reason, the experiment which we regard as life on Earth is periodically 'stirred' by comets from the edge of the solar system. It can be stirred vigorously – as when the dinosaurs were eliminated 65 million years ago, leaving the decks clear for mammals to take over – or, as this book suggests, it can be stirred more gently – just enough to change the odd dynasty or move some populations. Jupiter itself was stirred vigorously in July 1994 when all twenty-two major fragments of Shoemaker/Levy 9 impacted there.

Comets are loosely compacted, but deeply frozen, hard, masses of rock and ice and organic materials, debris left over from the formation of the solar system. The common term 'dirty snowball' only half does them justice. 'Snowball' implies fun – nice children throw snowballs. A comet is more like the ice/gravel/mud/excrement 'iceball' of the playground psychopath. There is another factor worth mentioning. A snowball is typically thrown at a velocity or around ten metres per second; a comet is typically travelling at 20 to 50 km (12 to 30 miles) per second! So do not think of dirty snowballs; think of 'psychopathic iceballs'. As it approaches the sun, some of the comet's volatile material evaporates into a cloud called a comae, which is stretched out into a tail by the solar wind.

While the asteroid population in the inner solar system is relatively stable, and as lumps of rock or nickel-iron the asteroids themselves are pretty stable, comets are a bit more diverse. Normally a few kilometres or miles across, they can be captured into fairly stable orbits which can be of long or short periods – a few years or thousands of years. These long-return types will normally appear out of the blue and are not much different from a completely new comet – they appear, pass through and disappear and as long as they have not hit us we can forget about them. Then there are giant comets up to hundreds of kilometres across. Clube and Napier believe that these turn up very infrequently but that they break up in the inner solar system – it may be these giants which provide the bulk of the smaller 'regular' comets. Clube and Napier reckon that a giant comet entered the solar system some 20,000 years ago and that most of the comets that have been seen by enquiring humans over the last 5,000 years are the debris from successive break-ups of its fragments. If left orbiting long enough, all the comet's volatiles will eventually burn off and only the rocky core will be left, effectively indistinguishable from an asteroid. So there are at least two broad classes of hazard from comets: interaction between a live comet and the Earth and interaction between a dead comet and the Earth, with the latter being indistinguishable from the asteroid hazard.

A number of scientists have gone to great lengths to point out the hazards of both these classes of astronomical object and have worked out from the numbers of Earth-crossing objects that 'by any standards we should have been hit in recent millennia'. They ask an essentially pointed question: 'We must have been hit, so where is the archaeological or historical evidence?' For example, W. B. Masse recently stated that his findings indicated that impacts capable of directly or indirectly killing at least one quarter of the Earth's human population occur on the average every 5000–6000 years.

Strangely, he suggests a specific date for an impact, namely 2807 BC. While the tree-ring chronologies do not seem to support that idea, there is what appears to be a severe Europe-wide oak downturn, inevitably of unknown cause in 2740 BC. John and Mary Gribbon mention a minimum of 1,300 (more like 2,000) Earth-crossing asteroids in the greater-than-1-km range, and point out that some of these may be dead comet nuclei. Duncan Steel, one of the scientists who has actually been involved in the search for Earth-crossers, puts it in more deadly scientific terms with his 'estimate of about 2,000 Earth-crossing asteroids larger than the *minimal global catastrophe* threshold, a diameter of one kilometre.' Steel does some sums on known asteroid parameters and comes up with the fairly standard estimate that, taking into account their mean collision probability and orbital period, 'a figure of once every 100,000 years is a useful benchmark … for (collision with) the larger bodies.' Though he qualifies this by saying that the estimate could be out by a factor of a few in either direction, that is, it might be more like 200,000 or 300,000 years, or, just as likely, 50,000 or 25,000.

For every object greater than 1 km in diameter, there will be many more half that size, and huge numbers of little ones. The Gribbons mention estimates that, as well as the 2,000 big ones there may be about a million in the 0.1 km to 1.0 km range and a staggering 500 million bits down to 10 m (32 ft) across. The 20-megaton Tunguska object may have been only 40 m (130 ft) across: *small* does not mean *safe*. I have mentioned earlier the recent observations from satellites and from infra-sound listening stations (which can detect explosions in the atmosphere around the globe) showing that on average the Earth is hit by a handful of 2–6 m (6–19 ft) objects every year. There is no doubt that this planet is hit by objects which are either asteroids or bits of comets.

We need to think a little bit more about this idea of being hit – what does it mean in reality. Well, there are hits and there are near-misses. We can imagine the simple case. A boulder whizzes in and hits the Earth directly at high velocity. Depending on the size of the boulder and the velocity, there is an explosion ranging from the equivalent of a few kilotons to hundreds of millions of megatons. It is clear that nothing in the latter class has occurred in even the last few million years, almost certainly not since 65 million years ago – though we did witness those impacts on Jupiter in July 1994. In this direct-hit scenario it is immaterial whether the object was an asteroid or a dead or live comet; size and velocity are all that matter. However, near-misses are a different thing altogether. A near-miss with an asteroid is just that: 'woosh – that was lucky', and, as mentioned, we have had several of those in recent times. A near-miss with a comet, whether it is dead or alive, may be very different. Because cometary nuclei are 'loosely packed' there is a tendency for them to be torn apart by the gravitational fields of the Sun or the planets in any close situations. So we can be pretty sure that cometary nuclei are not travelling alone; there is likely to be a whole hierarchy of fragments. A near-miss with a comet, dead or alive, might mean that even if we are not hit by the main fragment, we may be hit by a whole host of smaller fragments. This could happen in a single pass or it could happen over a number of orbits. Such activity might lead to loading of the Earth's atmosphere with dust and maybe even volatiles and, as Clube and Napier, and Bailey and Steel, and Verschuur and others would argue, with the possibility of multiple Tunguska-class impacts – the 'cosmic swarm'. Simple mathematics indicate that for every comet that would hit us, about 4,000 pass closer to us than one Earth–Moon distance.

This introduction to cometary hazards tells us that the real problem on the timescale of civilization is the debris associated with a 'close pass' comet, irrespective of whether the comet was dead or alive. As we will see, the principal difference would be the scale of visual display: a live close-pass comet would fairly certainly blow your mind. Looking back over the last few chapters, those questions, deriving from those precisely-dated environmental downturns, have led to a scenario which suggests that the Earth may have had one, or a few, close brushes with comets and their debris in the later second millennium BC and just possibly another in the sixth century AD.

It is not possible to paint such a scenario without drawing attention to another worker who came up with just such a scenario almost fifty years ago. Many readers will have noted strange echoes in this book from the still-resonating works of Immanuel Velikovsky, mentioned earlier in the context of volcanoes at the Exodus. I am not a follower of Velikovsky and would side entirely with Carl Sagan and others in denouncing Velikovsky's ideas about Venus having been a comet, of Venus having made close passes to Earth, of exchanges of various kinds between Earth and the passing Venus, etc., etc. In addition, I would be the first to state that Velikovsky's desire to shorten the Egyptian chronology is wrong, and, as I have pointed out elsewhere, it disagrees with my own chronological work.

However, I would not disagree with *all* aspects of Velikovsky's work. Velikovsky was almost certainly correct in his assertion that ancient texts hold clues to catastrophic events in the relatively recent past, within the span of human civilization, which involve the effects of comets, meteorites and cometary dust. After all, I have arrived at the same scenario, spurred on by those anomalous tree-ring events. Unfortunately, Velikovsky's more lunatic ideas had the effect of scaring off most scientists from having anything to do with him or his ideas or the issue of recent bombardment events. His principal failings were, in my view, threefold. First, his thesis was too large; anyone reading *Worlds in Collision* is left breathless at the range of subjects covered. Second, he couldn't be neutral and really believed his own thesis (perhaps one should say theses) to a point where he was blind to common sense. Comets are quite enough of a handful in themselves without involving Venus and Mars passing by and the Earth standing still. However, his greatest failing was chronological. Everywhere in his work is the desire to see connections – from Mexico to Samoa, China and India to Israel, similarities in ancient tales are seen as good-enough grounds to make concrete associations. The Exodus, Phaëton – all are drawn into pan-global reconstructions. Velikovsky seems not to have realized that without good chronological reasons for making linkages, the linkages are just so much wishful thinking; at best they could be called interesting. When a precisely dated event acts as a focus to explain, to suck-in, other loosely dated phenomena in the same general time period, the danger is that one creates an artificial horizon. Velikovsky takes hypothetical and undated catastrophic events and sucks in many pieces of either poorly or entirely undated ancient history or mythology to create major horizons which, with the exception of the Exodus, have no location in real time. However, now is the moment for yet another re-examination of Velikovsky.

VELIKOVSKY'S WORLDS IN COLLISION

When Velikovsky published *Worlds in Collision* in 1950 he ran into a storm. Some scientists were so incensed by the content of his book that they went to the extraordinary lengths of attempting to have it banned: they thought that the content was 'dangerous'. In the following decades the result of this assault by some scientists had two effects. First, most scientists either read and dismissed the whole book or did not bother to read it at all. Some lay readers decided that Velikovsky had been attacked by establishment scientists and therefore he must be correct; thus in some ways he became a martyr figure and guru for a particular type of anti-establishment audience. This latter set of converts cover a variety of degrees from mildly interested to devoted follower. There are still many people today, almost half a century later, who feel that re-habilitating Velikovsky is their life's work.

But what is it all about? Velikovsky was a catastrophist in a relatively uniformitarian world; he believed that ancient history contained a disguised story of major environmental effects on the Earth caused by extraterrestrial forces, namely comets. Now, there would appear to be nothing wrong with such thoughts today; after all we now know that comets pack a wallop. But what Velikovsky did to upset those original scientists was to suggest that the comets which caused havoc on earth about thirty-five and twenty-six centuries ago were not comets as such, but the planets Venus and Mars.

His thesis ran along the following lines. At two different dates, Venus, in the second millennium BC, and Mars, in the first millennium BC (the former having shot out of Jupiter as a comet), roamed around the inner solar system narrowly missing, but having dire effects upon, the Earth and then settled down into their present stable orbits. As if this flagrant abuse of Newtonian mechanics was not enough, Velikovsky went on to postulate all sorts of theories about electrical discharges between passing planetary bodies, magnetic fields strong enough to stop the rotation of the earth, etc. It was for this wild swipe at scientific orthodoxy that Velikovsky fell foul of scientists in general.

I am going to ignore completely the mistaken ideas about electrical discharges and the Earth stopping, reversing, etc.; these were not central to his book. I also ignore some of his main chronological failings. Velikovsky did not have a very good basic chronology to work with back in 1950. However, he did search through an incredible amount of ancient literature, chasing up just about every ancient source from China, the Mediterranean, Europe and the Americas in his search for support for his basic thesis. It is this ancient history archive which I think should be mined, not dismissed. This is probably the stage to explain why I think this is reasonable. It was when I read the final part of *Worlds in Collision* that I spotted a major flaw, which explained why Velikovsky had felt obliged to invoke planets doing impossible things.

Through the course of the book he had been talking about Venus and Mars having endangering the Earth during the last few millennia. But fundamentally, Velikovsky did not understand anything about comets; he had not had the benefit of Clube, Napier or Steel, etc. As if to comfort his readers, at one point he says that no planet at present has a course which poses a danger to this planet: '...only a few asteroids – mere rocks, a few kilometres in diameter – have orbits which cross the path of the earth.'

A *mere rock* a few kilometres across, say 10 km or 6 miles across, can pack a 100-million megaton punch and would easily end all intelligent, and most other, life on this planet. That adjective 'mere' tells us why he went to all the trouble to try to invoke planets acting like (and in his view actually being) comets. He did not know about the hazard posed by relatively small objects, and, just in case there is any doubt about his mistake, he repeats the notion by noting that a possibility exists of some future collision between planets, 'not a mere encounter between a planet and an asteroid'. This failure to recognize the power of comets and asteroids means that it is reasonable to go back to Velikovsky and delete all the physically impossible text about Venus and Mars passing close to the earth. We can then safely ignore everything about the earth stopping revolving (and starting up again), toppling over, associated changes in ancient calendars, used to show the changes in rotation rates etc. In other words, we can get down to his main thesis, which is that the Earth experienced dramatic effects from heavenly bodies particularly in the second millennium BC. This thesis seems to me to be entirely reasonable, given what we now know about the likely return times for impacts of various sizes, and the circumstantial case for cometary involvement in the two environmental events in the mid- to late second millennium BC.

Velikovsky has done a pretty thorough job of combing the sources for us. He describes the phenomenon which would most likely accompany a comet passing close to the Earth. This phenomenon, he explains, would be a rain, a torrent, of meteorites. Any cometary astrophysicist would agree. And Velikovsky goes on to remind us of the biblical reference to great stones cast down from heaven at the time of Joshua and the associated hail of stones which slew the host of the Canaanite kings. Joshua comes, by tradition, shortly after the Exodus of the Israelites from Egypt, so this is clearly the main period of interest (if only anyone knew the dates of Exodus and Joshua, we would know when this shower of meteorites might have taken place). Velikovsky reminds us that in the book of Joshua there is a record, apparently from this time, of the earth quaking and trembling. So by quite early on in *Worlds* we see the general thrust of the argument, which Velikovsky paraphrases as follows:

> *A torrent of large stones coming from the sky, an earthquake, a whirlwind ... It appears that a large comet must have passed very close to our planet and ... a part of the stones dispersed in the neck and tail of the comet smote the surface of our earth a shattering blow.*

There we have it. Velikovsky believed that a realistic interpretation of a well-known part of the Old Testament was that some time in the mid- to late second millennium BC we had a close brush with a comet. What he does next is look for support for his idea in the historical traditions of the natives of the Americas. He finds that Mexican annals record a cosmic catastrophe in the remote past during which the night did not end for a long time. Here he is looking for a link with the Joshua observation of the sun and moon standing still. The problem for Velikovsky is that he has no time control on the Mexican reference; it just happened in the *remote past*. This should have caused him to stand back from the evidence and define a defensible approach. Only if some very specific information linked the independent references could they then be used in support. Usually he fails to do this, though none-the-less he does draw out some interesting pictures about the nature of recorded cosmic catastrophes which are of general use. Unlike Velikovsky, I intend to accept only supportive information if it adds to the picture and if there are good chronological grounds or associations which seem reasonable to me.

However, let us paraphrase this first Mexican event just for reference. In these records, associated with one or more catastrophes, 'the night did not end for a long time', the world was dark, there was a fourfold night and sometimes the Sun would rise just above the horizon and then stay still. Velikovsky ends his first key chapter by recognizing that he is not dealing with a single remembered event, but more likely several. In the Americas, according to Velikovsky, another catastrophe had occurred 52 years before the one just described, that is, the one Velikovsky wants to associate with that of Joshua. He uses this second event to search backwards in biblical sources, looking for something catastrophic about half a century before the Joshua incident. He knows that in Hebrew 'history' the Wandering in the Desert traditionally took forty years and the various battles involved in conquering Palestine took a number of years (he cites a source stating that the conquest took 14 years). He feels it reasonable to ask whether a date 52 years before the Joshua cosmic event might coincide with the Exodus. He was actually working back towards the Exodus because that is the event he really wants to deal with. We have already seen in this book how the Exodus does indeed sound like a catastrophic event. Not only that, but a seriously catastrophic event around a time when there is a notable hint of cometary activity recorded in both Chinese and Hebrew sources. The difference is that the scenario in this book has been arrived at by another route. But having recognized that Velikovsky, with the nonsense removed, is talking about a catastrophic event at the time of the Exodus, let us see what he deduced about the event. On the basis of his reading of ancient history, in the middle of the second millennium BC there was a global catastrophe when 'a new comet came very close to the earth'.

However we got here, we certainly have arrived at the same place. Our problem is that the logic chain used in this book has placed the eruption of Santorini and something cometary at the same time. So we need evidence to separate out phenomena relating to volcanic/tectonic effects from those associated with comets. What do we have at the time of the Exodus that would segregate the symptoms of the two phenomena? As an example, red rain and water turning to blood could well be volcanic/tectonic, while the hail of stones seems more likely to be related to a comet – it seems unlikely that Santorini could have shot stones as far as Egypt! Velikovsky notes that the Midrashim, in a number of texts, states that naptha, together with hot stones, poured upon Egypt. The memory is of strange rains and hails associated with an utterly consuming fire. One of the references seems to say that even the waters were affected by fire. Overall, if Velikovsky got this part of his story correct, it seems that at the Passover there was a major destruction in an all-consuming conflagration.

This is interesting because fire could just as easily be a by-product of tectonic/volcanic events in the Eastern Mediterranean. We saw in the last chapter how outgassesing might spew out massive quantities of methane and hydrogen sulphide. Another symptom of an outbreak of tectonic activity in the Mediterranean area could well be massive conflagration. One other notable plague in the Exodus was the plague of darkness. It is clearly stated that the Israelites were blinded and choked by this unearthly darkness. Again, according to Velikovsky, rabbinical sources suggest that during the plague of darkness most of the Israelites perished, and at the same time these sources describe a strong west wind that lasted for seven days. The ash dispersal pattern from the Santorini eruption is towards the East, that is, there must have been a prevailing westerly wind.

There is no very easy way to segregate the volcano and outgassing phenomena, though let us just take Velikovsky at face value and outline a couple of his other comments about the Exodus. It is traditionally told that the final plague occurs when the Angel of the Lord passed over, killing the firstborn in the houses of the Egyptians but sparing those in the houses of the Israelites. Velikovsky interprets the selective nature of this plague, one that has puzzled many biblical scholars, as the selective effects of an earthquake. He reasons that the Egyptians lived in stone houses which would have collapsed with fatal consequences, whereas the Israelites lived in tents or light huts which would have been largely unaffected by an earthquake. So he sees the 'smiting' as a 'severe blow'. The trouble is that a severe blow could be either tectonic- or impact-related. However, he is on firmer ground with the seventh plague, the plague of 'barad', which he believes are meteorites.

If we approach the last couple of paragraphs with an open mind it is possible to see aspects of earthquakes, fire and meteorites. Maybe we do have combined tectonic and impact effects at the same time. However, there is one other symptom of the Exodus proceedings which I am pretty sure Velikovsky did not fully appreciate when he noted it down and which may, in its own way, be one of the clearest references to a symptom of an impact. As we have just noted, he sees the last plague on the last night in Egypt as an earthquake, and one associated with lethal hail. But it was also associated with an anomalously bright night. Velikovsky says that the Midrashim records the last night in Egypt being as bright as the noon on the day of the summer solstice. Later he repeats the statement that the bright night was on 'the night the great earthquake shook the globe'. What Velikovsky almost certainly did not know in 1950 was that one of the symptoms of the Tunguska impact was the anomalous brightness of the nights at the end of June 1908. He did not know about the miracle associated with Patrick, where 'on the night of his death no night fell'. Reviewing this overall package we end up with the possibility that the Exodus, according to Velikovsky, could be associated with volcanic/tectonic activity, outgassing activity, impact activity, or any combination. But to me the 'night as bright as the noon' is the significant indicator of events.

Velikovsky does not stop here; he goes on to quote biblical statements which refer to the Exodus and which appear to be quite specific. For example, parts of Deuteronomy verses 4 and 26 are used to describe the phenomena which were associated with the bringing of the Israelites out of Egypt: 'and the Lord brought us forth out of Egypt with a mighty hand, and with an outstretched arm, and with great terribleness, and with signs, and with wonders.'

As mentioned earlier, the image of the hand and arm in the sky is a recurring motif and seems to be a cometary image. We have already seen it in Beowulf and in Arthurian legend, and we will see it again in the context of the Celtic god Lug. To be fair, the image could presumably also be a description of the eruption column from Santorini being moved by upper-atmosphere winds. Tectonics or impacts: they are difficult to separate.

THE BATTLE IN THE SKY

If one were forced to make a judgement, up to here Velikovsky's evidence would seem, with one or two exceptions, to be mostly consistent with tectonic activity and we could explain almost all the observations by some combination of eruptions (Santorini?), earthquakes and, just possibly, outgassing. To be fair, there is also the 'arm in the sky' and the apparent hail of meteorites. It is not possible to be certain either way. Just when one is starting to despair of making any sense of the issue, Velikovsky moves into the compellingly widespread notion of two 'gods' in the sky doing 'battle'. We have already seen how in Greek mythology Phaëton, the son of Apollo, is shot out of the sky by Jupiter when he loses control of the chariot of the Sun. Bob Kobres interprets that imagery as a twelfth-century BC cometary incident. But there is much more to the story and it is interesting to see how Velikovsky handles it. He sees the comet, passing close to the earth, changing in form with extensions growing from the serpent-like tail. It may have looked like a writhing animal with numerous heads and waving limbs. Velikovsky sees this image as the basis for the widespread mythology, found essentially world-wide, of a fight in the sky between a light-god (seen as good) and a serpent monster (seen as evil). In most cases the force of good overcomes the evil monster and in some cases the dragon is thrown to Earth. This story takes many forms: the Archangel Michael and Satan, Marduk and Tiamat the dragon, Isis and Seth, Vishnu and the serpent, Krishna and the serpent, Thor and the Midgard serpent, Zeus and Typhon, Arthur? Beowulf?

However, this is a subject-area clearly fraught with difficulty. Is anything dated? Are there any grounds for linking any of these myths in real time? (Apart from Arthur and Beowulf, as we have seen.) One uneasy aspect is that the battle image may be a recurring motif. The most common criticism of attempts to insert cosmic catastrophes into, say, the seventeenth or the twelfth centuries BC comes in the form of referral to earlier similar examples. In other words, the idea is dismissed because the event is presumed to be simply a re-statement of earlier Sumerian or Egyptian examples. Those who study these early stories may have been obscuring an obvious hazard by assuming that all the descriptions stem from a single very early source, which may itself have been mythological. Are we starting to see a different and more frightening story, previously obscured by poor chronology, where the myths are re-invented every time one of the events occurs?

Let us look at a few of these different events to see if they stand up to scrutiny. Put simply, did impacts really happen? Fortunately, from the point of view of the possible Exodus–Santorini–1628 BC event, Velikovsky decides to use Apollodorus' description of what seems to have happened around this time, that is, the battle between Zeus and Typhon. Classical authors carry some authority, and, moreover, this version of the 'battle in the sky' myth has some interesting details. According to Appollodorus, Typhon:

> *overtopped the mountains and his head often brushed the stars. One of his hands reached out to the west and the other to the east, and from them projected a hundred dragon's heads. From the thighs downward he had huge coils of vipers which … emitted a long hissing … His body was all winged … and fire flashed from his eyes. Such and so great was Typhon when, hurling kindled rocks, he made for the very heaven with hissing and shouts, spouting a great jet of fire from his mouth.*

This classical depiction certainly does read as though there were some cometary goings-on in the ancient sky. If we want to think in cometary terms then the most likely explanation is that a comet fragmented in the vicinity of the Earth with one part possibly missing the planet and another fragment or fragments possibly impacting. Certainly these myths habitually see a dragon (remember those bolides/dragons from previous chapters) falling or being thrown to the ground and in some cases going underground. People who had witnessed a fireball, or dragon, passing over the horizon, and who had felt the resulting earthquake associated with the airburst/impact, naturally assumed that the dragon had gone underground. Subsequent tectonic effects and earth rumblings would be attributed to the beast groaning there. The problem as always is that the story does not come with a date. Without one, it is impossible to relate it to the Exodus story. However, Velikovsky found sources which suggest a date for Typhon. He starts by quoting Pliny:

A terrible comet was seen by the people of Ethiopia and Egypt, to which Typhon, the king of that period gave his name; it had a fiery appearance and was twisted like a coil, and it was very grim to behold; it was not really a star so much as might be called a ball of fire ...

Velikovsky's problem is to ascertain when this event took place, and in his book he asks quite specifically if king Typhon's comet was at the time of the Exodus.

He then cites earlier authors, for example Hevelius, writing in 1668, who in turn cites 'certain authorities' to the effect that at the time the Israelites were on their march from Egypt, at a date given as AM 2453 (= 1495 'BC'), a comet shaped like a disc was seen in Syria, Babylonia and India. So we can be fairly certain that the assertion that there was a comet at the time of the Exodus long predates Velikovsky. This is important, because, as indicated previously, the suggestion that there might have been a comet at the time of the 1628 BC tree-ring event, which in turn might be Santorini, which in turn might be the Exodus, came about through links to *Chinese sources* by an indirect route. That *cannot* have been the route that these earlier writers followed.

Velikovsky goes on to state that the Typhon comet is mentioned not only by Pliny, but also by Lydus, Servius, Hephaestion and Junctinus and he proceeds to give more descriptive detail. Apparently the comet was seen as an immense, slow-moving, red-coloured globe. The ancient writers' views seem to be mixed as to whether it was of a fiery or of a bloody redness. It was also described as 'like a sickle', which might be a description of a globe partly illuminated by the sun. What seems clear is that the comet is recorded as causing destruction 'in rising and setting.' Servius writes that it caused many plagues, evils and hunger. Overall, if one wants a pre-existing description of the hypothesized comet at the Exodus, then clearly here is one.

Velikovsky continues with his quest. He notes that Campester, as recorded by Lydus, was of the opinion that if the Earth ever again ran into Typhon, the former would be destroyed in the encounter. Given the nature of such predictive writings (based on actual past experience) the original Typhon encounter must have been distinctly catastrophic in character. He notes that another seventeenth-century writer, Bochart, also maintained that there were close associations between the plagues of the Exodus and the phenomena associated with Typhon: 'the flight of Typhon is the Exodus of Moses from Egypt'. Although it is not a watertight story by any means, it leans very heavily in the direction of a comet at the time of the Exodus and a widely remembered cosmic event of catastrophic character.

Velikovsky has given us some interesting clues which as far as I know have not been adequately exploited. I will now use Velikovsky's encyclopaedic gathering of relevant information to see what picture of the Typhon comet might emerge.

If we take Velikovsky's research from ancient literature at face value, we have reference to the comet being a *globe* which can present as a *crescent*. Velikovsky seems to have wondered if this latter description meant that the comet was close enough for the earth's shadow to obscure part of the cometary disc. The problem with this idea is that a cometary nucleus may be solid but it will have a large comae – the surrounding cloud of gas which reflects sunlight and can be extremely bright – so it is not clear whether the crescent description would actually work in reality. It is, for example, very difficult to assess just how close a comet with, say, a 10-km, or 6-mile, nucleus, would be in order for it to look as large as the sun (by simple trigonometry, without a comae, the nucleus of a 10-km comet would look as large as the sun if it was 1,000 km, or 600 miles, from the Earth's surface).

Actually, the distance does not much matter; the big step prompted by this Typhon description is the realization that a frighteningly close brush with a comet could well bring the comet itself, or parts of its associated debris, within a few thousand kilometres of the earth. What, I asked myself, would actually happen in a close approach? I sought out Gerry McCormac, a colleague who had trained and worked as an atmospheric physicist. Most atmospheric physicists have long since thrown Velikovsky out, and indeed McCormac had never read any Velikovsky. When asked what he thought would happen if a comet approached very close to the earth, his reply was startling:

If it came within the earth's magnetosphere it would probably be spectacular ... the sky would go purple or green, particles from the comet would spiral down the lines of force and it is likely that you would have amazing auroral displays and coloured streamers ...

'Oh,' I said, 'you mean like Quetzalcoatl the Central American sky serpent with his feather arrangement represented as flames of fire?' Suddenly a new series of possibilities had opened up. One had to try to imagine a cometary body, or associated debris, passing within the earth's magnetosphere and possibly producing a fabulous, moving, coloured display. So I asked if there would be any other associated phenomena – noise maybe? He replied: 'Well, the Eskimos [Inuit] say that at the time of aurora they sometimes hear a hissing noise … but! … scientists who took up sensitive listening equipment did not manage to record anything.'

Yet again, as with the smell of rotten eggs at Lake Nyos, we have eyewitness testimony, in this case of noise associated with aurora, but because scientists cannot duplicate it in a few experiments the testimony is disregarded. But the Inuit have lived in the far north for millennia, they have witnessed a lot of auroral activity; if they say that they sometimes hear the aurora, who are we to say they do not? In fact, there is a whole literature on the subject of auroral sounds and, indeed, sounds heard directly from bolides, even comets. Colin Keay has written extensively on these phenomena. Leaving aside auroral sounds (apparently sometimes they are heard and sometimes not), the problem is with meteors or bolides, where there is an apparent contradiction. People have claimed that they have heard an incoming fireball and in fact *heard* it and turned round to *see* it. There is the contradiction: the flash of light from a fireball is travelling much faster than any related sound (in the same way as we see a high-flying jet and hear it some time later). Traditional wisdom holds that we cannot actually hear fireballs coming in, we may hear the rumble and explosion only some time later, usually after we have seen them. Keay has accumulated information showing that some people genuinely do hear fireballs as they come in and *before* they see them: how? The plasma trail from a large fireball may generate Extra Low or Very Low Frequency radio emissions; if an observer happens to be standing beside a suitable object (or perhaps if he or she is wearing a suitable object like glasses or headgear), that object can act as a transducer for the electromagnetic signal – thus the observer actually 'hears' the incoming fireball as it enters the atmosphere, before seeing it. The technical name for this phenomenon is 'geophysical electrophonics'. What do observers claim that they have heard? It appears that the sound is most like hissing, shooshing, popping, wooshing or clicking; it seems we can believe Apollodorus' comments about 'Typhon … emitting a long hissing'. A lot of pieces of evidence are beginning to fit. In a recent article Keay provides a real gem: two Chinese researchers, Zhuang and He, have found in old reports the statement that the very bright Comet De Cheseaux in 1743 produced sounds when it appeared. Obviously we cannot hear across the vacuum of space, so the likely explanation, according to Keay, is that particles from the comet's tail must have been interacting with the magnetosphere. Apparently sometimes we *can* hear comets!

In the 1990s, new scientific information is making sense of ancient reports which previously have been dismissed. Keay states the case quite bluntly:

> *Geophysical electrophonics can provide a physical explanation for many episodes hitherto assumed to be supernatural, such as celestial noises accompanying tongues of fire and similar manifestations, described in many scriptures, scrolls and ancient writings ...*

CONCLUSION

By now it should be clear what the package of information is beginning to look like. Having mined Velikovsky's accumulation of ancient sources, it appears that, at the time of the Exodus, which could easily be 1628 BC, and quite possibly as Santorini was erupting, there is a reasonable case for a comet being somehow involved. The comet known as Typhon may have been passing very close to the earth: astonishingly, frighteningly, incredibly close, putting on a display of at least six components which we can reasonably envisage:

• A bright head, perhaps as bright as the sun and blood red
• That head 'wrapped' in a comae or halo like mantle
• A tail, as of a serpent, and flaming or multicoloured
• Incredible auroral displays with changing patterns and streamers, 'heads', 'tails', 'arms', 'manes', etc.
• Direct electrophonic sound-effects, not necessarily heard by everyone
• Impacts of accompanying debris ranging from 'hail' (meteorites) up to perhaps 'Tunguska class' or beyond with accompanying earthquakes, possibly the 'thunderbolts' of old legends.

Such a phenomenon would have been awe-inspiring and any debris recovered from the ground would be considered as sacred stones. Indeed, there is a whole literature concerning the idea of 'sacred stones'. To give but one example, recently Graham Hancock wrote:

> *some of the serious biblical scholarship argued that the Tablets of Stone contained within the Ark of the Covenant had, in reality, been two pieces of a meteorite.*

From the point of view of this book, it is particularly interesting that Hancock goes on to suggest that the Holy Grail was also a meteorite. As the Grail is intimately tied in with Arthurian legend, we see yet another faint link between the time of the Exodus and the time of Arthur.

CHAPTER 13

•

MERLIN, LUG AND MICHAEL

All the pieces of the jigsaw are now in place. It appears that there may have been a catastrophic set of happenings in or around 1628 BC involving a close-pass comet and volcanic activity. We have what may be some reasonably accurate descriptions of what it was like at the time with incredible coloured sky displays, assorted impacts and general mayhem. It is not impossible that versions of this may have happened more than once, especially if the responsible body exhibited even temporary periodic behaviour. We can imagine that, in later times, even lesser displays might have triggered off fear of a return and, indeed, this is just what Duncan Steel envisages for his admittedly earlier and less well-documented 'Stonehenge' bombardment episodes. (Steel suggests that the earliest construction at Stonehenge, the circular bank known as a 'henge', was actually an artificial horizon to aid in the prediction of impacts associated with meteor showers.) But we know that some of the other possible dates for return apparitions could include those same old narrowest-ring dates 1159 BC, 207 BC and AD 540. Events originally assumed to be purely volcanic now seem to have a cosmic dimension. The point is that, whether the cometary involvement is in the form of direct interaction with a live comet or in the form of one of Clube and Napier's 'cosmic swarms', in either case, the issue is raised of bombardment of the planet triggering volcanic eruptions. Presumably the causal mechanism would be impacts, causing earthquakes and triggering volcanoes. This scenario sounds reasonable; it is just that it has not been observed in recent times. It would have the great advantage of explaining why, when volcanic eruptions are extremely common, the very severe events, like 1628 BC or 1159 BC, stand out so clearly. So with that in mind now that we have a faint glimmer of what the answer might be, let us make an excursion into some varied ancient literature and see what we can find. Can we make any sense of previously obscure ancient detail? What follows is in no particular order, it is simply a recent 'stream of consciousness' triggered by a few chance finds of what might loosely be termed 'dragon images'.

Because of our interest in the AD 540 event and its proximity to the traditional date of the death of Arthur, it was inevitable that we should take some interest in Merlin. In *The Quest for Merlin*, Nikolai Tolstoy unearths some interesting imagery in regard to Merlin. What follows is a brief synopsis. For example, Merlin saw a ghastly vision in the sky which drove him to lifelong exile in the forest. What ghastly vision in the sky, one might ask? First, Tolstoy sets the tone by quoting from the poem *Cad Goddeu* which is from the *Book of Taliesin*. Apparently this contains many details of the legend of Merlin, and Tolstoy wonders if the text might actually derive from things written by Merlin. I would have thought that Merlin's mythical status would make this unlikely, but that is irrelevant. We are interested in things attributed to Merlin and, by association, to the sixth century. Tolstoy tells us that Merlin claims to have 'wounded a great scaly animal', which recalls the cosmic serpent of the ocean, Leviathan, wounded in the Old Testament. Tolstoy sees some similarity with northern mythology, where Thor attacks the Midgard Serpent which is described as encompassing the earth. If we turn to Gibbon's *Decline and Fall of the Roman Empire*, he says something strange about a comet which appeared eight years after the well-attested AD 530 apparition of Halley:

> *Eight years afterwards (AD 538–9), while the sun was in Capricorn, another comet appeared to follow in the Sagittary: the size was gradually increasing; the head was in the east, the tail in the west, and it remained visible above forty days... The nations, who gazed with astonishment, expected wars and calamities from their baleful influence; and these expectations were abundantly fulfilled ...*

While this certainly adds credence to the AD 536–45 environmental event, it also provides an image of a comet which would partly explain the concept of a dragon encircling the earth – head in the east, tail in the west. Tolstoy notes that these examples are variants, as we have seen, of a world-wide myth involving the slaying of a serpent or dragon which is also a ritual originally celebrated in Ireland at the feast of the god Lug, *Lughnasa*. Who is Lug? Tolstoy tells us:

> *The name 'Lug' derives from a Celtic root meaning 'light' and the god was conceived as bright, youthful and glorious above all the other gods ... and like to the setting sun was his countenance and his forehead; and they were not able to look in his face from the greatness of his splendour ... The glory of his appearance was like that of the sun itself ...*

This is the bright face of Lug of the Long Arm (more literally, 'long reach'). A Celtic god as bright as the *setting* sun with a long arm: is that not reminiscent of Apollo and of the blood-coloured comet Typhon? But, remember, we have arrived at Lug by opening a book on Merlin. Tolstoy elaborates further by telling us of a New Year festival from Babylonia which took place at the temple of the god Marduk, located at the site of the world navel or *Omphalos* (centre of the Earth). It was Marduk who slew the monstrous Tiamat. Similarly Tolstoy reminds us that, in ancient Israel, the New Year Festival included aspects of Yahweh wounding the serpent Rahab. There is a widespread association of dragon fights with New Year festivals, and Tolstoy points out that such festivals also occurred in ancient Ireland. As he puts it, these were 'ceremonies of cosmic renewal' which took place at the Irish Omphalos (Uisnech) and provincial Navels. Of them all, the one which was best known was the festival of the god Lug.

But just when we are getting used to the imagery of Lug of the Long Arm, Tolstoy tells us that the poem *Cad Goddeu* makes best sense if we imagine that it is uttered by Merlin as an incantation of Lug. According to Tolstoy, Merlin seems to be a priest of Lug or, just possibly, he is a Celtic god like Lug, and Tolstoy goes on to note that one of several attributes which link Merlin and Lug is that each had a 'virgin birth'. The message seems clear. Apparently logical steps, starting with spaced tree-ring phenomena, running through volcanoes and comets, led to the linking of the Exodus to cometary phenomena. In turn there is a distinct impression that the happenings around AD 540, with those notable environmental events, resemble a rerun of aspects of the Exodus. It is then possible to find that others, studying the complex field of mythology, have already linked Yahweh with the Celtic god Lug, whose description might as well indicate a comet, and with Merlin, who

(a) was born of a virgin impregnated by an incubus which was between the earth and the moon
(b) throws thunderbolts and
(c) wears a feathery cloak (remember Quetzalcoatl).

Merlin is undoubtedly associated with the sixth century AD where the AD 540 event, if not the whole period, has bombardment imagery. A pattern undoubtedly exists. These repeated associations do not need to be there; but they are. One begins to wonder if we are close to an overall answer and if we can test it by independent routes. In an earlier chapter it was observed that 'wormwood' occurs in Chinese texts at the end of the Xia/start of the Shang dynasties in a reference associated with 'Heaven's bright terrors'. It was noted that 'wormwood' also occurs in Revelation chapter 8 vv. 10–11 in the clear context of a 'star falling from the sky' and causing problems on earth:

And the third angel sounded, and there fell a great star from heaven, burning as it were a lamp … And the name of the star is called Wormwood: and the third part of the waters became wormwood; and many men died of the waters, because they were made bitter.

But since that was noted we have seen how many of the characteristics of the apparitions in the sky could be accounted for by contemplating a comet, or its associated debris, passing so close to the earth that it runs through the magnetosphere, thus putting on a pyrotechnic display which would account for much of the strange and extreme imagery of Revelation. A close comet would produce incredible auroral displays in colours including purple through green. If we read on in Revelation, after the star Wormwood falls from the sky:

And the four angels were loosed ... and the number of the army of the horsemen were two hundred thousand thousand ... and I saw the horses in the vision and them that sat on them, having breastplates of fire [red], and of jacinth [blue] and brimstone [sulphur-yellow]; and the heads of the horses were as the heads of lions [with manes]; and out of their mouths issued fire and smoke and brimstone ...

So here in Revelation we have a description of the colours of the huge number of maned beasts. In Revelation chapter 12 vv. 7–9 the image is further reinforced:

And there was war in heaven; Michael and his angels fought against the dragon; and the dragon fought and his angels,
And prevailed not; neither was their place found any more in heaven.
And the great dragon was cast out, that old serpent, called the Devil and Satan he was cast out into the earth, and his angels were cast out with him.

The Archangel Michael and his angels defeat a dragon and his angels and throw them on to the Earth from heaven. This sounds like an attempt to describe yet again something like the Phaëton myth, which could just as easily be a close comet with atmospheric happenings, coloured skies and fragments falling to earth. However, the new ingredient is Michael: who is Michael? He is the Angel of the Lord at the Exodus. Remember, we now know that there seem to have been catastrophic visitations associated with comets in 1628 BC and 1159 BC; we have also a fairly good idea that something with cometary associations took place around AD 540. We also seem to be reading about something involving a close cometary approach. This close approach would have been truly awe-inspiring, not to mention terrifying. There is the auroral display as charged particles spiral down the magnetic lines of force; we can imagine this as billowing tendrils of incredible colours, constantly moving – the 'feather cloak' phenomenon that could account for the images of beasts with manes, arms in the sky, and even heads. If the main object has already separated into several pieces, as a comet close to a planet is wont to do, it might appear as a complex body. But whether there is one or more main components, the object is certainly not alone. A hierarchy of smaller objects is also moving with the main object. Each of these smaller objects is a miniature version of the large object, with their own halos and streaming tails, some of them falling to earth. It may have resembled a very dramatic meteor shower. If some of the impacting fragments were large then witnesses on earth would have heard distant explosions of kiloton to megaton size, and felt the earth quake and there may have been hissing or other sound-effects directly associated with the sky effects. Basically, it is hard to do justice to what such an experience might have been like. People caught up in earthquakes talk about disorientation; anyone witnessing a close cometary approach would be pretty sure that the end of the world had indeed come: this is just what eyewitnesses to the Tunguska event believed was happening.

Once this scenario has been developed we know what we should be looking for in ancient descriptions. We have to start looking at ancient writings in a new way, namely, that at least some of the early writers were making serious attempts to describe phenomena about which they had no understanding. We also must remember that for the early events, perhaps for most of the events, the writers had not been actual eyewitnesses, but were working from handed-down verbal descriptions (successive generations may have found it more and more difficult to believe what they were being told). My feeling is that, as with parts of the Irish annals, in many cases people were probably being as factual as could reasonably be expected.

AN AFTERNOON IN THE LIBRARY

I went to look something up about an apparition of St Michael which is supposed to have happened in the late fifth century AD. The reason was that the previous year I had bought a small, leather-bound copy of the *Examination of John Fox's Calendar of Saints*, printed in 1603. When I bought it I did not realise that at the front was a 'Catholike Calendar' which listed the saints associated with particular months. Leafing through the list, I came upon dates such as 'Ann. Chr. 540': 'Siluerij PP. & Mart. This Pope being persecuted by Theodora the Empresse wife of Justinianus, for that he would not restore an heretical Bishop ... sent into banishment.' The list appeared accurate because under the month of March for 'Ann. Chr. 491' it referred to:

Patricij Episc.&Confessoris ... this Patrick being brought up in all kinds of learning … was sent … to preach Christian religion to the Scotts and Irishmen whome he converted … working infinite miracles among them.

The year AD 491 is one of the traditional dates for the death of St Patrick. A few pages away there was 'Ann. Chr. 536',the same year as Stothers and Rampino's dry-fog year. Imagine my surprise when I read:

Apparitio S. Michaelis. This is the memory of a famous apparition of S. Michell the Archangell on the mount Garganus in Italy, whereof you may read in Sigebert in his chronicle an. 488 and many others …

Traditionally, the apparition of St Michael on Mount Garganus was in the late fifth century; however, here is a seventeenth-century book which places a 'memory' of the apparition in AD 536! What is not in doubt is that St Michael is the Archangel who slew the dragon (the Antichrist). Why would an apparition of Michael be remembered under AD 536? Remember that 536 is the year of the 'dim sun' which Stothers and Rampino had picked up from ancient Mediterranean sources. If there was 'an apparition' it might give some clue as to the nature of the AD 536 event – it might in fact be the answer. Was a comet seen in the sky that year or did someone witness something fall to earth? I was not encouraged by the reference to Sigebert's chronicle date – who was Sigebert and what calendar were the writers of the list actually using? As I searched the library for any reference to a Sigebert, I found a book on the sixth-century Gregory the Great. On page 12 a date caught my eye: 'The huge and magnificent baths of Caracalla … had been dry since 537 …'

Nothing to do with St Michael, but a nice chance find. Why were the baths dry – was it social change or war or had some tectonic movement altered the water supply or brought down an aqueduct? The answer is about as mundane as we could reasonably expect. Norwich's book *Byzantium* tells us that at the start of the siege of Rome in March 537 the Goths had indeed cut all the aqueducts supplying the city. The baths were dry as a direct result of human activity. A few pages later there were lurid descriptions of the tribulations of people in Italy at this time, of which a few words will suffice: 'The fields, which for two years had been left uncultivated, were silent and deserted.' The inhabitants of Tuscany had taken off to the mountains where they were living on acorns, and occasionally each other. In Bower's *History of the Popes* (1750), it turned out that there was just a single line devoted to the year AD 540: 'The following year 540, nothing happened worthy of notice …' This is not quite what the trees thought! This particular comment by Bower is odd because there are other years where he gives no information, but they are not commented on in any way. It is almost as if Bower, by this unusual negative comment, is pointing out 540 to us. It is that old problem for historians when there is no history – 'no history' is taken to mean 'nothing happened' – but sometimes things happened that were not recorded, and sometimes the records themselves were destroyed. I read through the entries for the years AD 536 to 545. We know, not only from Stothers and Rampino, but also from the dendrochronological story, that something pretty strange was happening in this period. In the relevant pages associated with the history of the popes there is just one whisper of actual conditions. In a footnote, under AD 536, it mentions that Sophronius tells a story about Pope Agapetus. Apparently Agapetus is supposed to have unjustly imprisoned a bishop:

> *But he had not been long thus confined, when his innocence was revealed in a Vision to the Pope, and the Vision was confirmed by the most Stupendous Miracle, wrought in the Sight of the whole City of Rome.*

One is left wondering what a stupendous miracle might look like? Could this have something to do with the memory of the apparition of St Michael mentioned above? Moving on, Russell's book entitled *Satan* produced:

> *Gradually the idea grew that Michael was God's agent in the destruction of the Devil. Devotion to Michael existed in the very early church; by the fifth century it was growing rapidly, particularly at Constantinople and the East, and it then extended to Italy and became important in the reign of Gregory the Great (590–604) when Mt Gargan became a centre for devotion to Michael.*

If Michael, in Revelation, fought with the Dragon in heaven and cast it to the earth, why was his cult becoming more important in the fifth and sixth centuries? Was this in line with Sophronius' miraculous happening at Rome? Was it in line with Clube and Napier's more active sky and increased risk of bombardment between AD 400 and 600?

The biggest surprise was an English translation from the German by A. H. Keane of a book by W. Bousset, *The Antichrist Legend*, published in 1896. The imagery in the text really is quite surprising. Bousset starts by pointing out that apocalyptic writers do not invent their ideas, rather they hand down memories from primeval times. Bousset is saying that the writer of Revelation, rather than having a premonition of the end of the world, is using either past, or possibly contemporary, human experience as the basis for his imagery. Thus, when it is suggested that 'a star called Wormwood will fall from the sky and poison the waters' it most likely means, as we could have anticipated, that some time in the past a star did fall from the sky and poison the waters (if the

Chinese texts mean anything, the wormwood and poison at the end of Chieh's reign give us a hint for the likely date for the event, possibly the same date as the Exodus). Bousset goes on to relate Revelation to earlier Babylonian myths and to discuss the manner in which the dragon (slain by Michael) had been anthropomorphized into the Antichrist: a 'shameless and terrible dragon who is to bring disorder into the whole world'. Bousset quotes from an earlier discourse on the Antichrist:

> *In the opening of Ephr. Gr. [Discourse on the Antichrist] we have the*
> *following description of the Antichrist, which nowhere recurs in later writings*
> *... there shall be – signs and wonders*
> *Wrought by the Dragon – in great abundance*
> *When he shall again – manifest himself as God*
> *In fearful phantasms – flying in the air*
> *And show all the demons – in the form of angels*
> *Flying in terror – before the tyrant*
> *For he crieth out loudly – changing his forms also*
> *To strike infinite dread – into all men ...*

Such a passage really encapsulates the whole issue. It could almost be a direct description of a close-approach comet and its associated debris. Here is the Dragon, flying in the air, associated with demons/angels, producing signs and wonders – phantasms – even changing in form. Bousset puts it another way: 'The Antichrist perishes in an attempt to fly aloft and thus prove himself God, and by God is hurled down.' Sounds very much like the Phaëton story. Bousset again, quoting from Philip's *Dioptra*, describes other attributes of the Dragon: 'But also ... by changes of forms and colours one from another ... flying on high like an angel, nay like a demon, and fashioning portents and wonders unto deception.'

More and more relevant imagery emerges from the text:

> *And suddenly shall the sun shine again at night ...*
> *He shall bid fire fall from heaven and the sun stand still on its course ... The*
> *sun shall he turn to darkness and the moon to blood ... The sun shall he cause to*
> *rise in the West ...*

If we take Bousset at face value, then all these factors linked to the Antichrist are remembered primeval images associated with apocalyptic happenings at the time of an ancient comet. He even tells us that the chief plague to prevail at that time (the period of the Antichrist) was a long drought coupled with a terrible famine. Did the event about which Bousset was hypothesising and which we are attempting to reconstruct coincide with an important incident involving the Israelites – did it happen at the time of the Exodus? Did it happen at the time of Troy? Or did it happen at both?

Though one cannot prove a case here, the sheer abundance of relevant literature allows some surprising linkages to be uncovered. Can we find any links between the Dragon in Revelation and the Exodus? In Revelation it is the Archangel Michael who slays the Dragon and throws him down to the earth. But Bousset at his page 231 says: 'On Michael, the Dragon-slayer, and his analogy to Horus, vanquisher of Typhon, and to Apollo, the python killer, see Dietrich, Abraxes, 122 *et seq.*'

With Bousset we have come full circle – we have already seen that earlier writers such as Bochart in the seventeenth century link the flight of Typhon to the Exodus of Moses from Egypt, that is, they place the Typhon comet at the time of the Exodus. Revelation – Michael – Horus – the Dragon/Antichrist – Typhon – Exodus; they all appear to be linked, even Apollo.

Before leaving Bousset let us just jot down a few other images from his writings, bearing in mind that he has told us that premonitions are not invented, but are memories of past happenings. In Matthew chapter 24 the question is raised of how the last days (the end of the world) can be recognised, and a series of 'signs' are given. Bousset comes up with a long list of signs, of which the following are of interest:

Probably the sign ... is to be conceived as some manifestation in the heavens, perhaps a flaming sword ... (there is a tradition that) suddenly a sword shall fall from heaven, that the just may know that the leader of the holy army is about to descend ... (or again) ... Then shall be seen a fiery chariot and a brand streaming through the stars to forewarn the peoples of the fire.

There are numerous versions of these signs:
'...a mighty sign with sword and trump ... there shall from heaven come a great star down ... signs in the sky; a bow ... and a horn and a brand... the banner of the Messiah shall be seen the Cross that is again to appear...' Each of the items would be entirely consistent with the description of a comet. Just to reinforce the concept of the use of past phenomena associated with the Exodus to predict future events, Bousset points to Revelation:

It may have been a Jewish expectation that, in the night when once the people of Israel were liberated from the land of Egypt, in the same night would come to pass the great deliverance from Antichrist (the end of the world) ... at midnight in the hour when the angel made Egypt desolate ...

The signs which will mark the end of the world are those signs that were played out at the Exodus. Bousset is quite specific about how the end will be observed:

God or Christ, surrounded by the angelic hosts, comes to sit in judgement, and before Him rushes a fierce, fiery storm that burns up the world ... Against the earth shall the Lord send fire ... lasting forty days ... the air be agitated ... the stars shall fall out ... And before His glory shall run – the serried hosts of angels and archangels all breathing fiery flames – and a river full of fire – with frightful crash.

Bousset is at pains to stress that all this imagery is very old:

The account of the last conflagration has been handed down from age to age with wonderful persistency, so that it stands out clearly ... in the Sibylline literature as well as in the Old High German Muspilli lay ... we are told everywhere with the fullest details that the last fire is to consume the ocean, the rivers and the springs.

Whereas by the time we get to Revelation the only echo is in the line 'and there was no more sea'. So our starting-point, with St Michael in Revelation, is a relatively late version of the vision of the end of the world. Bousset also provides the following description of The End:

A trumpet blast shall send forth from heaven a sound of much wailing (or moaning) ... the trump suddenly gives out a fearful blast from heaven, and lo, it rings harsh through the firmament, everywhere with reverberating note ... and thrice shall the horn be sounded by Michael the Archangel ... and Michael and Gabriel shall come from heaven and sound the trump ...

This passage seems to be about as accurate a description of an impact event as one could reasonably imagine. The components are essentially in the right order. Twentieth-century experience tells us that we might hear a hissing or moaning followed by a tremendous explosion with associated earthquakes; the ancient sources describe the moaning, the blast and use the words 'ring' and 'reverberate'. But it is noticeable that it is not a single event, the word 'thrice' would be consistent with *multiple* impacts. These 'end-of-the-world' descriptions, based on the memories of some previous catastrophic happenings, suggest that our hypothetical close-approach comet did indeed involve several distinct fragments; or perhaps we may dispense with the comet, and have just the Clube and Napier 'cosmic swarm'.

However, if we take the line that these ancient texts preserve a core of truth, it is also interesting that all the descriptions, whether detailing the Exodus or the end of the world, differentiate between God, who is the Lord of Creation, and the Angel of the Lord, who appears to be the cometary agent. This differentiation shows us that the ancient writers believed in a Greater Power who actually sends the comets. If they were right, we might do well to understand the rules of this greater God. After all, we saw what Shoemaker-Levy 9 did to Jupiter in July 1994, within a mere 400 years of the invention of the telescope.

CHAPTER 14

•

REINFORCING THE CONNECTIONS

Even if comets or their debris were somehow involved with ancient catastrophes, this story falls well short of proving the case, indeed, the case will not be proven until space debris is located in appropriate stratified deposits. However, one preliminary test of any theory is that it is continually reinforced. A few examples of reinforcement are included below.

Norma Goodrich, in her volume *Merlin*, notes that, on the basis of her researches:

(a) Merlin predicted his own death one year in advance
(b) he died in AD 536 and
(c) he died during an eclipse of the sun.

The significance of the date is obvious given Stothers and Rampino's dim sun records for AD 536 and the presumably related apparition of Saint Michael, and, indeed, much of what is presented in this book. Merlin has been suggested to be either a priest of, or a god such as Lug of the bright countenance and the long reach. We should remember also that premonition in these years seems to have been rife, for instance, the Chinese abandonment of their capital in 534, and Gildas and his warnings.

In a recent work entitled *Saints Preserve Us* by Sean Kelly and Rosemary Rogers they paraphrase the history and attributes of Saint Michael: 'He appeared to Moses in the burning bush', while 'his tears formed the cherubim.' In addition he had 'a tremendous wingspan' and his wings were 'the colour of green emerald'. The manifestation of the Angel of Yahweh is laced with cometary imagery; also if Michael is dated to the time of the Exodus, he is also the Archangel in Revelation who throws the Antichrist to the ground. Rereading Sagan and Druyan's *Comet*, I found that they footnote the following: 'Even 'apparition' – the word we use today to describe the presence of a comet in our skies – is an echo, with ominous and supernatural overtones, of our ancient belief about comets,' thus adding significantly to the 'memory of an *apparition* of St Michael' recorded for AD 536. So the Archangel who was at the Exodus, which may have been in 1628 BC, is also mentioned in association with AD 536. Everywhere one looks there are repetitions of the same basic scenario. To recap: the reason why it is respectable to question whether the AD 536–45 event may have been cometary in origin (for cometary read 'impact-related') was because the ice-core workers failed to come up with any good evidence for a large volcanic signal at this time; indeed, several cores seem to have stopped or run into problems just around the middle of the sixth century. So the quest for an AD 540 'comet' represents a respectable scientific question. In earlier chapters I pointed out that I had been surprised when an independent worker, Don Carleton, posed the same question about a possible impact around AD 540; indeed, it seemed to me to be intuitively significant that the question could be asked from two essentially independent viewpoints.

If my question about AD 540 cometary associations is a free-standing scientific question, is it possible to find independent evidence for the same question being arrived at by yet another route? The answer seems to be in the positive. Let us consider Goodrich's *Merlin* a little further. The book was published in 1988 and has no mention of volcanoes or dust-veils associated with AD 536–45; neither Stothers nor Rampino and their 1983 or 1984 papers on the AD 536 dry-fog issue are cited. With Goodrich's background in French and comparative literature, it is unlikely that she would be familiar with the relevant scientific literature. As a working hypothesis, let us assume that Goodrich did not know about the AD 536 'dry fog' that Stothers and Rampino had originally assumed to be a volcanic dust-veil. As the Irish narrowest-ring work was published only in 1988 we can take it that she did not know about that.

Thus we have the scientific question: could there have been an asteroid or comet-related impact around AD 540, that is, in the window 536–45? Reading Goodrich we can glean the following. King Arthur died in AD 542 (Goodrich uses this alternative date rather than 539). Merlin was Arthur's wizard-advisor. Associated with Merlin's prophecy we see statements relating to Aurelius, who was the first person to be called Pendragon. Aurelius sends for Merlin, who informs him that he will be killed in the battle. But before the battle 'Merlin's massive red dragon will blaze across the sky' and as soon as he sees 'the dragon burn above them as it crosses the sky' Aurelius should attack. This cometary/fireball imagery is directly associated with Merlin; though it becomes even more specific. Quoting from the *Huth-Merlin,* Goodrich notes the images associated with the arrival of the Saxons: 'On the third day a red dragon breathing flames appeared in the sky and flew straight forward with a great wooshing sound, directly over the Saxon warriors. It was not Merlin.' To find a reference to 'Merlin's massive red dragon blazing across the sky' is good enough, but then to find a description of a red, fire-breathing, wooshing, dragon and be told that it was not Merlin is surely a coded way of saying that it could easily have been Merlin, but in this case it was not. Presumably Merlin was sometimes a red wooshing fire-breathing dragon in the sky, who just happened to die in AD 536. Surely this has to be the answer. Conventional history may have largely let us down – maybe conventional history is suffering in this case from just a hint of suppression – but mythology, which could not be suppressed, seems to provide the missing evidence.

So in response to the scientific question, 'could the AD 536–45 environmental event have been caused by a comet-related impact?', there is a pre-existing reference to a fiery dragon in the sky in the correct year, AD 536. If we want to know what the effects may have been, we can turn to Merlin's prophecies – by definition these 'prophecies' refer to things that have already happened, but, more importantly, as they are *Merlin's* prophecies, clearly they are associated with Merlin. Reading them we find that they are strewn with catastrophic imagery, including famines and fire-breathing worms that destroy forests. Rather than pick through them, it is easiest to go to the place where Goodrich sums up Merlin; for this she uses a French source:

Les Prophecies de Merlin [*sic*] *contains his so-called 'Merlin prophecies' …
but in general terms only: floods, mountains that collapse, fire seen in the sky,
comets, rivers that change course, coastlines that become altered, seas that dry up,
torrential rains, droughts, marvellous stones, cyclones, the moon out of orbit, the
stars awry or off the ecliptic, the sun displaced and huge storms at sea.*

The reader may be saying, yes, but we read all this in previous chapters. The difference here is that Goodrich has told us when, according to her researches, Merlin died. Goodrich's Merlin, who could sometimes be mistaken for a wooshing fiery dragon in the sky, and whose prophecies contained the catastrophic images just noted, died in AD 536 during an eclipse of the sun. Could there be something cometary or impact-related around AD 540?

It is not being suggested that Merlin ever existed; for the purposes of this book it is of no matter whether he existed or not. What is important is that in a period in northern Europe when there is essentially no relevant written history, long-standing myths place catastrophic happenings associated with a 'dragon' at, in someone's view, exactly AD 536 – a date where we have other allusions to 'the memory of an apparition of St Michael, and a stupendous miracle'. Did we have a close pass with a comet or did the earth experience a shower of cometary debris? Probably.

But, if that hint of an apparition of St Michael associated with AD 536 means anything, what is the difference between Michael and Merlin? Probably none. We have already noted that Merlin may be the god Lug. Then again, Michael, the Angel of the Lord, was in the burning bush prior to the Exodus. So the similarities already noted between the two events and all the personalities are further compounded; there is a continuous spectrum from Michael to Merlin to Lug, all with the same imagery.

Again it turns out that there is nothing very original about this in the realm of mythological studies. David Day casually says in his *Quest for King Arthur*:

> *Merlin the Magus became a dominant figure in popular culture that took him well beyond the realm of Arthur ... As a mystical, messianic wise man, he was considered the equal of history's other great magi: Zoroaster, Moses, Solomon, Pythagoras, Jesus, Simon the Magus, Empedocles, Virgil and Faust.*

From this list we can extract three main characters: Merlin, Moses and Solomon. Of interest here is the fact that Moses met Michael at the Exodus, while after David's experience with the Angel of the Lord, Solomon builds the Temple. Michael and Merlin–Lug are both mentioned in AD 536. And to close the loop we can turn to Tolstoy, who says:

> *A recent study of the thirteenth century Robert de Boron's romance of Merlin has detailed remarkably close parallels existing between the characters and careers of Merlin, and those of both Antichrist and Christ ... in truth Merlin was Cernunnos and Lleu, Devil and Christ ...*

But, Michael, the Angel of the Lord, flings the Antichrist, the Devil, down on to the Earth. If Merlin is both Antichrist and Christ, then he may be a fiery wooshing dragon but, by implication, part of him also fell to Earth. The similarity in both the timing, and in the dragon elements, to the Beowulf story, suggests that two separate oral traditions are both recording similar events at around the same time – very notably the AD 530s. But again there is more to the Beowulf story than meets the eye. Klaeber points out that there are strong Christian elements deeply ingrained in the poem; Beowulf is likened to the Christian Saviour and Grendel is the impersonation of evil and darkness – an incarnation of the Christian Devil. Encoded into the Beowulf poem, set in the sixth century – pushing right up towards the AD 540 event – is a version of the Revelation story of Christ and Antichrist. We have just seen that this is exactly what Tolstoy said of Merlin – 'he is Christ and Antichrist'. It seems that two independent sources – the Merlin mythology and the Beowulf poem – encoded Revelation imagery into the AD 530s. Why? Because something happened in the AD 530s that was reminiscent of both the Exodus and Revelation.

To summarize: a loose paraphrase of these various associations allows us to make the following assertions: At 1628 BC, 1159 BC and AD 536, there are environmental events associated with dust-veils. The events are loosely associated with references to comets. All three events can be loosely associated with references to the Angel of the Lord and to plagues.

If we want independent duplication of some of the serpent aspects of these ideas, we can turn to the works of two influential students of myth, namely J. G. Frazer, who wrote *The Golden Bough*, and Robert Graves, who, with R. Patai, wrote *Hebrew Myths*. Frazer says: 'It has been argued that King David belonged to a serpent family and that the brazen serpent ... represented the old sacred animal of his house.' While Graves, discusses the Creation as deduced from other biblical texts:

> *The Brazen Serpent made, according to Hebrew tradition, by Moses at God's command and revered in the Temple Sanctuary until the reforming King Hezekiah destroyed it, suggests that Yahweh had at one time been identified with a Serpent-god ...*

Yet another clue linking the time of Moses, the time of David, and the time of Merlin (sixth century AD) is to be found in Stewart and Matthews' *Merlin through the Ages*. On the first page of their preface they note: 'In the primal stream of tradition that holds the deepest lore of Merlin and Apollo, both beings concerned with the light within the land, the sun at midnight.' We have already seen the sun at midnight at the Exodus; according to Velikovsky's reading, as the Angel of the Lord passed over, the last night in Egypt was as bright as the noon on the day of the summer solstice. Now we have Merlin and Apollo both associated with brightness at midnight: bright nights as were seen on the night of Tunguska 1908; in the 'light nights' miracle associated with St Patrick and Livy's record of 'light appeared in the night at Fregellae' in 206 BC.

The impact scenario, which seems to be well borne out in ancient history/mythology, gives us a very good picture of what past experience had led the ancients to anticipate at Doomsday. The world, from a human perspective, will end when either a comet (or substantial asteroid) collides directly with the planet, or when a close-pass comet results in just marginally less bombardment and conflagration. No mainstream scientist would disagree with that Doomsday scenario; sooner or later it will happen, the only question is when? The ancient stories consistently tell of 'signs'. This implies that in their worst experience there were precursors. It is this level of detail which suggests that their experience was not with an asteroid. Asteroids would not give warnings; comets by definition show themselves in advance. Even Clube and Napier's 'cosmic swarms' would almost certainly show a build up to Armageddon, and by definition a cosmic swarm is associated with cometary debris.

The other common feature of the three postulated ancient packages is plague. We see it clearly at the Exodus, at the time of David/Troy, and in the sixth century AD. Stories exist which link the concept of plague and impacts in the popular imagination. Graham Twigg writes about the sixth-century 'Yellow Plague' which affected Wales and Ireland:

In 550 [sic] the Yellow Plague was said to be roaming through the land in the guise of a loathly monster. This was in Wales but in Ireland too the plague was regarded as a living thing which roamed the land. The power of prayer against this creature was amply demonstrated when, at the prayer of St MacCreiche in Kerry, a fiery bolt from heaven fell upon it and reduced it to dust and ashes in the presence of the people.

It is likely that environmental downturns, associated with the loading of the atmosphere, produce crop failures which lead to famines and in turn produce disease, even pandemics. However, for many years Fred Hoyle and Chandra Wickramasinghe have suggested that comets actually *bring* plagues. Given the three episodes, listed above, with their associations, would anyone like to say that they are wrong? If the comets do not actually bring plagues, they do seem to *cause* them.

BACK TO ANCIENT HISTORY

This excursion seems to have taken us very close to backing up the idea of an AD 540 impact. We have conceptualised what may have occurred in the AD 530s and 540s. With that knowledge, we can now go back to the actual historical writings from the period and see if that understanding makes anything in the history more intelligible. We can start with some of the sources which Stothers and Rampino used in 1983, particularly Cassiodorus and Zachariah of Mitylene.

Cassiodorus was a senator and a praetorian prefect who, as secretary to King Theodoric, wrote letters and edicts. In the end, he collected together 468 of these which he had drafted between AD 506 and 538 and compiled them into a *Variae*. The *Variae* end just in the AD 536–45 window. What can we glean from his writings which might give some additional clues to what was going on? Given that we now know that the Earth was probably being bombarded, that is, there must have been unusual atmospheric loading from ablating meteoric debris and possibly exploding cometary fragments.

In Cassiodorus' book XII, letter number 25, he mentions the 'blue coloured sun', the cold summer, etc. This is the letter that Stothers and Rampino convinced themselves related to AD 536. S. J. B. Barnish, who translated the *Variae*, ran into a chronological problem with this letter. Although in the heading he notes 'date as XII.22', which would be the autumn of AD 537, in a footnote he mentions that Ruggini would date this to 'late spring 534'. So there is a dating problem, though it is most likely that the letter was written in AD 537 and referred back to the problems which had 'been going on equally through almost the entire year', which appears to be AD 536. What does he say that is relevant to our debate?

He starts by saying that people are often troubled when the 'order of things' is changed, because 'the clearly unusual is frequently a portent' – premonitions again? He writes that nothing happens without a reason and everything is part of God's plan. Then he writes: 'But who will not be disturbed, and deeply curious about such events, if something mysterious and unusual seems to be coming on us from the stars.'

What is this disturbing, mysterious something which seems to be coming on us from the stars? He does not tell us immediately, but it certainly involves the seasons not running on in their succession; he mentions perpetual frost and unnatural drought associated with harvest failures and dearth. He then describes the symptoms of the problem, including the fact that the sun is blue and gives no heat, the moon lacks its usual splendour etc. The people find these occurrences marvellous, and troubling at the same time.

This is the 'dry fog' event which Stothers and Rampino interpreted as a volcanic dust-veil. But we now have an idea that it was not a volcano that was responsible. The next few lines are potentially significant:

Something mysterious and unusual seems to be coming on us from the stars ... For things in mid space dominate our sight, and we can see through them only what the rarity of their substance allows ... for this vast inane, which is spread between earth and heaven as the most tenuous element, allows us to see clearly as long as it is pure, and splashed with the sun's light. But if it is condensed by some sort of mixture, then, as if with a kind of tautened skin, it permits neither the natural colours, nor the heat of the heavenly bodies to penetrate ... hence it is that, for so long, the rays of the stars have been darkened with an unusual colour ...

There is no doubt that Cassiodorus is describing something obscuring the sun, something apparently coming on us from the stars. Can we take this to mean loading by extraterrestrial dust; dust from ablating meteors perhaps, or for impacting debris? Maybe our best clue is that whatever is in the 'tautened skin' it absorbs the red light of the sun, leaving the sun blue, while it darkens the blue light from the stars. Perhaps the 'tautened skin' might be a description of a high-altitude, yellow layer of heavy elements including sodium, material normally ablated from incoming meteoric debris. Let us pause for a moment and add in the comment from Zachariah. who also wrote during this period: 'And the stars in the sky had appeared dancing in a strange manner, and it was the summer of the year eleven [AD 533]. And it lasted about six or seven years, until the year three [540].'

Modern atmospheric scientists refer specifically to 'dancing stars' as a phenomenon experienced by astronomers when the atmosphere is turbulent, something entirely consistent with the idea of an atmosphere loaded with dust. These several pieces of information from Malalas, Cassiodorus and Zachariah seem to imply that the phenomenon started as early as AD 533; an observation which makes the Chinese abandonment of AD 534 even more interesting. There should now be enough information here for us to interpret what was actually happening.

BACK TO THE TREE-RINGS

This would seem a good place to follow up the previous scenario by looking again at the tree-ring chronologies which are available for recent millennia. We can do this by looking at new, independent tree-ring evidence which is becoming available from American bristlecone pines, foxtail pines and temperature-sensitive Fennoscandian pines. When we look at the 1628 BC and 1159 BC events, which first showed up in the Irish oak records, in the new temperature-sensitive records we seem to see that both events sit inside temperature *troughs*.

Up until recently it has been assumed that the tree-ring events were volcanic in origin. But a volcano is usually a sudden unexpected incident – volcanic events should show up abruptly in the tree-ring records. Do they? Maybe not, maybe something has already started to cool the earth before the volcanic events. So could it be that cometary dust was causing cooling on earth and during that cooling there was a tendency for large volcanoes to be triggered? If that were the case then the volcano-related effects in the tree-rings may be secondary effects.

If this were true it would free up the whole chronological situation. Instead of seeking key events marked in the tree-rings, maybe we should see broad periods of downturn. If we invoke broad periods, as we seem to be seeing in Fennoscandian and American tree-rings, then we could easily fit the Shang dynasty or the New Kingdom or the Hebrew '470' years to the cool episodes. The comets observed at the start and end of the Shang, the comet seen at the fall of Troy, could all be signs of a *period* of downturn caused by

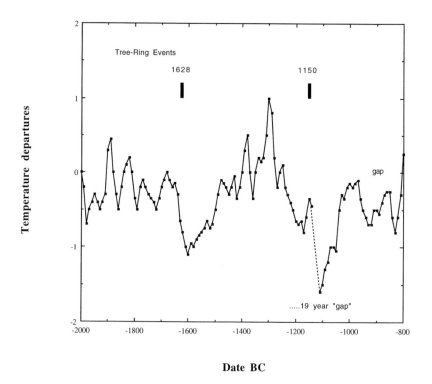

Although 'floating' and hence not precisely dated, this provisional temperature reconstruction from Fennoscandian pines, published by Keith Briffa, hints that the 1628 BC and 1159 BC events may sit in pre-existing temperature troughs.

extraterrestrial factors; the volcanoes act only as signposts to point us to the important periods, they would not need to rigidly define the periods. Perhaps we are getting towards a working hypothesis for what really happened in the relatively recent past. At least it seems that we now know *when* to look and roughly what to look for. The dates 2345 BC, 1628 BC, 1159 BC, 207 BC and AD 540 will not go away.

No sooner does one write a line like that than Richard Warner raises the name William Whiston who was professor of mathematics at Cambridge immediately after Newton. It seems that Whiston heard a lecture given by Edmond Halley at the Royal Society in 1694 in which Halley, according to Duncan Steel, 'discussed how the biblical flood may be an account of a cometary impact'. Whiston published *A New Theory of the Earth* in 1696, wherein he proposed that the 'great flood began on the seventeenth day of the second month from autumnal equinox in 2349 BC' when a comet passed close to the earth: 'Much water came from the tail, through which the Earth passed

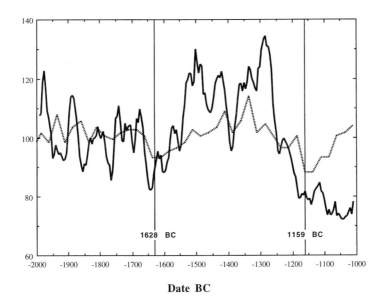

Date BC

The Fennoscandian temperature reconstruction presented with Val LaMarche's smoothed, temperature-sensitive, bristlecone pine chronology from Campito Mountain. In this case the bristlecone pine chronology is precisely dated and it seems evident that the 1628 BC and 1159 BC events sit in episodes of reduced temperature.

but Earth also stretched and cracked and water emerged from below.' This raises the 2354–2345 BC tree-ring event again as well as making it fairly clear that Whiston was using Usher's chronology. Even though we do not have any grounds to believe Usher's chronology, 2354 to 2345 BC is another one of the original list of tree-ring/volcano events reported in 1988, which seems to be associated with trees recording an innundation of Lough Neagh. A highly circumstantial case links it with quasi-mythological records of Irish lakes breaking out and an ancient date for the biblical Flood. We have seen that all the other main dates, AD 540, 44 BC, 207 BC, 1159 BC and 1628 BC, appear to be linked with cometary activity; now we have, by loose association, a pre-existing suggestion of a comet affecting the earth at a date within the range of yet another of our tree-ring events.

In 1997, Marie-Agnès Courty announced that she had found a regional occurrence of 'a layer with an uncommon petrographic assemblage, dated at ca. 2350 BC' in northern Syria. This petrographic assemblage occurs with widespread archaeological debris and comprises tephra along with various glassy spherules and small fragments of 'black, vesicular, amorphous material made of silicates' etc. It occurs at the transition between the Early Dynastic and the Early Akkad and seems to be part of Manelkehr's 'earth wide event at 2300 BC'. If these Syrian glassy balls are proven to be of extraterrestrial origin, we will have our answer. But there is more to Courty's uncommon petrographic assemblage. She originally published the Syrian information with Harvey Weiss, who says this about the catastrophic event which Courty now puts at around 2350 BC:

> *Hundreds of years after the event, a cuneiform collection of 'prodigies', omen predictions of the collapse of Akkad, preserved the record that 'many stars were falling from the sky'. Closer to the event, perhaps as early as 2100 BC, the author of the Curse of Akkad alluded to 'flaming potsherds raining from the sky'.*

This is a fantastic association for the 2350 BC events. To me, it proves the case. We have seen that gradually each of the 1628 BC, 1159 BC, 207 BC, 44 BC and AD 540 events have taken on a cometary/bombardment hue. Logic would have suggested that 2350 BC might be of the same character. Now we can see that ancient texts actually tell us about a bombardment at that time and Courty and Weiss can demonstrate what sounds very like impact debris. QED? It also makes one wonder just exactly how Beaumont came up with that bold-type line of his, mentioned in the preface:

THE FLOOD IMMORTALIZES THE COLLISION OF A FALLEN PLANET, LATER TERMED SATAN, ACTUALLY A COMETARY BODY, WITH OUR EARTH.

If Beaumont was correct, then the Revelation image of a Star called Wormwood falling from the sky may relate to this episode just as easily as it could to the happenings at Exodus. We could go back to Clube and Napier and their ideas of decayed cometary orbits which are now loops of dust, studded with boulders, which the Earth's orbit intersects. From *time to time* the Earth's orbit takes it progressively further into the annulus of dust and debris. In the outer reaches of the annulus the atmosphere might just pick up dust – producing cooling on Earth – but if it enters the core of the annulus it might suffer actual Tunguska-class, or larger, impacts. It is possible that the mechanism as we orbit through the annulus is something like: Increasing dust – cooling – impacts/volcanoes – less dust – warming.

CHAPTER 15

◆

CONCLUSIONS

When I started writing this book I wanted to know what caused the various, abrupt, environmental downturns which appeared in the oak tree-ring records. I had hoped other information, archaeological, ancient-historical and mythological, would help in defining the likely causes of the downturns. At face value the core story seems to be saying, yes, at 2345 BC, 1628 BC, 1159 BC and AD 536, perhaps also at 207 BC and 44 BC, the Earth experienced the effects of close-pass comets, or cosmic swarms of cometary debris. Terrifying apparitions were seen in the sky that were associated with optical, and possibly aural, effects. Fireballs and associated atmospheric detonations gave rise to frightening noise, earthquakes and tsunami. People experiencing these phenomena identified them with the attributes of various deities. In this chapter I address some issues which have worried me as the story has emerged. First, are there easy alternative explanations? Second, where are the doubtful bits in the story?

THE BLAME-BY-ASSOCIATION SCENARIO

It is important to take care not to create a completely false scenario. Critics of the original volcano story, such as Dave Pyle and Paul Buckland and colleagues, objected particularly to the linking of specific volcanoes, like Santorini or Hekla 3, to the dated tree-ring events. Unfortunately, the linkages go back to the original papers of Hammer and LaMarche, and nothing can now be done to extinguish the resulting debates. The only way forward is to date the eruptions very precisely by location of their tephra in the Greenland ice-cores. We have, so to speak, to play the game to the end. So how, in the case of the thesis presented in this book, might the package of information, from tree-rings to myth, be interpreted differently? An alternative scenario might be that comets have no effect on Earth but occasionally do get a bad press. We can imagine the following. A large volcanic dust-veil causes hemispheric, possibly global, cooling. It affects trees, leaves acid in Greenland, brings crop failure, famine and disease – exactly our original scenario. Comets seem to have been seen very often in the past. What happens if a bright comet appears at, or even close to, the time of the dust-veil? The comet gets the blame. After all, the humans suffering on the ground have little knowledge of volcanoes and dust-veils. They can blame only what they see. This blame by association has the great advantage of explaining the general dread of comets in ancient societies; sometimes comets were associated with really dreadful conditions, although, if this scenario were true, the comets were being blamed for all the wrong reasons.

Will this scenario stand up? Not entirely. The ancient descriptions repeatedly discuss thunderbolts and fiery dragons. It is hard to believe that all those descriptions are strictly earthbound; merely local falls of volcanic bombs and auroral or lightening phenomena. Also, the descriptions include elements which were well observed at the one definite airburst from space about which we have documentation, the 1908 Tunguska explosion over Siberia. The ancient descriptions, around the times of the environmental downturns in the trees, do seem to indicate fireballs and at least atmospheric impacts. A reasonable surmise is that close-pass comets, or their debris, almost certainly did skim by in recent millennia.

If we accept that as a premise, we still have to ask whether these close passes were one-off affairs. In each case, did the comet appear from nowhere, make a close pass of the Earth and disappear? Or did the comet enter some sort of short-period orbit so that people on Earth were treated to a series of repeat encounters? Several of the texts and myths seem to hint at differing descriptions through time, something which would suggest returns. This is also the implication of the predictions associated with the Chinese abandonment in AD 534, with Gildas' warnings and with Merlin knowing of his own death in advance. Overall we have enough evidence to support the bombardment hypothesis so that the alternative scenario of blame by association does not need to be invoked.

CONFESSIONS ON THE OTHER DOUBTS

The direction which emerged during the course of this book came as a surprise to me, and everything after Chapter 5 turned out to be just a matter of 'following my nose' through a lot of strange information. Hopefully the reader has also found the direction to be both interesting and thought-provoking. However, from Chapter 6 onwards I have had some misgivings about the quality of some of the evidence. We have robust, well-replicated tree-ring chronologies telling us when there were some dramatic environmental downturns in recent millennia. Unfortunately the quality, particularly the dating quality, of some of the other records used to build up the pictures of the events has fallen short of anything that could be called robust. I have given some thought to these problems and will elaborate on a few of the relevant issues. However, another confession is more interesting from a chronologist's point of view. In this book, and in the previously published *A Slice Through Time*, I have quite ruthlessly attempted to force all relevant evidence to conform to the narrow 'point events' at 2354–2345 BC, 1628–1623 BC, 1159–1141 BC, 208–204 BC and AD 536–45. This has been quite evident, for example, when I have tried to force the New Kingdom in Egypt and the Shang dynasty in China to fit between 1628 BC and 1141 BC. I also have to confess to having presented Warner's gleanings from the Irish Annals in a wholly uncritical fashion, even though the observations have not been used to prove anything. I have also pointed out other chance coincidences, such as Usher's date for the biblical Flood, which at 2349 'BC' would conform wonderfully to the 2354–2345 BC event, even though I would have the gravest doubts as to whether his chronology bears any resemblance to reality. Similarly, in treating mythology I would have to confess that it all seems capable of wide interpretation, and we are at the mercy of the interpreters.

Given this list of weaknesses, it is fair to say that although the story which emerged was of great interest, I would not have been surprised if it had begun to unravel in the harsh light of scrutiny. Thus I want to address some of these issues, in particular the aspect of forcing the various arguments to fit to the tree-ring dates, and the quality of some of the other evidence; what emerges, surprisingly, is that even when one addresses the doubts, the arguments and the logic still hold sway.

FORCING THE ARGUMENTS TO THE FIXED DATES

While I have expressed self-doubt on this general issue, it is fair to point out that the evidence at and around the AD 540 tree-ring decline – let us call it the Merlin event – suggests a very tight fit for that environmental event with the calamity which seems to have befallen most of humanity at the time. Similarly, the evidence around the 207 BC tree-ring downturn seems to conform with other available evidence right down to the fact that the Han dynasty traditionally starts in 206 BC. We now begin to see that the 2354–2345 BC tree-ring downturn, previously only supported by the tephra evidence for an eruption of the Icelandic Hekla 4, is gaining support from seriously anomalous deposits of melted material and tephra from Syria, where there is no obvious local volcano. Even a cursory glance at the five main events shows that there is now good support for the existence of three of them in other records; other records which show events that are highly catastrophic in character, namely something tectonic or bombardment-related about 2350 BC, at the time of a widespread collapse of civilisation in the Near East, a dynastic change following famine in China at 207 BC, and a Dark Age trauma, including the serious Justinian plague, at AD 540. In fact, when these three events are reviewed, it is clear that no 'forcing' is involved. In each case, tree-ring records point to downturns and these coincide with recorded events of catastrophic character.

To take the Irish Annals: in reality, with the exception of the close associations of the 148 BC Corlea track to the roadway mentioned in the *circa* 140 'BC' tale of the 'Wooing of Étaién', and the references to 'failure of bread' in AD 536 and 539, the early Annal references are not used to prove anything. They are listed to provide colour to the initial arguments on spaced events. Indeed, the basic story could have been written without using the Annals at all, so that any doubts about their reality, or relevance, appear groundless. Perhaps the most interesting aspect is their frequent reference to 'lakes breaking out'. It is possible that these actually are a very obscure guide to outbreaks of tectonic activity and should not be ignored. *Beowulf*, which might have been considered a weak link, turns out, with its Revelation imagery and its sixth-century context, to be a powerful addition to the AD 540 story. Having said that, let us now address the weak areas as they relate to the 1628 and 1159 BC events.

When we come to look at the other spaced evidence, there are some aspects which do not generate concern. The growth anomalies in the Anatolian tree-ring chronologies spaced 470 years apart speak for themselves; I would be very surprised if they are anything other than the 1628 and 1159 BC events, given the sheer weight of the available radiocarbon evidence. Similarly, the close coincidence between the current conventional date for the end of the Middle Kingdom in Egypt, *circa* 1640 BC, and the 1628 BC tree-ring event, means that there is no real point of contention here. But when we come to the date of the start of the Shang dynasty, we have more problems. Although one traditional date for the start of the Shang is 1617 BC, other estimates move progressively further and further away. Pang suggests 1600+/- 30 BC, but Pankenier opts for 1554 BC on the basis of his dating of the reference to 'five planets criss-crossed' in the reign of Chieh, the last emperor of the Xia dynasty. By correlating this reference to the five planets to an astronomical observation at 1576 BC Pankenier sees the Xia ending at 1555 BC. Similarly, another 'five planets together' reference towards the end of the Shang is used to define a date, already associated with an apparition of comet Halley, in 1059 BC; the resultant date for the end of the Shang dynasty being 1046 BC. If Pankenier is correct on this issue, the dates of the start and end of the Shang bear no close resemblance to the 1628 and 1159 BC events; nor do they conform in any way to Chang's traditional suggestion of 1617 and 1122 BC. However, everything may not be rosy in the field of astronomical retrocalculation. Pankenier disagrees radically with Pang on the date of the eclipse of the moon in the '35th year of King Wen'. Pang gives 1137 BC, while Pankenier gives 1056 BC. This can be coupled with considerable doubt over the interpretation of the 'five planets criss-crossing' in November 1576 BC (see Appendix). All in all, it is not clear that the attested global environmental event at 1628 BC can be ruled out as a contributory factor in the demise of the Xia dynasty. The tension in the Shang dating is well exemplified by the observation by Pankenier that there is much happening in Chinese history that involves a sky god between about 1610 and 1550 BC. It seems very strange that this misses the global 1628 BC event; I would hazard a guess that it is these Chinese dates that are slightly wrong.

What comes out of this discussion is that the end of the Xia/start of the Shang dynasty could still fit to around 1628 BC. The situation at the end of the Shang/start of the Zhou is almost certainly more diffuse. So, as with the remarks about the Egyptian chronology, things seem reasonably tight in the seventeenth century BC and less well defined in the twelfth century BC.

One other weak line of evidence relates to the Old Testament Hebrew chronology: the 470-year spacing. The problem with this is that there are no good grounds for believing the Usher chronology. However, there is no doubt that the spacing has been around for quite a long time. The story does not stand or fall on the basis of these biblical spaced events, even though I have used them quite extensively. What is perhaps most intriguing is that the biblical stories do seem to preserve a memory of comets – the Angel of the Lord – close to the spacings in the tree-ring records. People have undoubtedly quibbled about the validity of the 480-year spacing between the Exodus and the building of Solomon's Temple. While the number 480 can by made up from multiples of mystical numbers, the same does not apply to the 470-year spacing between the catastrophic events at the Exodus and the famines at the time of David; 470 years in the later second millennium BC, given the tree-ring evidence, is a great spacing to exist under any circumstances and could be a real remembered interval. More worrying than the interval is the move which would be required in the time of David. I imagine many people would object strongly to David moving from *circa* 950 BC to *circa* 1150 BC. In fact, this is an interesting issue. We would assume that David, or indeed Solomon, would be well dated, but we would be wrong. Peter James, the revisionist author of *Centuries of Darkness*, has long argued that the Egyptian chronology needs to be revised downwards with a resulting shortening of the *circa* 1200–800 BC Greek Dark Ages. I do not subscribe to his views on the shortening of these chronologies, but I can use his arguments to show some of the tension in the conventional dating. In a recent article, confirming that he has not changed his revisionist views, he points out several things relevant to the issue of the dating of David and Solomon. He says, discussing the conventional chronology which he wishes to revise:

The conventional model raised far too many questions ... Why are the glories of King Solomon's reign in Israel, ground plan and even the furnishings of his temple, reflected in Late Bronze Age Levels supposedly 250 years before his time ...?

One answer, from the perspective in this book, and the 480-year spacing from the Exodus to the construction of Solomon's temple, is that King Solomon is wrongly dated and should come in the twelfth century BC. James also points out that in 1993 the 'House of David' stela was found at Tel Dan in northern Israel. The stela which 'can be historically dated to 825–800 BC' appears to have come from a level conventionally dated to the tenth or eleventh century BC. James uses this as an argument to reduce the conventional chronology by about two centuries. The irony for the revisionists is that you could use the same logic to suggest that, on the conventional chronology, both David and Solomon should have their dates *moved back* by a couple of centuries – to the *twelfth century*, just where the logic of this book would put them. I cannot resist putting in another chance find at this point. In a brief 'teachers' helper', *The Preceptor's Assistant*, published in 1854, the author, David Williams, gives a chronological table of events, discoveries and inventions from the creation of the world. He uses Usher's dates for the Flood and the Exodus, but two of the other dates in his table are interesting:

1193 The siege of Troy commenced
1148 David reigned sole king of Israel

It could be just a typographical error – or did Williams know something we do not? It certainly does not weaken our case.

REMARKS

Let us make a final review of the story. We now have a set of environmental events at 2354–2345 BC, 1628–1623 BC, 1159–1141 BC, 208–204 BC and AD 536–45. We have seen quite a lot of evidence for connections between various of these events. There are connections between the happenings of the sixth century AD and those associated with the Exodus in what was presumably the seventeenth century BC. Some people may scoff at the suggestion, but it is now possible to show that a contemporary writer in the AD 550s made exactly the same connection, and even gives a hint of heavenly bombardment (see Appendix). There are connections between the events in that all now seem to have references to extraterrestrial occurrences. Mythology links several of them quite explicitly, and the mythological connections suggest some cosmic linkages to the same events. Connections just keep on emerging. For example, when Courty pointed out her anomalous deposits around 2350 BC she mentioned that this fell between the Early Dynastic and the early Akkad. If we look up Akkad we find that, yes indeed, the conventional dating is *circa* 2350 BC but we also find that the famous king of this period, Sargon, set up a dynasty at that time which lasted for about 150 years. But Sargon has the same story associated with his birth as Moses. As J. J. M. Roberts puts it in the *Grolier Multimedia Encyclopedia*: 'The story of the baby Moses in the reed basket on the Nile, for example, is a typical legend about a famous man's childhood. The same basic story is also told about Sargon, king of Akkad (*c.* 2350 BC).'

Clearly, a typical legend here means that the story is a widespread myth and has no significance. Nevertheless, it does form a faint link between the personalities at around 2350 BC and at the Exodus, and it is an easy link to make. Much early material in the Old Testament can be traced to earlier stories, for example, similarities between the biblical Flood and the Epic of Gilgamesh are well recognized. Other stories and connections are less easy, but it is probably worth including one further example which gives some hints of the sort of ideas which go towards substantiating the notion of catastrophic happenings. The following paragraphs are based on notes taken at a lecture given by Gunnar Heinsohn in Cambridge in July 1997.

Heinsohn has studied the origins of Bronze Age civilization and feels that it is not simply the use of a new metal which separates the Bronze Age from the previous stone-using, Neolithic; rather, it is the use of cult centres which mark out the new age. Heinsohn comes to the issue by asking what was the origin of human sacrifice? As he sees it, scholars since the later nineteenth century, that is, post-Darwin, have increasingly given up trying to understand the origins of sacrifice. However, in the less enlightened eighteenth century people were pretty clear how sacrifice had arisen. There had been a great 'destruction' and cult centres, where sacrifices took place, were established.

During rituals at these cult centres people threw stones or grain, covered each other in ashes, stomped around in a frenzy and, in some cases, took laxatives so that they excreted. At the culmination of the ritual a victim, dressed in unusual costume, would be killed. The sacrificial victim could be hung up on a pillar and venerated, or totally consumed by fire. Heinsohn explains these rituals as catharsis, a release from the pent-up emotion of people who had been through terrible trauma. Some terrible catastrophe, whose origin is hinted at by statements involving a flaming sun among the stars, had decimated the population. The traumatized survivors needed to exorcise the stress/terror/pent-up emotion. The result was a re-enactment of a ritual version of the terror and a culmination in the sacrifice – death. This provided the release which the people needed. The victim was therefore of service to the greater community; the bulk of the guilt would be taken by the priest. The people recognized the role of the priest in taking the guilt from them and in turn looked after the priest. Thus, according to Heinsohn, we can explain the rise of sacrifice and cult centres as a necessary social response to some terrible catastrophe. The logic of his argument places the catastrophe and the origins of kingship and sacrifice in the third millennium BC. There exist a few lines of ancient Akkadian text which basically say that there was a time when there was no king, a time when there was no counselling and that kingship descended from heaven; the origin of kingship and the need for counselling came from the sky in the form of a calamity. As we have seen already, Sargon, the first king of the Akkad, seems to have come to power around 2350 BC, and Courty certainly has strange material which, whether it is volcanic or cosmic, fell from the sky at around 2350 BC. It appears that the threads of several stories weave together at some of our events.

USING EPISODES RATHER THAN SPACED EVENTS

I confessed to trying to force the other evidence to conform to the precisely dated tree-ring events; however, when we look at the evidence, not all that much forcing actually happened. The associations are basically good for four of the five events. As recognized previously the weakest event was probably that in the twelfth century. However, even if one were concerned by the failure to fit all the events tightly to other evidence, there is an easy way to remove the concern. This is to simply broaden the events out in time. As shown in the last chapter, there is some American and Fennoscandian tree-ring evidence which suggests that the 1628 and 1159 BC events took place in cool episodes, that is, the dramatic point events are superimposed on longer-term environmental downturns. If we broaden the point events out to longer episodes, rather in the way that the Intermediate Periods in Egypt are broad episodes, the tension in the story disappears and the Shang dynasty or the New Kingdom can sit comfortably between broad seventeenth–sixteenth century BC and broad twelfth–eleventh century BC episodes. This approach means that there is no need to think of dynastic changes taking place at precisely 1628 BC or 1159 BC; rather the point events are merely part of the package of decline, in some cases the prime mover, in others the last straw which collapses a system. The initial strict adhesion to the environmental events was necessary to obtain the story. Once we have the story we can afford to be much more flexible in our interpretations.

When it comes to mythology there is little need to alter any perceptions. Mythology tells the same story whether we force it to the point events or simply refer it to broad episodes. In this sense it does not matter whether the similarities between the happenings at AD 540 and the Exodus relate to AD 536 and 1628 BC or whether they are thought of as the sixth century AD events and the seventeenth century BC events. The connections are just the same. Then there is the issue of Santorini. I have to confess to having been worried at forcing everything to the 1628 BC date for Santorini, and then linking that to the Exodus. However, I was simply using Wilson's prior linkage of Santorini with the Exodus and imposing a fresh date. In retrospect, the story does not founder on the date of Santorini or even on the attribution of the Santorini eruption to the Exodus. The important thing is the identification of the extraterrestrial events and the mythologies surrounding them. So whether an actual bombardment took place in 1628 BC or simply in the broader window of the seventeenth–sixteenth centuries BC hardly matters at all. Similarly the references to comets do not have to be at 1628 BC or 1159 BC, they can be in the broad downturn episodes, again as symptoms of a more flexible story. It is the fact that some cometary-related event took place around the seventeenth century BC, which was similar to something that happened around AD 540, that is important.

Despite the points made above, I do not feel any requirement to move from the tree-ring dates. If the trees got 208 BC and AD 540 exactly right, then logically the 2345 BC, 1628 BC and 1159 BC events are only kept from also being correct by the poor archaeological and ancient historical chronologies. Now that we know what to look for, the evidence will be forthcoming to prove (or disprove) the volcano/bombardment events and refine their dating to the tree-ring events.

THE REAL CONCLUSION

The story associated with the five main tree-ring events is so robust that it probably is correct, though, as alluded to in the text, it is the twelfth century BC event which is the least well supported – even though it is the most profound event in the Irish bog trees. Maybe we should not worry; four out of five extreme growth reductions linking with other evidence for catastrophic events would not be bad going. All things considered I would not abandon the 1159 BC event yet either. A bombardment event would actually help to explain the long-standing dilemma associated with the widespread destructions and burnings around the eastern Mediterranean in the twelfth century BC. Robert Drews sets the scene well when he tells us about what he terms 'the Catastrophe': 'the end of the Bronze Age was arguably the worst disaster in ancient history, even more calamitous than the collapse of the western Roman Empire …'. It seems that many major sites were totally burned and totally destroyed at this time. The problem was (and is) that there were almost no bodies or precious objects. This evidence, coupled with Egyptian references to marauding hordes – the 'Sea Peoples' – led to the assumption that the cities were destroyed by invaders who took away the inhabitants for slaves and carried off all the objects as booty before destroying and torching the cities. But that package actually creates a problem; almost by definition, if no traces are left it is hard to prove that the invaders existed. Other researchers proposed that the widespread total destructions were actually caused by a huge earthquake. Unfortunately it is almost unimaginable that you could have severe earthquakes and not have lots of buried artefacts and people. Drews points out that there are other theories to explain 'the Catastrophe' involving concepts such as drought and 'system collapse', but he dismisses these in favour of the theory that the introduction of new slashing swords, and close-order fighting formations, allowed the 'invaders' to defeat everyone in the eastern Mediterranean and destroy and burn their cities. The problem as always seemed to be that there ought to have been at least a few dead warriors and some weapons, but, by and large, there were none.

What we seem to have here is a failure to recognize all the possible origins for destruction and fire. We now know that at some of our other events, especially in the sixth century AD and at the Exodus, there are hints of warnings. The approach of a comet, or preliminary bombardment associated with a cosmic swarm, might well give people time to pack up and leave; just as Noah had time to build the Ark, the Israelites had the whole build-up of the plagues before they left Egypt and the Chinese saw fit to abandon their capital in AD 534. In the twelfth century BC the people probably still died in 'the Catastrophe' which, if it was extraterrestrial, would have involved destruction and fire from above, but they would already have fled their towns and cities. This would suggest that all the destruction took place either at the same time or in a few concentrated episodes. Drews, referring to six major destroyed cities, points out that 'What gold, silver, and bronze items archaeologists found in these cities had been secreted in pits or hidden in wall caches.' This is reinforced by details from the site of Kokkinokremos in Cyprus, where a bronzesmith put raw materials and tools into a pit, while a silverworker hid two silver ingots and a goldsmith hid his whole stock in another pit. Apparently 'They were all hoping … that they would return and recover their treasures, but they never did.'

It is the information that the only valuables were hidden and never recovered which suggests that the people who fled the cities were indeed killed. So the entire scenario – abandonment, complete destruction, burning, valuables hidden, no one returning and the onset of a centuries-long dark age – would be consistent with extraterrestrial bombardment. Ironically, Drews came very close to this conclusion at one point. He says, in discussing the unusual nature of the total destructions of the twelfth century, if they *were* actually due to earthquake:

> *Damage is one thing, however, and destruction is another. In all of antiquity only a few cities are known to have been destroyed by an 'act of God'. Whatever may have happened to Sodom and Gomorrah, we do know that Thera and Pompeii were covered by volcanic eruptions. And very occasionally we do hear of a city destroyed (rather than damaged) by an earthquake.*

His best parallels for the total destruction which he surveyed in the eastern Mediterranean, in the twelfth century BC, were the very cities which had been destroyed when 'the Lord rained down brimstone and fire from heaven' upon them. That was the occasion when two *angels* warned Lot that he should remove his family, 'because we are going to destroy this place'. There is a possibility that the twelfth-century catastrophe was extraterrestrial, just as Kobres suggested earlier.

New reinforcing or linking information continues to emerge which makes the story even more convincing. For example, we saw earlier a weak link between the *circa* 2350 BC King Sargon and the biblical Moses, the main Exodus character, through their similar 'basket in the reeds' stories. We have also seen that Heinsohn argues for a cult of sacrifice following a catastrophic event in the third millennium BC. Pankenier points out that Tan'g, the first emperor of the Shang dynasty, following on the catastrophic demise of the Xia dynasty with its references to 'wormwood' and 'Heaven's bright terrors', is confronted with a five-to-seven-year famine so severe that Tan'g offers himself as a human sacrifice. This suggests that Heinsohn's ideas on the origins of sacrifice lying in the aftermath of catastrophic events may not be too far from the truth, and, yet again, we see parallels between occurences in western Asia and the East linked by catastrophic events. Ironically, having just stated above that we could have written the story without using anything from the Irish Annals, we are reminded that at Warner's 1620–1544 'BC' catastrophe 'Tigernmas died, with three-quarters of the men of Ireland. This reign was followed by seven years without a king.' Did an Irish king sacrifice himself after the 1628 BC event which shows so clearly in some of the Irish trees? Earlier we saw how the find of an unfinished sixth-century dug-out boat in Lough Neagh hinted at a possible seiche, or a water-level change around AD 540. On its own, it is flimsy evidence. However, recently, Euan MacKie published a note on a unfinished dug-out from Loch Doon in Scotland which also dates to the sixth century on radiocarbon evidence. It was found in the last century along with others in a *near vertical position* buried in sands and silt. Given

The unfinished, sixth century, dugout boat from Loch Doon, Scotland. Another unfinished sixth century dugout was found in Lough Neagh, Ireland. The most likely explanation of the loss of these objects is a widespread seiche around AD 540

that information and the unfinished condition of the dug-out, it seemed to MacKie that it must have been swept away in a storm. Could it actually have been a major tectonically induced seiche, or an impact?

Thus, we find that the evidence is not so weak after all, and examples like *Beowulf* or the unfinished dug-outs are actually quite robust. It is also apparent that we have very real associations of ancient history and mythology with the main catastrophic events originally identified in the Irish oak sequences. These events, although originally assumed to be purely volcanic, on the basis of the links to the well-spaced ice-core acidity levels, increasingly show all the signs of actually being extraterrestrial in origin. At or around 2354 BC, 1628 BC, 1159 BC, 208 BC and AD 540 the earth was subjected to environmental dislocation either by the effects of close-pass comets, by dust loading from such comets and their components, from direct bombardment or dust from the trail of dead comets, that is, some combinations of close approaches, impacts and dust. None of the events have a *proven* cause, though the circumstantial evidence in each case is well-nigh overwhelming.

The conclusion therefore is that a very strong case exists for the contention that we do not inhabit a benign planet. This planet is bombarded relatively often – if the story in this book is correct, we have been seriously bombarded at least five times since the birth of civilization, that is, in the last five millennia. As should be apparent from Tunguska, and the rapidly increasing number of recent terrestrial craters being identified and dated, we have probably been less seriously bombarded at least fifty times in the same period. If we include the fact that the bulk of the planet is covered in water, and that many serious impacts will be virtually undetectable airbursts, then the actual numbers of less serious events may be many more than 50. But even working with this number would imply, as astrophysicists have already pointed out, that we can expect a Tunguska class of impact on average at least once a century. Our problem is that as an intelligent species we have taken our eye firmly off the ball; most scientists and historians have opted for a non-catastrophic world. Press people to acknowledge Tunguska, or the 1994 Shoemaker-Levy 9 impacts on Jupiter, and most resort to fatalism – 'nothing can be done' or, 'it is not worth trying to do anything'. As the first species capable of recognizing the problem, it behoves us to assess the risks seriously and to begin the long haul of doing something about mitigation. There seem to be four options. Option one is to work out strategies for identifying and deflecting any incoming missiles from space. This option means identifying all the asteroids and dead comet fragments, in earth-crossing orbits, big enough to cause a global catastrophe – generally this is assumed to mean anything more than 500 metres (550 yards) in diameter.

Unfortunately it is not clear that we can protect ourselves from a 'cosmic swarm' of smaller, Tunguska class, objects. Nor is it likely that we could deflect a live comet that was discovered on a collision course with Earth, least of all a newly discovered long-period comet.

Option two is to broaden the target by dispersing human populations on to the Moon and Mars, in the first instance, something we can probably do. The third option, as conveyed by ancient writers, is to conform to the rules of the Lord of Creation and ask to be spared from impacts. This latter option is actually more difficult for humans than either of the former, because it would involve conforming to sets of rules which broadly involve 'living life right'. To take just the Christian version, it involves, apart from honouring the Lord, 'loving thy neighbour as thyself' something humans find extremely difficult in practise (it would involve, for example, not polluting the planet or harming the environment; it would involve relationships with other species). But that message, difficult as it may be to practise, was conveyed by the Son of God whose birth was announced by the Angel Gabriel and whose Second Coming is foretold in Revelation. The message there seems to be clear.

The fourth option is different from the other three, which all involve humans as the end product. In this latter case we have to consider, as an intelligent species, what really matters in the long run. We now know enough to recognize that, in the long run, it is DNA that matters. So, the fourth option is to start seeding resistant packages of DNA into deep space. This is very much in keeping with Hoyle and Wickramasinghe's ideas that resistant packages of DNA arrive from space (maybe some previous intelligent species did this long ago). We know that if DNA fetches up somewhere, on some distant planet around some distant star, it will eventually evolve into something interesting. Humans have a pretty poor record of caring for other species; perhaps some day, somewhere, some new species (whose form we cannot even imagine) might owe its existence to our recognition of cometary hazards on this planet.

Finally, this particular story started with the dendrochronological study of oak trees in Europe. I have induced much mirth among colleagues over the years by attributing certain things to oaks. For example, in *Tree-Ring Dating and Archaeology* I wondered why oaks 'had been granted the gift of immortality' because they could tell us their dates long after they were dead. In the 1980s I started using the phrase, 'The trees do not lie' in consideration of the fact that they present a less biased story from the past than do most human recorders. This is particularly the case in terms of environmental downturns, which are evident from the trees and much less evident in human history (for what may be an extreme case of tampering with the human historical record see Appendix). Now, let us consider this current story. If the

The Lisbon earthquake of 1 November 1755 and its associated tsunami. Waves from this quake arrived in the West Indies and Ireland and water levels in lakes and wells across northern Europe were affected, with significant seiches recorded in Scotland and Germany.

story is true, the oak trees, particularly the oak trees in Ireland and Britain, are pointing us to events where the planet has been bombarded in the not-too-distant past; a concept which had, until recently, all but disappeared from mainstream human consciousness. The question asked of the Irish oaks was, 'In your view which were the worst events'? Their answer revealed a series of dates where it seems our own ancestors were profoundly affected and, interestingly, where the information supplied by mythology seems more directly relevant than almost any contemporary writings. Given the events the oaks chose, maybe they are telling us that extraterrestrial hazards are the most serious; we seem to have, in the broadest terms, 'oaks warning us'. It turns out that there is nothing very new about this idea. In J. G. Frazer's mammoth set of volumes on myth, *The Golden Bough*, he tells us that:

> *The worship of the oak tree or of the oak god appears to have been shared by all the branches of the aryan stock in Europe ... [who]... associate the tree with their highest gods, Zeus and Jupiter; the divinity of the sky, the rain, and the thunder ... One of the most famous sanctuaries in Greece was that of Dodona, where Zeus was revered in the* oracular oak *... the god whose voice was heard alike in the rustling of the oak leaves and in the crash of thunder.*

Clearly the ancients listened to the oaks; perhaps we should.

APPENDICES

APPENDIX 1

ATTEMPTING TO DATE THE SHANG DYNASTY

Much of the story in this book hinges around the events at the start and end of the Shang dynasty. The information given below gives at least a glimpse of how complex the dating of this dynastic unit is.

The seventeenth-century and twelfth-century 'events' and their possible relationship to the chronological limits of the Shang dynasty are entirely outside the writer's control: 1628–1623 BC and 1159–1141 BC turned up from narrowest Irish tree-rings, while the suggested dates for China, Egypt and Ireland are derived from the published statements of other workers. Also, one cannot force 496 years (one suggested length for the Shang) between 1628 and 1141 BC. So we must be open to the possibility that the Irish dates may not be the answer. This becomes even more likely when reading Pang's information on the end of the Shang. According to Pang, there is clear evidence for environmental effects due to volcanic activity in the fifth year of King Chòu (the last Shang ruler) who ruled somewhere in the twelfth century BC:

Additional evidence ... comes from a reference to a lunar eclipse that took place in the thirty-fifth year of King Wen, who lived one generation before Chòu. This event has been precisely dated by astronomers, at January 29, 1137 BC.

If Pang, and indeed the astronomical fix, is correct, then the end of the Shang must be *after* 1137 BC. This would break the link between the Irish tree-ring event at 1159–1141 BC and the Shang termination event. In 1993 Tony Caprio and Chris Baisan from the Laboratory for Tree-Ring Research at the University of Arizona pointed out that they had evidence for frost-rings in a new foxtail pine chronology, from the Sierra Nevada, at 1132 BC. Here was a marvellous revelation. We know frost-rings are very good indicators of explosive volcanic eruptions; now we have frost-rings at 1627 BC and at 1132 BC. From 1627 to 1132 BC is a total span of 496 years. This tree-ring evidence suggested two volcanic events at exactly the right interval to fit *precisely* with one of Chang's prior suggestions for the length of the Shang. Even more impressively, Chang has stated that one set of traditional start and end dates for the Shang were thought to be 1617–1122 BC; within a decade of the frost-ring dates in the American trees. When this 496 year spacing was first noted, it seemed to me that the Shang dynasty could be dated 1627–1132 BC, until proven otherwise.

However, it will be obvious to the reader that, in reality, I want the two Irish tree-ring events 1628 BC and 1159 BC to bracket (and hence date) the Shang dynasty. However, it is important to be objective. Let us look again at the facts:

- Two fixed points, 1628 BC and 1159 BC, in Irish oak
- A frost-ring in bristlecone pines at 1627 BC
- A frost-ring in foxtail pines at 1132 BC
- Three estimates of the length of the Shang are '496' years, 'more than 500' years and '600' years (i.e. flexible length)
- Descriptions of dust-veil-like phenomena in the last year of king Chieh (last Xia king) and in the fifth year of king Chòu (last of Shang)
- Traditional 'dates' are 1766–1122 BC, or 1617–1122 BC, though the 'end' has also been variously dated to 1111 BC, or even 1027 BC
- Comets are recorded as 'When Chieh executed his faithful councillors, a comet appeared' and 'When king Wu Wang waged a punitive war against king Chòu, a comet appeared with its tail pointing towards the people of Yin'
- Pang suggests 'A lunar eclipse in the 35th year of king Wen, who lived one generation before Chòu ... (dates to) ... 1137 BC'.

Let us try to make some sense of all this. Obviously 496 years would not fit between 1628 and 1159 BC, nor will 496 fit between 1628 and 1141 BC. But then 496 is not necessarily a reliable figure. However, 496 years is exactly the spacing between the 1627 BC and 1132 BC dates for frost-rings in western America, which was the reason for suggesting that 'the Shang should be dated 1627–1132 BC until proven otherwise.' So that looked good, given that we do not have to believe all the detail in the Chinese early histories. But, if we do accept a historical basis for the detail we must take a different line. Pang's 1137 BC eclipse in the thirty-fifth year of Wen Wang has to be before the end of the Shang. It seems likely that (from given information) Wen Wang reigned for 15 years. His son Wu Wang in his eleventh year defeated Chòu. But the last year of king Chòu was his forty-eighth reign year. Unfortunately, the dust-veil description relates to king Chòu's fifth year.

```
                    1137 BC
Wen Wang            eclipse       Wen Wang        Wu Wang
————————————————x—————————X—————————X——Zhou dynasty—
                    year 35         year 50         year 11


                            King Chòu
————————x——————————————————————————————X    end of dynasty
      year 5                               year 48
```

If we accept the 'historical' detail, the idea of either 1628 to 1159 BC or 1627 to 1132 BC bracketing the Shang would be impossible. However, if we take the historical information at face value, and accept the eclipse date, we can suggest that the Shang dynasty ended in 1137 minus 15 minus 11, that is, about 1111 BC. Interestingly this date is one of the traditional dates calculated for the end of the Shang by the Buddhist monk, Yi Hsing in AD 721. If this were the case, then the dust-veil in Chòu's year 5 would fall about 1154 BC, which would, of course, help enormously the whole 1628/1159 BC volcanic story. But if this attractive scenario were true, it negates the link to the 1132 BC frost-ring and does not do much for the 496-year length of the Shang (this goes to show just how hard it is to tie anything down in the distant past).

If we accept the attractive 1111 BC end for the Shang, we also have the date of the comet (it appears at the time Wu Wang defeats Chòu, that is, the last year of the Shang) and it clearly has no connection with the dust-veil description of 1154. However, a dust-veil in 1154 would help to interpret the secondary defoliation noted in 1153 BC in the Irish oaks. This can be summed up as 'you win some you lose some'. It is necessary to caution the reader at this point. Despite all this discussion, it is still technically possible that the 1159 BC dust-veil caused the end of the Shang. This is because there is no guarantee that the ancient Chinese historical information is completely real or completely accurate; it might be, but then again it might not. Anyone wanting to play this game for themselves should note that James Legge, who translated much of the early history of China into English in the nineteenth century, was quite happy to state that Chòu's dates were 1154–1123 BC.

There is no doubt that Chinese history does tend to place the Shang to Zhou dynastic transition around the twelfth and eleventh centuries BC. If we go back to Legge, writing in the 1860s, we find that he has compiled an outline of the three dynasties with 'dates'. His text notes some odd phenomena which may be relevant to the 1628 and 1159 BC issues. Legge listed the dynasties by reign with any natural phenomena noted. For brevity's sake, the 'periods of calm' are conflated:

'BC' dates from Legge

1989–1951 ... nil

1951–1942 ... in 5th year there was an eclipse of the sun

1942–1621 ... nil

1621–1611 ... in 8th year inauspicious portent – ten suns appear together

1611–1595 ... nil

1595–1588 ... in 7th year Mount T'ae shook

1588–1557 ... in 10th year the five planets went out of their courses.
In the night stars fell like rain. The earth shook. The E and Loh became dry.
in 29th year three suns appeared together
in 30th year there was a fall of mount K'eu
End Xia

1557–1545 ... in 2nd–7th year drought and famine (5 or 7 years)

1545–1539 ... nil

1539–1527 ... in 7th year sky overspread with mists for 3 days

1527–1166 ... nil

1166–1123 ... in 35th year the king ... was frightened to death by a great thunderstorm

1123–1110 ... in 3rd year Yuen-water thrice ceased to flow in one day

1110–1101 ... in 3rd year an earthquake in Chow

1101–1049 ... in 5th year there was a shower of earth in Poh
in 32nd year conjunction of 5 planets in Fang
in 35th year a great famine in Chow
in 43rd year part of mount K'aou fell down
in 48th year, the E goat was seen (a prodigious thing, a 'spirit like animal' variously described)
End of Shang

1049–1043 ... nil

1043–1006 ... in 2nd year great storm, thunder lightning and wind

1006–980 ... nil

980–961 ... in 14th year the regular stars were invisible
in 19th year a comet. The heavens were dark and tempestuous

961–906 ... nil

906–894 ... in 1st year there were two sunrisings in Ch'ing (899 BC by retrocalculations)

From this list we can see that in the second millennium BC there was an empty period from '1942–1621 BC', an eventful period from '1621–1557 BC' (the end of the Xia), an empty period from '1527–1166 BC', and finally an eventful period from '1166–1049 BC' (the end of the Shang). These eventful periods conform quite well to the longer episodes of downturn associated with the seventeenth and twelfth centuries BC indicated by the temperature-sensitive American and Fennoscandian tree-ring series.

Into this overall framework we can introduce these revised datings from David Pankenier. He opts for 1554 BC as the start of the Shang on the basis of a 1576 BC date for the reference 'five planets criss-crossed' which occurs in the reign of king Chieh, the last emperor of the Xia dynasty. Similarly, another 'five planets together' reference towards the end of the Shang is used to define a date, already associated with an apparition of comet Halley, in 1059 BC; the resulting date for the end of the Shang is 1046 BC. If Pankenier is correct on this issue, the dates of the start and end of the Shang bear no close resemblance to the 1628 and 1159 BC events; nor do they conform in any way to Chang's traditional suggestion of 1617 and 1122 BC. However, Pankenier disagrees radically with Pang on the date of the eclipse of the moon in the '35th year of King Wen'. Pang gives 1137 BC while Pankenier gives 1065 BC. Someone has to be wrong here. This is as good a place as any to challenge Pankenier's interpretation of the 'five planets criss-crossing' in November 1576 BC. Legge originally translated this as 'the five planets went out of their courses' and gave it a date of around 1578 'BC'. Pankenier states that the proper translation should be 'the five planets criss-crossed' and he suggests that this happened in November 1576 when the planets moved 'contrari-wise' which he interprets as follows: 'the time and place of observation changed from the NW horizon after sunset to the SE horizon before dawn'.

In order to test that hypothesis I used the *Macformat Redshift* astronomical programme which allows one to view the heavens from anywhere on earth at any time and date within the period of interest. I confirmed the accuracy of the programme by checking both the 1953 BC five-planet alignment and the 899 BC double eclipse. I then looked at the Chinese sky for November 1576. There was a problem: in November 1576 BC the planet Mars is on the opposite side of the sun from the other four main planets. The almost linear arrangement is Saturn, Jupiter, Mercury, Venus, the Sun and Mars. Thus throughout that month Mars always set before the Sun and it would not have been possible to see that the five planets were lined up. Similarly, at dawn, Mars would have been visible for a short time before the sun rose, rendering both Mars and the four planets, which rose after the Sun, invisible. If this set of observations is correct, and I can see no reason for it to be wrong, this frees up the fix on the 'five planets criss-crossed'. Thus I searched the century before 1540 BC for an alternative planetary configuration which might satisfy the description.

The best alignment that I could find, which would satisfy the original description of the five planets' behaviour, occurred in August 1638 BC. On 15 August, Saturn was high in the sky but aligned with Mars, Venus, Jupiter and Mercury which were *following* the Sun. When the Sun went below the horizon, the five planets were in a straight line at twilight. Tracking the programme forward for five nights, it was quite startling to see the two pairs of planets, Mars/Venus and Jupiter/Mercury, reverse their positions, as follows:

```
Saturn              Saturn
    Mars                Venus
        Venus               Mars
        Jupiter                 Mercury
            Mercury             Jupiter
                Sun             Sun
            15 Aug 1638 BC      20 Aug 1638 BC
```

This configuration, where the planets are all together on the same side of the Sun, set after the Sun, and undoubtedly criss-cross, would seem to make it possible that the tenth year of king Chieh was 1638 BC. The fall of the Xia dynasty would then be twenty years later in 1618 BC, allowing the Shang to start in 1617 BC, one of the traditional dates as given by Chang.

If this were correct, then the 1628 BC dust-veil would come in the immediate run up to the end of the dynasty. If we look at Legge's list, we see that it shows:

1588–1557 in 10th year the five planets went out of their courses. In the night stars fell like rain. The earth shook. The E and Loh became dry.
in 29th year three suns appeared together
in 30th year there was a fall of mount K'eu
End Xia

Now at this distance in time, and given the damage and confusion associated with the *Bamboo Annals*, wherein individual lines of text on bamboo strips can be misplaced in time (possibly, on occasion, even ending up in the wrong reign), we cannot be certain that all the effects associated with the tenth year actually happened in that year. What are the chances that the sentences 'In the night stars fell like rain. The earth shook' actually belong to a reign-year between the tenth year and the 29th year, say, the twentieth year?

That is, is it possible that they belong to 1628 BC, perhaps when the volcano Santorini was erupting, or when the Egyptians suffered a plague of meteorites, or when there was a comet in the sky, or when a star called Wormwood fell to the earth and poisoned the waters, or when Moses threw his rod to the ground and it became a serpent, or when Michael wrestled with Satan and threw him to the earth, or when Tigernmas died with three-quarters of the men of Ireland, or when the plague of hail broke every tree; and absolutely certainly when there was notably reduced growth in oaks from Ireland, England and Germany and within a year of those widespread frost-rings in American bristlecone and foxtail pines?

One can play these games endlessly, simply because back in the second millennium BC things are avowedly flexible, with the exception of *some* astronomical retro-calculations. But we do have to note that Pankenier would date the end of the Shang to 1046 BC, very much later than the twelfth-century dates preferred by Pang, by some traditional histories, and, it has to be said, by me. If he is right then we have to be wrong, and that is perfectly fair. But is he right? For example, by committing himself to 1554 BC for the start and 1046 BC for the end of the Shang, he commits himself to a defined *length* for the dynasty – an inclusive length of some 509 years. If that length were correct and if the dynasty actually started in 1617, as suggested above (and by one tradition), then logically it should end around 1109 – very much in line with the 1111 BC date noted above.

What makes Pankenier so sure that the Shang ends in 1046 BC? It is the reference in the *Bamboo Annals* to the five-planet conjunction in the 32nd year of Chòu, the last Shang emperor. This conjunction, which according to the annals was in the constellation 'Fang', that is, Scorpio, is believed by Pankenier to actually have happened in May 1059 in the constellation Cancer (a five-planet conjunction with minimum separation < 7° did take place at that time). For this to be the same conjunction, the reference to Scorpio in the annals has to be wrong, and Pankenier is able to state that the reference to Scorpio 'is a demonstrably late interpolation into the text'. However, Pankenier also tells us why the five-planet conjunction is so important. In early Zhou times (let us say about 1000 BC) the doctrine of 'Heaven's Mandate' has already been articulated. By late Zhou times it has become axiomatic that the 'Mandate' is actually tied up with 'five-planet conjunctions'. Indeed Pankenier lists the three important ones for us, and, of course, we have seen two of these already:

1953 BC, February (start of the Xia, allegedly)
1576 BC, November (towards end of Xia, though see text)
1059 BC, May (towards end of Shang).

Taken at face value, it would appear that there really were five-planet conjunctions at around the start of the three dynasties in the second millennium BC. Or, as Pankenier puts it,

> *Using the 1059 BCE date of the Zhou mandate conjunction as a benchmark, it became possible to interpret similar accounts in pre-Han sources such as Mozi, where the precedent-setting portents associated with all three dynastic foundings in the second millennium BCE are cited in chronological order.*

However, if by late Zhou times – a thousand years after the events – people have decided that the 'Heaven's Mandate' concept *does* refer to five-planet conjunctions, then how convenient to attribute the conjunction (which we know happened in 1059 BC, but only from retro-calculation) to the reign before the start of the Zhou dynasty. It is by means such as these that ruling groups legitimize their position (for example, William the Conqueror used the cometary apparition of AD 1066 to link back to a comet associated with Arthur, thereby legitimizing his claim to the throne of England). For all we know, the placing of the five-planet conjunctions at the start of new dynasties might be a manipulation by late Zhou writers to conform to their interpretation of the Heaven's Mandate concept.

We should remember several things in this respect. The 1059 BC conjunction was in the wrong constellation; the 'demonstrably late interpolation' actually tells us the texts have been tampered with. As described above, the 1576 BC 'conjunction' would not have been visible because of the Sun's location, and hence is extremely dubious; 1638 actually offers a better interpretation. Pang and Pankenier disagree on the date of the total lunar eclipse which is used to back-up the 1059 BC dating (Pang puts it in 1137 BC, Pankenier in 1065 BC). Overall, the conjunction theory seems in need of additional justification. Moreover, there is no known physical mechanism which can explain how a planetary conjunction could *cause* a dynastic change. In contrast, as this book has tried to show, cometary interactions – 'Heaven's bright terrors' – wormwood, dim suns, yellow fogs, summer frosts, crop failures, certainly could bring down any dynasty. Readers can decide for themselves whether the early Chinese preoccupation with revealed wisdom in the form of 'bright manifestations' displayed by Heaven, the appearance of an auspicious 'phoenix' in conjunction with the rise of Zhou is, as Pankenier suggests, to do with planetary conjunctions in constellations, or whether it relates to 'cosmic swarms' and 'feathered serpents' like Quetzalcoatl.

APPENDIX 2

ICELANDIC MYTHOLOGY: THE RAGNARÖK

Given the suggestion that there have been one or several visitations of Earth by some combination of close-pass comets and impacting debris we can start to think about some of the wider possibilities. Imagine that something passing close to the Earth did look as bright as the sun and that associated with that object were showers of meteorites up to Tunguska class and beyond. The symptoms would be loading of the atmosphere and dimming of the sun and moon, probably resulting in cooling and crop failures; famines and plagues. On the physical side, impacts of sufficient size over land would induce earthquakes, while those over the oceans would cause tsunami. If the earthquakes were large enough, or in the right geographical locations, it is possible to imagine the triggering of volcanic eruptions – why not? The earthquakes themselves might trigger outgassing events involving methane or hydrogen sulphide or ammonium that could poison the atmosphere. The point about such a scenario is that if it happened it would produce effects out of all proportion to normal single-factor occurrences. The sort of events we have been looking at do seem to be in a class of their own. After all, if the 1628 BC or AD 540 events really were as devastating as seems likely from the available records, they would appear to represent a different class of effect. They might represent the sort of environmental downturn which just might bring down dynasties by affecting tree and crop growth over large areas. Therefore with that series of unpleasant events in mind I read about the Ragnarök. Given that the events outlined there represent essentially the End of the World, some of the imagery is interesting to say the least. We have to remember that such mythological tales are really disguised memories of things which have happened in the past. A recent encyclopaedia entry tells us the following:

> In Norse mythology, Ragnarök is an apocalyptic vision of the last days of the world, the twilight of the gods when the sun grows dim, the forces of evil are let loose, and gods and giants slaughter one another and all creation ... The battle will be signalled by Heimdall, who will sound a mighty blast on his horn.

The Ragnarök says that one day the 'Monstrous Winter' will come. This apocalyptic winter will be recognized by its severity and duration. It will last for three winters with no summers in between. If such a combination of circumstances were to come about, any society would be severely stretched, in particular, any agricultural society: two completely failed harvests would see to that. Are the writers of this mythology preserving the memory of just such an event from the past? Might they be remembering things that actually happened around 3200 BC or 2345 BC or 1628 BC or 1159 BC or even AD 540? We will look at a series of observations from Branston's *Gods of the North* and see what else fits.

The myth tells us that before the Monstrous Winter there will be three other winters where the whole world will be embroiled in war. This certainly recalls the AD 540 event, where we have that curious spacing between the AD 536 event and the more severe AD 540 downturn. However, this is merely a distraction. The real story is as follows. At Ragnarök a Wolf swallows the Sun and another the Moon while the 'stars turn from their steadings in heaven'. There are earthquakes, 'the earth and the mountains shake', and the forests are destroyed, 'woods are torn up by the roots'. The Fenris Wolf, who has flames coming from his eyes and nostrils, rakes the earth. At this point another Wolf, Fenrir, breaks loose and causes floods or more likely tsunami: 'a great bore of waters inundates the land'. We read of the World Serpent bucking and boiling up out of the sea. While that sounds like Leviathan, the more interesting association with the World Serpent is the 'clouds of poison' that he blows over the earth and sky. While all this is happening, the heavens split asunder and a tide of the sons of Muspell gallop through. These are headed by the fire giant Surtr, who is 'flinging fire before him and after him both, in his fist the supreme sword more dazzling than the sun'. Just about everyone then joins in with Loki, the father of Fenrir, plus the Sons of Hel (Hel being Fenrir's brother) and the Children of Muspell, who 'form an army on their own – a blazing host'. Thereafter there is a good deal of skirmishing by gods, wolves and serpents, until 'Surtr pitches flame over the earth and burns up the whole of heaven'.

It will hardly have escaped notice that this is laced with the same imagery of the dim sun and moon, swords, fiery serpents and blazing hosts that we have seen repeatedly associated with various environmental downturns. It bears more than a passing resemblance to the details in Revelation concerning the end of the world. Branston helps by elaborating some of the detail and giving the mythology additional context, although I repeat only one key aspect here, that concerning Surtr. According to Branston, Surtr's name means 'black': an incongruous name for a fire-being until we discover that Agni, the Hindu fire-god is called 'black-backed' when he passes through the forest, and at once we see his carbonised track; Surtr had in his hand fire 'the scourge of forests'.

Thus associated with the Norse mythology concerning some really unpleasant past experience and used as a model for the end of the world, is the concept of 'a fiery scourge of forests'. While Branston was thinking of forest fires, the attribute would sit equally comfortably with the aftermath of a 'Tunguska' event. This is made clearer when Branston quotes the Rig-Veda's description of Agni:

O Agni, thou from whom ... undying flames proceed, the brilliant smoke god goes towards the sky ... whose power spreads over the earth in a moment ... like a dashing army thy blast goes forth; with thy lambent flame thou seemest to tear up the grass ... thy brightness comes like the lightening of heaven; thou showest splendour like the bright sun ...

This does not sound like a simple 'forest-fire god'; this sounds very like the descriptions associated with the Tunguska event. Remember what the main elements of Tunguska were:

A fireball brighter than the sun associated with a deafening roar. There was a ballistic wave and a cataclysmic explosion which produced strong seismic shocks. At impact there was a gigantic pillar of fire which formed a blinding column and a thermal shock wave which scorched the conifers and ignited fires. As a result thick black smoke rose more than 12 miles resulting in a 'black rain' with associated thunder.

When Branston interpreted Surtr as Agni he gave us a pretty strong hint that the remembered awfulness had an impact dimension. The similarity of Ragnarök and Revelation in their depiction of the symptoms of the end of the world are further reinforced by a Celtic cosmic motif. In a personal communication, Chris Lynn drew my attention to the observation by Sayers that, in ancient Irish literature such as the *Táin bó Cúailgne*, a warrior vowing never to retreat – move from this spot – would normally couch the vow in terms such as 'unless the firmament with its shower of stars fall upon the surface of the earth, or unless the blue bordered fish abounding sea come over the face of the world, or unless the earth quake (we shall never retreat one inch from this spot).'

It is generally accepted that the Celts were saying that they were afraid of 'nothing' because the possibility of the heavens falling was so remote, but, of course, this is effectively a description of the most remote circumstance of which they could conceive – the end of the world. From our point of view, it is their description of the main elements which is most relevant. In their view the stars would fall from the sky, the sea would come over the land, there would be earthquakes and falling forests. Sayers then points out how congruent the visions of cosmic creation and destruction are in classical, biblical, Celtic and 'common Indo-European' models. So as one might expect, the universal vision of the end of the world has all the elements of an impact scenario. One reason why this is not better known relates to the perceptions of scholars of ancient myth. A good example is presented by something noted by Snorri, the great Icelandic mythologist. Santillana and Dechend, in *Hamlet's Mill*, footnote a comment about Snorri's comparison between Ragnarök and the Fall of Troy and note how the comparison was condemned by 'the experts': 'the logical outcome of their conviction that 'poetry' is some kind of *creatio ex nihilo*, whence the one question never raised is whether the poets might not be dealing with hard scientific facts.' Maybe Snorri was right after all.

APPENDIX 3

CONSPIRACY ... WHAT CONSPIRACY?

We have seen that tree-rings and mythology and odd little footnotes allow the building of a fairly conclusive picture wherein the earth appears to have been affected by atmospheric loading associated with bombardment – probably associated with one of Clube and Napier's cosmic swarms or a comet. So if that is correct and we were bombarded, why were we not told? Why would anyone want to suppress such information? Why, indeed? Let us see what we can come up with.

It was noted earlier that the similarities between the Exodus happenings and the AD 540 package of events were sufficiently great that the Christianization of Ireland (Patrick's mission if you like) may have been assisted by the environmental event. Thus, one net beneficiary of the event may have been the Church. So, could the Church have had a reason for suppressing the record of a natural catastrophic event? I am not the first to ask such a question about this period. Looking back to Peter Pritchard's letter about Arthur, I discovered that he had made some comments on the Arthurian Dark Ages; he had come to the conclusion that they were *deliberately* 'Dark': 'I hold that the Church has suppressed information which they saw as a doctrinal threat.' I am not going to go into Pritchard's reasoning, which basically sees Arthur as a rival Messianic figure to Christ. Suffice to say that the sentiment ties in with several other observations.

The sixth-century Byzantine writer and historian, John Malalas, for example, gave a considerable amount of detail for the years 526 up to 532, on average more than a hundred lines a year. But, AD 533 to 539 warrant only twenty-one lines in total; the eleven years from AD 540 to AD 550 warrant one hundred and six lines. This quantitative shift in the quality of Malalas' record would seem to suggest that the record may have been thinned; why else would an historian who has been recording widely suddenly dry up at an interesting time? Unfortunately for this line of reasoning it appears that Malalas, who had been writing at Antioch, was called to Constantinople in AD 532–3 and published his history up to that point. Only decades later, when revising his work, did he extend the record across our period. It is strange that such a traumatic period gets so little attention. And I have already mentioned the Cassiodorus letters, which run up to AD 538 and stop, and Bower's *The History of the Popes* which records for AD 540: 'The next year, 540, nothing happened worthy of notice.'

What is interesting in this context is the observation by Malalas of two things which happened in AD 532, the last year of his substantial record. First, there was another 'great shower of stars from dusk to dawn' (rather like AD 524). Then Justinian decreed, and sent throughout the Empire, his 'sacred edict' – this was a diatribe against heresy, particularly the heresy of Nestorios, Eutyches and Apollinarios. The principal point of Justinian's edict related to the fact that there were people who said that 'our Lord Jesus Christ the son of God and our God is man only'. Although these heresies had been around for a century or more, Justinian chose this moment to attack them in the most vitriolic terms. He refers to the 'sickness and madness of Nestorios and Eutyches (who is out of his mind)' and 'Apollinarios the destroyer of souls'.

Immediately after this, the record from Malalas drops to almost nothing. The happenings of AD 536 are not mentioned. But it does not end there. Turning to Caitlin Matthews writing on Mabon, the Celtic Divine Child, I noted the following statements:

Ashe, writing in the first Book of Merlin, *identified Merlin, Mabon and the primal god of Britain with one another ... It seems unlikely ... that we shall ever know the true status of Mabon, for his legend bears all the negative signs of having been heavily edited, or at one time banned, for religious propagandist reasons ...*

So information on another Merlin figure has all the signs of suppression. But it is Cassiodorus who gives us the best clue as to what may really have been going on. He had written that, although people are troubled by whatever marvels are going on in the sky, there is no need to worry. Why not? The answer is simple: 'But if this is to be ascribed to divine providence, we should not be troubled, since, by God's own command, we are forbidden to look for a sign ...' And he quotes the source of this, namely Matthew: 24. 1–4. The chapter says there will be no signs until near the end (though at the end, as we know, the sun and moon will be dim, the stars will fall from heaven and the sign of the Son of man will appear in the sky). The problem seems to have been that in the window of AD 536–45, in the wider window AD 532–45, or even AD 525–45, there were just such signs; signs in the sky, and on the ground; signs which may have indicated 'the end', perhaps reminiscent of the Angel of the Lord when he appeared at the Exodus, but signs that sixth-century Christians were 'forbidden to look for'. It looks as though the occurrences in this period may have been very confusing for the early Christians: there were signs but the end, bad as things became, did not come. Perhaps the powers that be had good grounds for suppressing the signs. What was the stimulus for Justinian's edict, or the subject of that synod of the Catholic hierarchy which took place at Auxerre, France, in 538? When we start to put all these pieces together – Malalas, Cassiodorus, Gildas, Justinian, Arthurian legend, etc. – we begin to see what just may be a picture.

In order to keep some sort of quasi-scientific handle on the foregoing, we can look at another set of observations relating to this particular period: the earthquake record for the Mediterranean produced by Phillips and Guidoboni. They have gone through the sources fairly exhaustively trying to make sense of the different references to the various tectonic events. The dates of earthquakes are interesting in themselves: AD 515, 518, 521–2, 523–5, 526 (Antioch) 526–7, 527, 528, 530, 532, 533, then nothing until AD 542, 543, 543, 544–5, 546, 548, 551, 551, and 554. There is that gap again, with nothing noted between AD 533 and 542; just like the AD 534–44 gap in the Anglo-Saxon Chronicle. This gap in the earthquake record is a direct reflection on the 'gap' in the Malalas record, because the authors lean heavily on the chronological integrity of Malalas. However, they also draw attention to the contradictions which occur even with the dating of the great Antioch earthquake of AD 526, which is described as the most important in the history of Byzantium.

Malalas dates the Antioch earthquake to May in the seventh year of the emperor Justin and also tells us who was consul. But this is contradictory, because apparently (according to these authors) the seventh year of Justin is AD 525, whereas the consul date is AD 526. Then both the time and day are contradicted by different writers; it was either on 20 or 29 May, it was either at 1.00 pm or 8.00 am. Theophanes places it at AD 527 and Cedrenus makes it 4 October. We can even find statements from the authors such as 'Both Glycas and Cedrenus relate this earthquake to the disaster at Pompeiopolis in

Moesia, but the latter seems to have occurred in 536 ...'. But according to the overall list there was no earthquake in AD 536 and that at Pompeiopolis is attributed to AD 527. It appears that there are some doubts about at least some of the texts. Apparently the *Syriac Chronicle of 1234* gives a date for the great Antioch earthquake as 'the seventh year of the reign of Justin II'. But Justin II is much later (AD 565–78) so Phillips and Guidoboni interpolate this as a reference to Justinian, whose seventh year would be AD 533. However, John of Ephesus also dates the event to the seventh year of Justinian, but this is interpreted as Justin I. How do these writers manage this amount of confusion on the most important earthquake in the history of Byzantium?

Phillips and Guidoboni go on to discuss the Pompeiopolis earthquake under the date AD 527. But they state that Malalas dates this earthquake to AD 528–9, whereas Theophanes says AD 536, though he is supposed to be using *Malalas* as his source. They continue about this Pompeiopolis quake as follows:

Furthermore, John of Ephesus and Pseudo-Dionysius of Tellmahre give the date as 538–39, but the latter's chronology is unreliable. Indeed, he records this earthquake shortly before mentioning the one at Antioch in 528 (this Antioch quake is two years after the great quake) ... which he wrongly dates to 539–40.

Three earthquakes at Antioch (the great quake), Pompeiopolis and Antioch (the quake two years later) are attributed to AD 526, 527 and 528 by modern writers trying to make some sense of the confusing and contradictory records available from the sixth century. All the attributions of earthquakes to the years AD 536, 538–9 and 539–40 are presented as contradictions or mistakes, and are moved back a decade into the AD 520s. If we really do know the date of the great Antioch earthquake, are we really sure it *was* 526? We used to be sure, but when confronted with this level of contradiction we might begin to wonder. Are some descriptions of things which actually happened in the late 530s being attributed to the mid-520s?

Let us review briefly the things which went on at the great Antioch earthquake (supposedly of AD 526):

• Sparks of fire appeared out of the air
• The surface of the earth boiled
• Buildings were struck by thunderbolts
• Much of Antioch collapsed under unusual circumstances
• Fire fell from heaven on the city
• On the third day a cross of light appeared in the western sky

- More fire came down as flames from heaven
- Moist dust came up from the depths of the earth
- The sea gave off a great stench.

However contradictory the accounts of the earthquakes may be, they are at least expected. Ancient texts are much copied and sections are misread, lost, damaged and misplaced. What we do not expect to find is such a coincidental set of problems in the ice-core records. Here, modern scientists are drilling through what is supposed to be a continuous depositional record of Greenland snowfall. Yet we have seen that, while the Crête core stopped at AD 553+/-3, just before that, in the sixth century, there are problems with both the Dye3 core and the GISP2 core; with moved dates and lost core respectively. How on earth does one explain that set of problems in the same century as all the historical problems? Could Greenland have been hit by something?

The problems are everywhere. Another Mediterranean writer of the early sixth century, Cosmas, author of the *Christian Topography*, gets muddled up around this period. Cosmas, a much-travelled merchant, gives up that occupation for religion and preaches a doctrine wherein 'the universe consists of only two places, namely the earth which is below the firmament, and heaven, which is above it'. McCrindle, writing about Cosmas, states categorically that Cosmas visited Adulê in Ethiopia in AD 525. Then he goes on to explain that Cosmas' visit to Adulê 'was made in AD 522, and that Justinus was at that date in the fifth year of his reign'. So, not only does McCrindle contradict his own dating for the Cosmas visit, he calls into question the statement attributed to Malalas above, that 'the great Antioch earthquake of 526 ... Malalas dates ... to May in the seventh year of the emperor Justin.' If Justin's fifth year was AD 522, how on earth was his seventh year AD 526? Something is definitely not right. Then again, we are forced back to Bower's comment when writing about the sixth-century popes, where he singles out the year AD 540 for his 'nothing happened worthy of notice' comment. He does not make such a comment about other years in the sixth century for which no relevant information was available; why earmark AD 540?

The icing on this particular cake comes from *Zachariah of Mitylene*, edited by E. W. Brooks. This twelve-book history credited to Zachariah is *A volume of records of events which have happened in the world* and is probably written by several authors. Believed to have been completed in AD 569, it forms a continual historical narrative from AD 448, exactly of the period of interest. It is possible to think of this as a test of the conspiracy theory for the simple reason that the conspiracy, suggested here, was already formulated before the details of Zachariah were discovered. Now, let us get this right. The 12 books of Zachariah each contain a series of chapters; however, only the first nine chapters are complete and they run up to, believe it or not, specifically the year AD 536. The remaining books are unfortunately fragmentary:

> *Of bk. 10 in which the history is continued to 548, we have the headings of the chapters complete and portions of the chapters themselves; the lost chapters I have been able in part to restore from Michael, Gregory, and the fragments of James of Edessa. Bk. 11 is wholly lost: of bk. 12 we have a fragment extending from the middle of ch. 4 to the middle of ch. 7, and dealing with the years 553–556.*

What makes this loss all the more interesting is the fact that, according to Brooks, books 1–9 are *practically complete*, 'setting aside small tears and obliterations', with only a few stray leaves missing; the bits we might be interested in vary from 'fragmentary' to 'wholly lost'. Given the observations already made on Malalas and Cassiororus, this sudden demise of the Zacharias record after AD 536 looks suspicious. But curiously, despite the loss of the key chapters covering AD 536 to the early 550s, something very interesting can be gleaned from those fragments of book 12 which have survived. The relevant fragment is bk. 12, chapter 5, entitled *The fifth chapter treats of the powder, consisting of ashes, which fell from heaven,* which deals with falls of ashes and dust in AD 556:

> *In addition to all the evil and fearful things described above and recorded below [mostly lost!], the earthquakes and famines and wars in divers places … there has also been fulfilled against us and against this last generation the curse of Moses in Deuteronomy, when he admonished the people who had just come out of Egypt …*

Here is someone writing in the mid-sixth century telling us about the unpleasant things which have been fulfilled against this last generation. For someone writing in AD 556, 'the last generation' would include those who had lived through the AD 536–45 events. So, the things which had been fulfilled against those who had lived through the AD 540 event could be identified in the writer's mind with Moses' curse from just after the Exodus. We have already seen that the events round AD 540 do look like a re-run of Exodus; now we have a contemporary source saying the same thing, though not in quite those words. Zachariah, or whoever was writing, does not say 'AD 540 looks like a re-run of Exodus'; what he compares AD 540 with is 'the curse of Moses in Deuteronomy'. There is a subtle distinction. The curses in

Deuteronomy should give us a clue as to what may have been fulfilled against that past, AD 540, generation; what do they include? Deuteronomy chapters 28 and 29 are easily available: the key items are curses in cities in fields and in stores. There will be pestilence, consumption, fever, blasting and mildew. It will rain powder and dust, there will be darkness, locusts, etc. Given that the generation who lived through AD 540 had clearly been afflicted with famine and plague, this curse of Moses seems entirely appropriate. Indeed, if that were the whole curse, we would not have learned anything new. The twist in Zachariah is that there is one last key element in Moses' curse, as follows:

When they see the plagues of that land, and the sickness which the Lord has laid upon it; and that the whole land thereof is brimstone, and salt, and burning, that it is not sown, nor beareth, nor any grass groweth therein, like the overthrow of Sodom and Gomorrah, Admah and Zeboim, which the Lord overthrew in his anger and in his wrath: Even all nations shall say, Wherefore hath the Lord done this onto this land? What meaneth the heat of this great anger?

The hint that Zachariah gives us, in telling us that the AD 540 generation had been afflicted by the curse of Moses, rather than by a rerun of the events of Exodus itself, is the mention of Sodom and Gomorrah. Once those cities are mentioned, Genesis supplies the answer: 'Then the Lord rained upon Sodom and upon Gomorrah brimstone and fire from the Lord out of heaven.'

There is a possibility that what actually happened at AD 540, or in the window AD 536–45, was impact-related. That there was something in the sky, 'something coming on us from the stars', something that may not exactly have been suppressed, but something which has been mysteriously overlooked.

APPENDIX 4

THE CELESTIAL BATTLE OF MU

Numerous references have been made in the main text, and in this appendix, to the end of the Shang dynasty in what is probably the twelfth century BC. There was a battle – the Battle of Mu – in which the 'evil' king Chòu, the last of the Shang, was defeated by Wu Wang, the first emperor of the Zhou dynasty. Traditional dating puts this around 1122 BC, though it could actually be a bit earlier or a bit later. Chang sets the scene with Wu Wang arriving on the field of battle at Mu Yeh and addressing his followers while carrying 'a battle axe yellow with gold' in one hand and a white ensign in the other – he was on his way to attack Chòu. Chòu had sent his troops to resist Wu Wang's progress into Shang territory, but they were defeated. When Chòu heard the bad news he 'put on his precious jade clothing, and went into a fire to his death'. What is quite surprising is that there is a whole other mythological story associated with this twelfth-century battle.

Derek Walter, in his book *Chinese Mythology*, puts it like this:

According to legend, the terrestrial or mortal battle was paralleled by another battle of gods, spirits and immortals. The events are recorded in the Book of the Making of Immortals, and the Catalogue of Spirits and Immortals, both of which are Taoist books compiled several centuries after the historical events. Many gods and spirits were annihilated in this battle, and several stellar dignitaries were replaced by newcomers to the celestial domains.

Here, it would appear, we are again, with details which are really quite strange. First it is necessary to see who was there.

Li Ching is one of Wu Wang's generals who is known as the Pagoda Bearer. He has a son, Li No-cha, who is famous for killing the Dragon King, Lung Wang. Li No-cha is thought by some to be the Hindu god of thunder, and is normally depicted holding a model of a golden pagoda, an image which may originally have been a thunderbolt. His description in some Chinese sources is of a monstrously tall figure with three heads, nine eyes and a host of arms whose voice makes the earth shake. Li No-cha is armed with a Heaven-Earth bracelet and rides about at high speed on a Wind-Fire wheel. However, the strange imagery of one of the mythical generals fighting for Wu Wang fails to prepare us for the beings on the side of Chòu.

Chòu has Lei Tsu, who is known as the ancestor of thunder. His middle eye (he has three), emits a beam of light. He rides at the speed of light on a black unicorn and can throw thunderbolts. He ends up being imprisoned and destroyed amid eight columns of fire. To go with Lei Tsu, Chòu has two marshals which we will call Heng and Ha for brevity. Heng is known as the 'Snorter' – when he snorts it sounds like a bell. However, it is the two beams of destructive light which come from his nostrils that mark him out as special. His companion is Ha, the 'Blower'. Ha gives us a whole new dimension to play with. When Ha blows there are clouds of poisonous yellow gas. To cut a long story short, Heng is captured by the Wu Wang side and ends up fighting for them against Ha. Both are killed, Ha by a bow and a spear and Heng by 'an ox-spirit, who spat a bezoar stone in his face'.

In this colourful set of descriptions, there are hints of happenings at the time of David. This book places David in the twelfth century BC. Amongst other things, David kills a giant by hitting him in the face with a stone shot from a sling. In the related Psalm 18 there are earthquakes, smoke, thunder, arrows, shot-out lightenings and 'the blast of the breath of thy nostrils'; indeed, in some texts Leviathan spouts fire from his mouth and nostrils. Of course there is nothing to link definitively the Chinese descriptions to the more general descriptions of the Old Testament. There is one thing, however, which serves to provide links among at least three of our main events. When Ha blows poisonous yellow gas at the end of the Shang dynasty, traditionally in 1122 BC, or possibly around 1159 BC, he reminds us of 'the earth emitted yellow fog' at the time of king Chieh, possibly around 1628 BC, but definitely at the end of the Xia dynasty. He also reminds us of the Yellow Plague which is recorded in Wales and Ireland in the AD 540s wandering around like a loathly monster. The 'yellow gas' could even remind us of how 'the sky has looked yellow and the air reddish because of the burnt vapours' as reported by the medical faculty of Paris in AD 1348 during the ravages of the Black Death.

A critic of this scenario would say, among other things, that these mythological records have little meaning and, in fact, relate to the introduction of Buddhism to China. Joseph Fontenrose tells us that 'Once the Buddhists and Buddhist texts had come to China … the Indic dragon myths became current in Chinese Mythology.' The important thing, as with the placement of the *Beowulf* and Arthurian imagery in the early sixth century AD, is that for some reason, even if the dragon imagery is imported from India, the Chinese place the imagery at exactly the point of the Shang/Zhou dynastic change. Fontenrose notes Li Ching and Li No-Cha, mentioned above, and points out No Cha's similarity to Indra. Then he makes another connection – that Indra had to fight not just one dragon/monster, but two, Vritra and Danu. He then points to the similarity with Beowulf, who had to wrestle not only Grendel but, the more hideous, Grendel's mother. And, of course, 'Apollo had to deal with the dragoness after he had disposed of the dragon.' So by placing Indra imagery at the end of the Shang dynasty, probably in the twelfth century BC, the Chinese myths allow yet another link between Apollo, 'a veritable plague demon' who appears in the twelfth century BC and the Beowulf imagery of the sixth century AD, not far from the Justinian plague. In every case these are images laced with dragons and things in the sky.

APPENDIX 5

WHY THE EXODUS TOOK PLACE IN 1628 BC

For many readers the most difficult aspect of the story in this book will be the moving of the Exodus from its traditional *circa* '1250 BC' date back to the period around 1600 BC. The story will founder on that very point. However, as pointed out in the text, there is nothing fixed about the date of the Exodus: even mainstream biblical scholars have no problem moving the date of the event over several centuries. So is there any scientific check on the general, if not the specific, seventeenth-century BC placement of the Exodus, as suggested here?

First it is necessary to recap the radiocarbon story as it relates to the date of the Santorini eruption. Numerous radiocarbon determinations have been carried out on seeds from the last phase of occupation just before the town of Akrotiri was buried by ash. The mean radiocarbon age is very close to 3355 radiocarbon years before present, with a suggested error of around +/-20 to +/-30 years. Unfortunately, the problem is that radiocarbon dates have to be calibrated to convert them to estimates of real age; that was the reason that the original European oak chronologies were constructed: to provide precisely dated wood samples to calibrate radiocarbon dates. Because the calibration curve is relatively 'flat' across the period from about 1670 BC to 1530 BC, that is, any samples of organic material which grew in that 140-year span of *real time* tend to give the same radiocarbon age of around 3300 to 3350 BP, it is impossible to use radiocarbon to get a closer real date for the eruption. In fact, the arguments between Peter Warren and Sturt Manning centre on whether the eruption was towards the older end of the 'flat' portion on the calibration (i.e. seventeenth century BC, Manning) or towards the more recent end (i.e. sixteenth century BC, Warren).

No one is seriously arguing that Santorini erupted anywhere other than on the flat portion of the calibration between 1670 and 1530 BC; just at which end of the flat portion. One piece of scientific evidence exists which is almost certainly crucial to this issue. In 1996 Hendrick Bruins and Johannes van der Plicht presented their radiocarbon measurements on cereal grains from the final destruction levels at Middle Bronze Age Jericho. This is thought to be the well-known destruction level at Jericho which is recorded in Hebrew texts and placed some forty years after the Exodus. These new radiocarbon dates from Jericho average out at 3311 +/-13 BP; very similar to the radiocarbon dates from Santorini. Thus the Jericho dates will calibrate out to the same range – from 1670 to 1530 BC

– as Santorini, making complete nonsense of the idea that the Exodus should be about 1250 BC.

But there is a nice twist which has to be significant. If the Hebrew records are correct, then the Exodus should be about forty years older than the destruction of Jericho and must lie *further back* on the flat portion of the calibration curve. On this reasoning, the very latest possible date for the Exodus would be 1570 BC, if Jericho lay at 1530 BC, the youngest possible calibrated date, that is, the Exodus must have taken place around 1570 BC *or before*. Since there is no good reason to imagine that the destruction of Jericho should lie at the extreme end of the flat portion of the calibration, it is likely that the Exodus is indeed before 1570 BC. In which case it might as well be at 1628 BC and link with the Santorini event, just where the logic of this book would place it.

APPENDIX 6

THE ROSUALT

In 1990 Seán ÓhUigin sent me an extract from P.W. Joyce's *A Social History of Ancient Ireland*. At that time I did not recognize its possible significance. It was not until 1997 that I rediscovered the correspondence and recognized what it might mean. Sean in his original covering letter had indicated that the piece might contain some hint of a 'major environmental disaster...some time in the latter half of the sixth century'.

In a section where he is writing about snakes and St Patrick, as well as monsters in lakes, Joyce goes on to describe a much larger and more deadly sea-monster – the Rosualt, the story of which is taken from the Book of Leinster and apparently set at the time of St Columkille, that is, in the sixth century. It appears that the monster was washed ashore on the plain at the foot of Croagh Patrick mountain. The plain is called Murrisk, which is a shortened form of *Muir-iasc*, meaning 'sea-fish'. So, some time in the sixth century a huge sea-monster was washed well inshore, a story which may preserve the memory of a great storm or a tsunami. However, it is the detail of what this sea monster could do – presumably did – while alive which is both interesting and alarming. Joyce wrote:

He was able to vomit in three different ways three years in succession. One year he turned up his tail, and with his head buried deep down, he spewed the contents of his stomach into the water, in consequence of which all the fish died in that part of the sea, and currachs and ships were wrecked and swamped. Next year he sank his tail into the water, and rearing his head high up in the air, belched out such noisome fumes that all the birds fell dead. In the third year he turned his head shoreward and vomited towards the land, causing a pestilential vapour to creep over the country that killed men and four-footed animals.

These are no ordinary attributes of a sea monster, especially not in the sixth century where we already know that the Yellow Plague of the AD 540s was able to move around the countryside as 'a loathsome monster' or 'as a pillar of vapour rising from earth to heaven and sweeping along the ground'. The question is, is this the piece of evidence needed to identify the phenomenon which caused the AD 540 event? Of course it is not sufficiently well dated for certainty. Nevertheless, given the sheer number of pieces of information on mists and vapours which now can be attributed to the sixth century, it does seem that there are hints of something foul in the atmosphere. Are we looking at hints strong enough to tell us that there was an ocean outgassing at around AD 540? Remember, we have not only the Rosualt but the Welsh legend of 'the innundation of Gwyddno's land' associated with an 'offensive smell' and 'poisoned water', while another Welsh legend has a 'magic mist that falls over the land, the seven cantiffs of Dyffid become barren and desolate'.

In Beowulf studies, attention has been drawn to the etymology of 'Beowulf, Beon and Grendel'. It turns out that according to Klaeber: Beowulf = 'sweeping wolf' i.e. 'the cleansing wind that chases the mist away.'

So an Irish tale set in the sixth century has a sea-monster blowing a pestilential vapour on-shore and an English poem, set in the sixth century, has a hero who wrestles with monsters and 'chases the mist away'. We could add in another sixth-century miracle associated with Saint Columba wherein he sees, from Iona, a dark cloud come up from the sea to the west which poisons people in Ireland. Overall, mythology does seem to support a noxious gas component to the story, but we must not forget that all the dragon imagery throughout the main text points to a cometary or fireball component as well. Can we find any hint of that in the Rosualt story? Perhaps there is just a glimmer.

When I mentioned the Rosualt story to Richard Warner, he noted the curious similarity between Rosualt and the name Sualtamh, one of Cuchulinn's fathers. Cuchulinn is the great hero-figure of Celtic myth, with many god-like associations. While there is no good etymological basis for seeing any similarity between the two names Rosualt and Sualtamh, the connection is so good that it is worth setting down anyway. Cuchulinn had more than one father. Another father of Cuchulinn is the god Lug, who we have met with earlier in the text. Lug is a god the radiance of whose face was like that of the sun itself; verily a comet god. Tolstoy quotes the following:

> Then arose Breas, the son of Balor, and he said: 'It is a wonder to me that the sun should rise in the west today, and in the east every other day.' 'It were better that it was so,' said the druids. 'What else is it?' said he. 'The radiance of the face of Lug of the Long Arm,' said they.

Now the only object as bright as the sun which can come up in the west is a comet or a fireball. Perhaps the package of events in the sixth century is both cometary – and outgassing-related. Here is one last quote from *Beowulf* by E. Talbot Donaldson. Writing in 1976 Donaldson tells us something intriguing about Grendel, Beowulf's monstrous adversary: 'I shall speak still more of Grendel … after heaven's jewel has glided over the earth, the angry spirit came, awful in the evening.'

We begin to wonder if the real-life scenario really was a close-pass comet, impacts, tectonic effects, tsunami and seiches, topped off with outgassing from the continental shelf? Maybe Don Carleton was correct when he postulated that 'a comet hit the Celtic Sea in AD 540'. But, as with all these things, there are always more connections. We saw the link, albeit tenuous, of the Rosualt to Lug (of the bright face who comes up in the west). At one point in Malory's *Morte D'Arthur*, Arthur has a dream which includes the following:

> Him seemed that a dreadful dragon did drown much of his people, and he came flying out of the west, and his head was enamelled with azure, and his shoulders shone as gold, his belly like mails of a marvellous hue, his tail full of tatters, his feet full of fine sable, and his claws like fine gold; an hideous flame of fire flew out of his mouth, like as the land and water had flamed all of fire …

Apart from sounding remarkably like Quetzalcoatl the feathered serpent, who from the Americas departed to the *East*, the associated drowning could as easily refer to a tsunami as to anything else. Perhaps it is not so strange that some writers place the legend of Lyonesse – wherein the land between the Isles of Scilly and Cornwall is inundated – in the same year as Arthur's death. If all these hints held together, the AD 540 event would appear to have involved a major crustal re-adjustment.

APPENDIX 7

THE GODDESS CYBELE

Although the 207 BC narrowest-ring event appears to tie in well to the general bombardment story, with Livy's 'stones falling from the sky'. Unfortunately, Livy regularly mentions such factors and this, of course, reduces the significance of his comments relating to the happenings around 207. To recap the story briefly, things were so bad in Rome in the vicinity of 208–205 BC that the Romans consulted the Sibylline Books, which advised that the Magna Mater, the goddess Cybele, be brought back to Rome to save the city. Now, the point about Forsyth's article on this subject was that it had never been fully understood why the oracle was consulted; Livy seems to record that it was because of the repeated falls of stones. The situation *appears* simple: stress in Rome – apparitions in the sky – bring back Cybele – everything improves. The detail is more interesting. As J.G. Frazer put it:

The worship of the Phrygian Mother of the Gods was adopted by the Romans in 204 BC towards the close of their struggle with Hannibal. For their drooping spirits had been cheered by a prophecy, alleged to be drawn from that convenient farrago of nonsense, the Sibylline Books, that the foreign invader would be driven from Italy if the great Oriental goddess were brought to Rome. Accordingly ambassadors were despatched to her sacred city Pessinus in Phrygia … It was the middle of April when the goddess arrived, and she went to work at once. For the harvest that year was such as had not been seen for many a long day, and in the very next year Hannibal and his veterans embarked for Africa.

It is difficult to see just why Frazer is so hard on the Sybilline Books; after all, by carrying out their prophecy, relief was obtained. But that is not the main issue. I have deliberately left out one sentence in the above quotation: 'The small black stone which embodied the mighty divinity was entrusted to them and conveyed to Rome, where it was received with great respect and installed in the Temple of Victory on the Palatine Hill.' Cybele, the mighty divinity, was almost certainly a meteorite, but not just any meteorite. She was brought from Phrygia: in mythology part of it is called 'Burnt Phrygia'. We must turn to mythology to find out just why Cybele was the goddess of choice to save Rome when it was in dire trouble, with apparitions in the sky. Here is a relevant quotation from Fontenrose:

We have seen that in Nonnos' version of the Typhon myth, Zeus's thunderbolts are either identified with or substituted for his sinews. In another version of the Titan war ... Kampe was killed by Dionysos, who commanded Zeus–Ammon's army against Kronos and the Titans. In this account the Titan war followed the Gigantomachy, and Kampe had a predecessor in Aigis, a frightful earth-born she-monster who breathed forth flames from her mouth. She appeared first in Phrygia and burned up that part of the country that was called Burnt Phrygia. From there she went to the Tauros Mountains of Cilicia and to the Lebanon Range of Syria, burning up all the forests as she went.

So Cybele, apparently an extraterrestrial object, was brought from Phrygia which has associations which would do justice to the Tunguska event. In fact, other references to the Typhon myth are even more specific:

Typhon's combat with Zeus ... [was] ... sometimes placed in Lydia or Phrygia: that part of Lydia and Phrygia called Katakekaumené (Burnt Lydia and Burnt Phrygia) was said to have been scorched either by Zeus's thunderbolts or by Typhon's fiery breath during the combat ...

Thus the Sybilline Books' 'goddess of choice' may well have been exactly the right goddess to call on in the circumstances. What better goddess to bring relief from possible extraterrestrial bombardment that a goddess who is herself an extraterrestrial object with catastrophic associations? Perhaps there is even more to the myths than one could reasonably expect. Note how Aigis burns up all the forests as far as 'the Lebanon range of Syria'. Courty's 'anomalous petrological assemblage' in Syria may not be so unexpected after all. But, again, there is more. These myths refer to the battle between Zeus and the 'dragon/monster' Typhon. Another god who battles a dragon/monster is Apollo who kills Python. The similarity between the two myths has often been noted. But Python was an enormous serpent which crawled forth from the slime left by the waters of the Flood (Usher date 2349 BC) and Apollo, who killed him, was present at the fall of, and indeed sent plague against, Troy (twelfth century BC). Thus an excursion triggered by mention of the goddess Cybele's arrival in Rome in 204 BC provides tenuous mythological links between events around three of the original Irish narrowest-ring dates. It turns out that 2345 BC, 1628 BC, 1159 BC, 207 BC and AD 540 really may be 'marker dates' after all – marked by extraterrestrial visitations, after the style of Clube and Napier's 'cosmic swarms'.

APPENDIX 8

MAKING SENSE OF THE GRAIL?

We have got to the point where we know, or think we know, that there was a close pass comet around AD 540 and perhaps others at dates already given. We now want to know if there is a description of such an event in mythology because there does not seem to be one in conventional history. We have already seen that Arthurian legend and some Celtic mythology seems to fit pretty well with the overall scenario, indeed, it provides at least some of the tone of the argument for an extraterrestrial dimension to the sixth-century events. It turns out that R. S. Loomis can supply us with the answer we need. Loomis was a major scholar of Celtic and Arthurian myth and among his works are two books, *Celtic Myth* and *Arthurian Romance*, published in 1927 and *The Grail*, published in 1963. Loomis makes a detailed analysis of the links between the main players in both the early Irish stories and their Welsh and Arthurian descendants. There is no doubt that Lug, the bright god who comes up in the West, must represent a comet. Cuchulinn is a re-birth of Lug. We have already seen that Tolstoy sees Merlin as either Lug or a priest of Lug; Loomis goes further and sees Arthur as the equivalent of Cuchulinn, the son of Lug.

However, the real progress comes when we look at the Grail legend. The Grail is a major motif associated with Arthurian tradition and people argue over whether it is a cup, a bowl, a meteorite, or just a concept. Many believe that it may be the cup used by Christ at the last supper and/or the cup used by Joseph of Arimathea to catch the blood of Christ at the crucifixion. One of Loomis' interesting comments is 'Wolfram von Eschenbach, author of *Parzival*, declared flatly that the Grail was a stone, much to the bewilderment of scholars.' Having seen that comment, the revelation comes when we examine the context of the Grail, namely the castle of the Fisher King. The main points are as follows: A standard motif is that the hero, Perceval, visits the castle of the Fisher King, the Grail castle, and sees a beautiful damsel carrying the Grail in her hands, the Grail giving out a brilliant light. Loomis gives us the alternatives:

It may be borne through a castle hall by a beautiful damsel; or it may float through the air in Arthur's palace, veiled in white samite...

So, we have a bright, veiled, object which moves through the air.

In the Grail Castle we also have a white lance from the tip of which a drop of red blood runs down. This lance is a highly important object. Loomis links the Irish tale of Conn's visit to the palace of Lug with Perceval's visit to the Grail castle, and says this:

> *Lug's spear was one of the four chief treasures of the Tuatha De Danann, the Irish gods.... one might expect to see it in Lug's mansion. What better explanation is there for the functionless lance in the Fisher King's castle? Later Chrétien informs us that it will destroy the whole realm of Logres (England) – a prophecy which accords with the origin of the lance in the spear of Lug, noted for its destructiveness:*

Even in late sources such as Malory's *Morte D'Arthur*, it is this lance which is used to deliver the Dolorous Stroke wherein the castle falls down. Loomis links the Grail castle with Celtic fortresses and generalises this into the similarity between the Grail castle and the Otherworld fortress of Curoi. But Curoi is Lug son of Lug, just as Cuchulinn is Lug son of Lug. So, there is a link to Curoi's fortress. But, the key that Loomis gives us is:

> *The castle of the Grail, then, is an Irish Otherworld fortress, and in a sense, Curoi's fortress. Again we have seen that Curoi's fortress, which revolved every night was really the sky....The Grail Temple was round. The dome was covered with blue sapphire, strewn with carbuncles which shone like the sun...*

So, when the brilliant, veiled, Grail floats through Arthur's castle or the Grail castle or the Fisher King's castle or Curoi's castle, it is floating through the sky. We also know that the associated lance, which is Lug's fiery spear, delivers the Dolorous Stroke or Blow. When that happens there is noise, mist earthquake and the country is laid waste – the whole 'Wasteland' concept. As Loomis puts it:

> *His (Lug's) approach is thus described "They saw a great mist all round, so that they knew not where they went because of the greatness of the darkness; and they heard the noise of a horseman approaching. The horseman (Lug) let fly three throws of a spear at them."*

All that is now needed it to add in Cuchulinn (Lug son of Lug) and his paroxysm which is almost certainly the description of the auroral display at the comet's close approach. So, putting that together, the Grail which is a bright object in the sky with a veiled appearance (a comet) is evident just before Lug's spear delivers the Dolorous Blow which causes the mist, the earthquake and the wasteland. QED there is a direct though disguised description in Arthurian legend and Celtic mythology of a close approach comet and its effects.

As always with this story, there is more. It turns out that Wolfram's Grail was wafted to earth by some of the angels which had remained neutral during Lucifer's rebellion. This is the meteorite version of the Grail, the *Lapis ex Celis* (stone from heaven) and links back through Lucifer to Revelation and the fall of the star Wormwood. But, of course, the story has earlier Irish, and then Welsh, roots. The original Grail was the Cauldron of the great god Dagda which came into Ireland with the Danaans; in Welsh legend Bran the Blessed obtained it from Ireland. Worth recording here is its relationship with the reputedly sixth century Welsh bard Taliesin. In outline it goes as follows (based on T. W. Rolleston's *Myths and Legends of the Celtic Race*).

The witch Ceridwen in attempting to brew a 'potion of knowledge' for her ill-favoured son Avagddu, sets Gwion Bach to stir the cauldron (Dagda's cauldron) for a year and a day in order to produce three magical drops. Unfortunately towards the end of the production the three drops intended for Avagddu end up on the finger of Gwion who swallows them and gains supernatural insight. Ceridwen, in a rage, chases Gwion who transmutes into a hare, a fish and ultimately a grain of wheat. Ceridwen transmutes variously into a greyhound, an otter and a black hen and swallows Gwion in his wheaty guise. Nine months later she bears him as an infant, places him in a leather bag and casts him into the ocean. Rather like Sargon and Moses, he washes up and is found. When the bag is opened the finders exclaim 'Behold a radiant brow' which in Welsh is Taliesin; 'Taliesin be he called'. So now we have a Lug-like bard called Taliesin, who is thought to be sixth century, who ends up at Arthur's court, which is also sixth century. When asked, Taliesin explains who he is and where he came from in what Geoffrey Ashe, in *The Quest for Arthur's Britain*, calls '... a long and baffling rigmarole. It looks like a riddle, and has been so construed by Robert Graves...' The poem contains the following lines, though I have re-ordered them here for maximum effect:

> *My original country is the region of the summer stars;*
> *I was in the court of Dön before the birth of Gwydion.*
> [Dön is the Irish mother-goddess Dana whose son Gwydion is equivalent to Arthur]
> *I have been in Asia with Noah in the ark,*
> *I have seen the destruction of Sodom and Gomorrah.*
> *I strengthened Moses through the waters of Jordan;*
> *I am now come here to the remnant of Troia.*
> [Referring to the traditional origin of the Britons in Troy]
> *I was in Canaan when Absalom was slain*

I was with my Lord in the highest sphere,
On the fall of Lucifer into the depth of hell;
I shall be until the day of doom on the face of the earth;

It is almost unbelievable (a riddle?) that a reputedly sixth century bard, who places himself at Arthur's palace, manages in a single poem to claim his presence at most of the main events in this book – the Flood, Sodom and Gomorrah, the Exodus, the happenings at the time of David (Absalom was David's son who died before him), Revelation and Doomsday – and to get in a mention of Troy. This is Taliesin who obtained his supernatural insight from Dagda's cauldron, the Grail; who is actually named for his radiant brow. The final icing is that while he was singing this poem 'a great storm of wind arose, and the castle shook with the force of it' – Arthur's castle, as we have seen, is certainly the sky. It may not be so surprising after all that Arthur's traditional death date is around AD 540. The only remaining question is whether there has been just one close-approach comet, or several, in the last 5000 years. The candidate dates are 2354 BC, 1628 BC, 1159 BC, 208 BC, 44 BC and AD 540.

Interestingly, Geoffrey Ashe got pretty close to the heart of the matter in his book *King Arthur's Avalon*. He put it as follows:

...were the romances purely fantastic; or did they reflect anything that actually happened or could happen? Some of them assert that the Grail finally vanished in Arthur's day and that no man has seen it since. On the other hand, the passages describing its apparitions are often so curt, so cryptic, so allusive, that they have the air of being hints at matters known to the author and to some of his readers but not described. As Sebastian Evans said: 'We feel as we read that the words employed are intended to convey some deeper meaning than the fiction bears on the face of it... It is also a secret written in cipher... Throughout, there is a continual suggestion of hidden meaning...'

I think it just possible that we now know what the hidden message might be.

GLOSSARY

airbursts – objects from space are moving so rapidly that most explode upon hitting the Earth's atmosphere; only solid stone or nickel-iron objects, or very large cometary fragments, survive to reach the ground

annulus –here, a ring of dust and debris left in the orbit of a dead comet; in the case of an Earth-crossing comet, the annulus of debris may pose a hazard and produce collisions with this planet

asteroid – an inert rocky or nickel-iron object metres to kilometres in diameter, orbiting within the solar system; up to 2000 such objects (diam. greater than 1 km) are believed to be in Earth-crossing orbits: these are called Apollo asteroids

Atlantis – legendary cradle of civilization mentioned by Plato; believed, by some, to have existed in the Atlantic and been destroyed in some ancient cataclysm; the destruction of Santorini has been suggested as the origin of the legend

aurora – beautiful, moving, luminous displays seen in the night sky; caused by interaction between the solar wind and the Earth's magnetic field; main colours green and crimson

back compute – see retro-calculation

Bermuda Triangle – area of the Atlantic Ocean off south-east Florida, associated with the sometimes mysterious disappearance of ships and aeroplanes and the appearance of mysterious lights

bolide – a large, abnormally bright, meteor is a fireball: an exploding fireball is called a bolide

bombardment event – here, an environmental downturn brought about by multiple extraterrestrial impacts on the Earth's atmosphere, loading the atmosphere with dust/debris; most likely source being one of Victor Clube's and Bill Napier's cosmic swarms

bottom simulating reflector – marine seismic reflection profiles often show an anomalous bottom-simulating reflection (BSR) below the actual sea-bed; it is inferred that this is caused by a layer of gas hydrate within the deposits

calibrated dates – radiocarbon age determinations which have been converted to calendar ranges by the use of a tree-ring-based correction curve

calibration – to compare against some known standard; the radiocarbon dating method was calibrated by measuring the radiocarbon ages of wood samples dated exactly by dendrochronology

calibration wiggles – the curve which shows the relationship between tree-ring age and radiocarbon age has both short and long-term fluctuations; the short-term variations are termed 'wiggles'

cambium – the layer of dividing cells immediately underneath the bark of a tree

catastrophist – someone who believes in, or is comfortable with the concept of, major catastrophes affecting mankind

Celtic Sea – area of the Atlantic Ocean south of Ireland and south-west of Britain

clathrates – *see* gas hydrates

climatology – here, study aimed at reconstructing actual climate records such as temperature or rainfall

conjunction – where several planets come close together

cosmic radiation – galactic cosmic rays are high-speed subatomic particles that enter the solar system in equal numbers from all directions; solar cosmic rays are emitted by the Sun; large numbers continuously strike the Earth

cosmic swarm – Clube's and Napier's term for multiple Tunguska-class impacts occurring in a short interval of time

crannog – an artificial island constructed in a lake, presumably for defensive purposes

crater lake – here, a lake in a volcanic crater

Dark Ages – periods for which almost no historical records survive; the best known are the Greek Dark Age c. 1200–800 BC and the Dark Ages c. AD 400–800

degassed remnant – the rocky, inert, core of a comet left when most or all of the volatile materials have 'boiled' away in repeated passages close to the Sun

dendrochronology – an all-embracing term for chronological studies involving tree-ring patterns, includes building regional chronologies and dating timbers

diffuse porous – where the vertical vessels within a growth ring are small and scattered throughout the ring

dragon – mythical winged monster normally capable of breathing fire; the enemy of various gods and heroes; equated with Satan; apparently inspired by incoming fireballs with smoky trails exploding with devastating effects

dry fog – term normally used by vulcanologists to describe a persistent, high-altitude, layer which reduces sunlight at the Earth's surface; normally assumed to be caused by volcanic dust and acid droplets; can also be introduced from outside as cometary material

dust veil – same as dry fog; indicates loading of the atmosphere by dust or droplets

earth-crosser – any solid object whose path through space causes it to cross the path of the Earth; repeated crossings through time increase the chance of a collision

environmental trigger – plagues do not just happen, it is reasonable to assume that some environmental event with resultant famines and/or population dislocation will normally trigger the spread of the disease

extraterrestrial – used here to denote anything that comes from outside the Earth and interacts with the Earth

fireball – term normally used to describe an object from space burning up in the atmosphere; can also relate, in a large impact, to descriptions of the actual explosion of the object, for example, Tunguska

fly-by – here, describing the situation where an extraterrestrial object passes sufficiently close to the earth to be a cause of concern, without actually impacting

gas hydrates – under certain conditions of temperature and pressure, for example some hundreds of metres down in the ocean floor, a water-ice lattice can store large quantities of gas such as methane or hydrogen sulphide; estimates suggest up to 10,000 gigatons of methane exist in this form world-wide

grids, of chronologies – a series of individual site chronologies covering a geographical region e.g. Ireland has a grid of nine modern oak chronologies

Holocene – the current, post-glacial, geological epoch; normally thought of as the last 10,000 years

Hyksos period – the Hyksos (literally 'ruler of a foreign land') were Syro-Palestinian invaders who ruled Egypt during the Second Intermediate Period, between the Middle and New Kingdoms (c. seventeenth century BC)

ice cores – vertical cores extracted from ice sheets allowing examination of the annual layers of compressed snowfall

impactor – here, an object that impacts the Earth or its atmosphere

Intermediate Periods – periods of disorder separating the Egyptian Old, Middle and New Kingdoms; it is as reasonable to assume that such episodes could as easily have been precipitated by environmental downturns, as by invasions or political upheaval

inundation – a significant flood event; in a coastal region an inundation could be due to a major storm surge or a tsunami

iridium – element relatively scarce on Earth but quite common in asteroid material from space; a significant layer is evident world-wide at the K/T boundary, 65 million years ago, when an object some 25 km in diameter impacted the Earth, assisting in the demise of the dinosaurs and more than 50 per cent of the marine invertebrate species existing at that time

kiloton impact – an impact explosion with the equivalent force of 1,000 tons of conventional high explosive

lake dwelling – a house erected on poles in the margins of a lake, presumably for security

ley lines – invisible straight lines running cross-country; believed by some to be lines of 'force' influencing the siting of major monuments at all periods

linear earthwork – a cross-country, earthen, bank/ditch system presumably designed as a boundary between groups; the Great Wall of China could be thought of as an extreme example

magma – the complex mixture of crystals, rock fragments, liquid, and gases present within the magma chamber deep below a volcano; source of igneous rocks

magmatic water – water which comes out of the magma chamber of a volcano during an explosive eruption

Mandate of Heaven – ancient concept whereby the ruling king/dynasty could only rule while they 'looked after their people'; failure to do so resulting in the 'withdrawal' of the Mandate; concept could be explained by dust-veils causing famine and political breakdown

marginal – any environment which is close to the limit for survival purposes

marker dates – if significant global downturns occurred in the past, then the dates of those downturns should recur in different places, again and again; such dates would be marker dates

medieval period – from c. AD 400 to c. AD 1600

megaton impact – an impact explosion with the equivalent force of one million tons of conventional high explosive

meteors – the streak of light produced when interplanetary particles burn up as they enter the Earth's atmosphere at high speed

myth – traditional narrative which usually involves supernatural or heroic characters; encapsulates deep-rooted ideas on natural or social phenomena

Nazca lines – massive geometric and animal shapes marked out in Peru's desert strip, west of the Andes; their scale has suggested to some that they were drawn to signal to a sky god

Neolithic, the – New Stone Age, marked by the shift to agriculture; new technology sees polished-stone axes and first manufacture of pottery; first occurrence circa 6000 BC; arrives Britain and Ireland c. 4000 BC

Oort cloud – J. H. Oort postulated that the Sun is surrounded by a very distant cloud of cometary material; individual comets are occasionally disturbed from the cloud through the effects of nearby stars or interstellar materials, and move towards the inner solar system

outgassing – the concept of large quantities of gas escaping from the layers of gas hydrate in the ocean bed, or for the layers of free gas observed to exist below the layers of gas hydrate

palaeoecologist – one who studies aspects of ancient ecology

palaeoenvironmentalist – one who studies past environmental change

plate boundaries – the Earth's lithosphere is divided into a number of rigid plates floating on the viscous underlayer of mantle; interactions at the edges of the major plates, for example the rim of the Pacific, produce earthquake and volcanic activity

polychrome pottery – pottery with surface decoration in several different colours

population dislocation – large-scale movement of humans normally resulting from failure of food supply, or fear of non-understood natural catastrophe

prehistoric – before written records i.e. before 3000 BC in Egypt or before AD 550 in Ireland

prodigies – here, something marvellous; especially events outside the ordinary course of nature

Pueblo – an Amerindian settlement in the American Southwest or Mexico

quasi-annual – any system which is essentially annual in character but where the records may contain errors; replicated tree-ring series are annual, ice cores or varve sequences are quasi-annual

Reed Sea – although traditionally at the Exodus the 'Red Sea' is supposed to have parted, it is believed that the original meaning was 'Sea of Reeds' probably indicating an extensive papyrus swamp in the vicinity of Egypt's present-day Lake Ballah

regeneration phase – where numerous trees start growing simultaneously due to changed conditions or reduction of human pressure on land

relative dates – dates a known number of years apart, but where the exact calendar dates are not known; as in tree-ring dates associated with a floating chronology

replication – here, where ring patterns or master chronologies are checked against each other to ensure absolute calendrical accuracy

retro calculation – loose term for back-computation of astronomical configurations or eclipses

ring porous – where the vertical vessels within a growth ring are noticeably larger at the start of the annual ring

Rosetta Stone – famous engraved block of black basalt bearing inscriptions in Greek and Egyptian that supplied the key to the decipherment of the Egyptian hieroglyphic script

seasoning – where timbers are left to dry and stabilize before use; not a significant factor in most ancient contexts

seiche – water movement in a lake induced by tectonic movement, i.e. earthquake

seismic sea wave – *see* tsunami

seismograph – sensitive instrument for recording earthquakes; also detects nuclear tests and extraterrestrial impacts

signature patterns – a particular configuration of wide and narrow rings that occurs in every tree in a region, across a specific span of years

solar cycles – quasi-regular oscillations in the behaviour of the Sun; the most well known being the 11-year sunspot cycle

stele – a stele is an upright stone slab or shaft that, in ancient times, served as a monument, memorial, or marker and was generally inscribed

stratosphere – the layer of the earth's atmosphere above the troposphere and below the mesosphere, i.e. between 9–16 km and 50 km; dust and acid injected into the stratosphere by volcanoes stays up for relatively long periods; material injected into the mesosphere and stratosphere from above will tend to reside there even longer

sub-fossil – trees which have died and been buried naturally and which, if left long enough, would have eventually become fossilized as lignite, coal or stone

sunspots – dark blemishes on the disc of the sun, indicating notable activity on the sun

tephra – here, particles of volcanic glass blown out by volcanic eruptions and carried long distances in the atmosphere or stratosphere

timberline – here, a line at high altitude above which trees cannot grow; dead stumps above the existing timberline indicate warmer conditions in the past

tracer – here, an identifiable chemical signal

trackway – normally a constructed timber path (narrow) or road (broad) across a wet area

transducer – here, an object which converts an electromagnetic signal into an acoustic signal; an extreme example is where certain people can pick up radio signals through the metallic fillings in their teeth

trauma – here, a significantly bad experience for trees and/or humans *tree-ring chronology* – a year-by-year record of mean tree growth, for a particular species in a particular geographic region

troposphere – the lowest 9–16 km of the earth's atmosphere; within the troposphere volcanic dust and acid wash out rapidly

tsunami – earthquakes or impacts over the ocean produce 'seismic sea waves' out at sea, as these waves approach land their height can be amplified by 40 times (an impact creating a five-metre deep-water wave could generate a tsunami 200 metres high); wave speed is generally about 500 km/h (300 mph)

Ulaid – tribal grouping likely to have been located in the north-east of Ireland

Usher – Archbishop Usher of Armagh, famous for his timescale of the Old Testament which starts in 4004 BC

wiggle match – if several stratified organic samples are dated by radiocarbon, it is possible to match the configuration of dates to the wiggles on the radiocarbon calibration curve, thus providing a link to the actual calendar age of the samples

REFERENCES

Allen, G. 1901, *The Evolution of the Idea of God*, Grant Richards, London

Alley, R.E., Meese, D.A., Shuman, C.A., Gow, A.J., Taylor, K.C., Grootes, P.M., White, J.W.C., Ram, M., Waddington, E.D., Mayewski, P.A., and Zielinski, G.A. 1993, 'Abrupt Increase in Greenland Snow Accumulation at the End of the Younger Dryas Event', *Nature 362*, 527–9

Baatz, D. 1977, 'Bemerkungen zur Jahrringchronologie der Romischen Zeit', *Germania 55*, 173–9

Bailey, M.E. 1995, 'Recent Results in Cometary Astronomy: Implications for the Ancient Sky', *Vistas in Astronomy 39* (4), 647–71

Bailey, M.E., Clube, S.V.M., and Napier, W.M. 1990, *The Origin of Comets,* Pergamon Press, London

Baillie, M.G.L. 1989, 'Do Irish Bog Oaks Date the Shang Dynasty?', *Current Archaeology 117*, 310–13

Baillie, M.G.L. 1991, 'Marking in Marker Dates; Towards an Archaeology with Historical Precision', *World Archaeology 23*, 233–43

Baillie, M.G.L. 1991, 'Suck-In and Smear: Two Related Chronological Problems for the 1990s', *Journal of Theoretical Archaeology 2*, 12–16

Baillie, M.G.L. 1994, 'Dendrochronology Raises Questions about the Nature of the AD 536 Dust-veil Event', *The Holocene 4*, 212–17

Baillie, M.G.L. 1995, Patrick, 'Comets and Christianity', *Emania 13*, 69–78

Baillie, M.G.L. 1995, *A Slice Through Time: Dendrochronology and precision dating.* Routledge, London

Baillie, M.G.L. 1996. 'Extreme Environmental Events and the Linking of the Tree-ring and Ice-core Records', in J.S. Dean, D.M. Meko and T.W. Swetnam, eds., *Tree Rings, Environment and Humanity: Proceedings of the International Conference,* Tucson, Arizona, 17–21 May 1994. Tucson, *Radiocarbon,* 703–11

Baillie, M.G.L., Hillam, J., Briffa, K.M., and Brown, D.M. 1985, 'Re-Dating the English Art-Historical Tree-Ring Chronologies,' *Nature 315*, 317–19

Baillie, M.G.L. and Munro, M.A.R. 1988, 'Irish Tree-rings, Santorini and Volcanic Dust-veils', *Nature 332*, 344–6

Barker, M. *The Great Angel: A Study of Israel's Second God*, SPCK, London

Barnett, R.D. 1969, 'The Sea Peoples', in *The Cambridge Ancient History, vol. 2*, ch. XXVIII

Barnish, S.J.B. 1992, *The Variae of Magnus Aurelius Cassiodorus Senator*, Liverpool University Press

Baxter, J. and Adams, T. 1976, *The Fire Came By*, Macdonald and Jane's, London

Beaumont, W.C. 1932, *The Mysterious Comet*, Rider and Co., London

Beaumont, W.C. 1946, *The Riddle of Prehistoric Britain*, Rider and Co., London

Becker, B. 1985, 'Die Absolute Chronologie der Pfahlbauten Nordlich der Alpen im Jahrringkalender Mitteleuropas', in Becker, B. et al. (eds), *Dendrochronologie in der Ur-und-Fruhgeschichte*, Schweizerische Gesellschaft fur Ur-und-Fruhgeschichte, Basle

Becker, B. and Schirmer, W. 1977, 'Palaeoecological Study on the Holocene Valley Development of the River Main, Southern Germany', *Boreas 6*, 303–21 (see also Baillie 1995)

Beegle, D.M. 1972, *Moses, The Servant of Yahweh*, William B. Eerdmans, Michigan

Betancourt, J.L., Dean, J.S. and Hull, H.M. 1986, 'Prehistoric Long-Distance Transport of Construction Beams, Chaco Canyon, New Mexico'. *American Antiquity 51*(2), 370–5

Bietak, M. 1996, *Avaris: the Capital of the Hyksos*, British Museum Press, London

Billamboz, A. 1992, Tree-Ring Analysis from an Archaeodendrochronological Perspective. The Structural Timber from the South West German Lake Dwellings, *Lundqua*, 34, 34–40

Bonde, N. 1994, 'The Dating of the Norwegian Viking Age Ship Burials. A Successful Norwegian-Danish Research Project', *Nationalmuseets Arbejdsmark*, 128–48

Bonde, N. and Crumlin-Pedersen, O. 1990, 'The Dating of Wreck 2, the Longship, from Skuldelev', Denmark, *NewsWARP 7*, 3–6

Bousset, W. 1896, *The AntiChrist Legend*, Hutchinson and Co., London

Bower, A. 1750, *The History of the Popes*, London

Branston, B. 1950, *Gods of the North*, Thames and Hudson, London

Briffa, K.R., Bartholin, T.S., Eckstein, D. Jones, P.D., Karlen, W., Schweingruber, F.H. and Zetterberg, P. 1990, 'A 1400-Year Tree-Ring Record of Summer Temperatures in Fennoscandia', *Nature 346*, 434–9

Briffa, K.R., Jones, P.D., Bartholin, T.S., Eckstein, D., Schweingruber, F.H.

Karlen,W., Zetterberg, P. and Eronen, M. 1992, 'Fennoscandian Summers from AD 500: Temperature Changes on Short and Long Timescales', *Climate Dynamics 7*, 111–19

Brown, see Pilcher et al. 1995

Bruins, H.J. and van der Plicht, J. 1996, 'The Exodus Enigma,' *Nature 382*, 213–14

Buckland, P.C., Dugmore, A.J. and Edwards, K.J. 1997, 'Bronze Age Myths? Volcanic Activity and Human Response in the Mediterranean and North Atlantic Regions', *Antiquity 71*, 581–93

Bulfinch, T 1993, *The Golden Age of Myth and Legend; the Classical Mythology of the Ancient World*, Wordsworth Editions Ltd, Hertfordshire

Burgess, C. 1985, 'Population, Climate and Upland Settlement', *British Archaeological Reports* (British Series) *143*, 195–229

Burgess, C. 1989, 'Volcanoes, Catastrophe and Global Crisis of the Late 2nd Millennium BC', *Current Archaeology 117*, vol. X, no. 10, 325–9

Caprio, A.C. and Baisan, C.H. 1992, 'Multi-millennial Tree-ring Chronologies from Foxtail Pine in the Southern Sierras of California,' Abstract in *Bulletin of the Ecological Society of America 73*, 133.

Cassiodorus, see Barnish 1992

Chambers, R.W. 1921, *Beowulf*, Cambridge University Press

Chang, K-C. 1980, *Shang Civilization*, Yale University Press, London

Clube, S.V.M. and Napier, B. 1990, *The Cosmic Winter*, Blackwell, Oxford

Cosmas, see McCrindle 1897

Courty, M.A. 1997, 'Causes and Effects of the 2350 BC Middle East Anomaly Evidenced by Micro-Debris Fallout, Surface Combustion and Soil Explosion',*Abstract O–5*, Second SIS Cambridge Conference on Natural *Catastrophes During Bronze Age Civilizations*, Fitzwilliam College, 11–13 July 1997

Dalfes, H.N., Kukla, G. and Weiss, H. (eds), 1996, *Third Millennium BC Climate Change and Old World Collapse*, Springer-Verlag, Berlin

Davis, E.N. 1990, 'A Storm in Egypt During the Reign of Ahmose', in Hardy, D.A. (ed.), *Thera and the Aegean World* III, vol. 3, The Thera Foundation, London, 232–5

Day, D. 1995, *The Quest for King Arthur*, De Agostini Editions, London

De Paor, L. 1993, *Saint Patrick's World*, Four Courts Press, Dublin

De Visser, W.M.W. 1913, *The Dragon in China and Japan*, Johannes Müller, Amsterdam

Douglass, A.E. 1919, *Climatic Cycles and Tree Growth I*, Carnegie Institute, Washington

Douglass, A.E. 1938, 'Estimated Tree-Ring Chronology: 450–600 AD', *Tree-Ring Bulletin 4*, 8

Drake, M. 1968, 'The Irish Demographic Crisis of 1740–41', in T. Moody, (ed.), *Historical Studies VI*, Dublin, June 1965, Routledge and Kegan Paul, London, 101–24

Drews, R. 1993, *The End of the Bronze Age: Changes in Warfare and the Catastrophe ca. 1200 BC*, Princeton University Press

Eckstein, D., Wazny, T., Bauch, J. and Klein, P. 1986, 'New Evidence for the Dendrochronological Dating of Netherlandish Paintings', *Nature 320*, 465–6

Ellis-Davidson, H.R. 1971, *Gods and Myths of Northern Europe*, Penguin

Expositors Bible Commentary, see Gaebelein 1990

Ferguson, C.W. 1969, 'A 7104-Year Annual Tree-Ring Chronology for Bristlecone Pine, Pinus Aristata, from the White Mountains, California', *Tree-Ring Bulletin 29*, 2–29

Ferguson, C.W. and Graybill, D.A. 1983, 'Dendrochronology of Bristlecone Pine: a Progress Report', *Radiocarbon 25*, 287–8

Fletcher, see Baillie et al. 1985

Fontenrose, J. 1959, *Python: a Study of Delphic Myth and Its Origins*, University of California Press, Berkeley

Forsyth, P.Y. 1988, 'In the Wake of Etna, 44 BC', *Classical Antiquity 7*, (1), 49–57

Forsyth, P.Y. 1990, 'Call for Cybele', *The Ancient History Bulletin* 4.4, 75–8

Frazer, J.G. 1930, *The Golden Bough*, Macmillan, London

Gaebelein, F.E. 1990, *The Expositor's Bible Commentary, Vol. 2*, Zondervan Publishing House, Michigan

Garmonsway, G.N. 1962, *The Anglo-Saxon Chronicle*, Dent and Sons, London

Geoffrey of Monmouth, see Thorpe 1966

Gibbon, see Low 1960

Gildas, see Winterbotham 1978

Goodrich, N.L. 1988, Merlin, Harper Perennial, New York

Grant, M.E. 1995 *The dating and significance of Pinus sylvestris L. macrofossil remains from Whixall Moss, Shropshire: palaeoecological and modern comparative analyses'*. Unpublished PhD thesis, University of Keele

Grattan, J.P. and Gilbertson, D.D. 1995, 'Acid-loading from Icelandic Tephra Falling on Acidified Ecosystems as a Key to Understanding Archaeological Environmental Stress in Northern and Western Britain', *Journal of Archaeological Science 21*, 851–9

Graves, R. and Patai, R. 1989, *Hebrew Myths. The Book of Genesis*, Arena, London

Grolier Multimedia Encyclopedia, 1993, for Apple Macintosh

Groves, cited in Hillam 1992

Hall, V.A., Pilcher, J.R. and McCormac, F.G. 1994, 'Icelandic Volcanic Ash and the Mid-Holocene Scots Pine (Pinus sylvestris) Decline in the North of Ireland; no Correlation'. *The Holocene 4,* 79–83

Hamilton, F.J. and Brooks, E.W., (eds.), 1899, *The Syriac Chronicle Known as That of Zacharias of Mytilene,* Methuen and Co., London

Hammer, C.U. 1984, Traces of Icelandic Eruptions in the Greenland Ice Sheet, *Jökull,* 34, 51–65

Hammer, C.U. and Clausen, H.B. 1990, 'The Precision of Ice-Core Dating', in Hardy, D.A. (ed.), *Thera and the Aegean World III, vol. 3,* The Thera Foundation, London, 174–8

Hammer, C.U., Clausen, H.B. and Dansgaard,W. 1980, 'Greenland Ice Sheet Evidence of Post-Glacial Volcanism and its Climatic Impact', *Nature 288,* 230–5

Hammer, C.U., Clausen, H.B., Friedrich, W.L. and Tauber, H. 1987, 'The Minoan Eruption of Santorini in Greece Dated to 1645 bBC?,' *Nature 328,* 517–19

Hancock, G. 1992, *The Sign and the Seal,* Heinemann, London

Handler, P. 1989, 'The Effect of Volcanic Aerosols on Global Climate', *Journal of Volcanology and Geothermal Research 37,* 233–49

Hankey, V. and Warren, P. 1974, 'The Absolute Chronology of the Aegean Late Bronze Age', *Bulletin of the Institute of Classical Studies, 21,* 142–52

Härke, H. 1991, 'Bede's Borrowed Eclipses', *Rastar (Newsletter of the Reading Astronomical Society),* Oct., 12

Herrin, J. 1987, *The Formation of Christendom,* Fontana Press, London

Hillam, J. 1987, 'Dendrochronology – 20 Years On', *Current Archaeology 9,* (12), 358–63

Hillam, J. 1992, The Dating of Archaeological Sites in the United Kingdom, *Lundqua* 34, 146–9

Hillam, J., Groves, C.M., Brown, D.M., Baillie, M.G.L., Coles, J.M. and Coles, B.J. 1990, 'Dendrochronology of the English Neolithic', *Antiquity 64,* 210–20

Hollstein, E. 1980, *MittelEuropaische Eichenchronologie,* Phillip Von Zabern, Mainz am Rhein

Horrox, R. 1994, *The Black Death,* Manchester University Press

Hoyle, F. and Wickramasinghe, C. 1993, *Our Place in the Cosmos,* Phoenix, London

Huber, P.J. 1977, 'Early Cuneiform Evidence for the Existence of the Planet Venus', in D. Goldsmith ed., *Scientists Confront Velikovsky,* Cornell University Press, Ithaca, 117–44

Huber, B. and Giertz, V. 1969, 'Our 1000 Year Oak Chronology', *Conference*

Report of the Austrian Academy of Science 178, 32–42

Hughes, M.K. and Brown, P.M. 1992 'Drought Frequency in Central California since 101 BC' Recorded in Giant Sequoia Tree-Rings. *Climate Dynamics 6*, 161–7

James, P.J. 1991, *Centuries of Darkness*, Jonathan Cape, London

James, P.J. 1996 'Updating the Centuries of Darkness', *British Archaeology 13*, April 1996, 8–9

Jeffreys, E., Jeffreys, M. and Scott, R. 1986, 'The Chronicle of John Malalas', *Byzantina Australiensia*, (Australian Assoc. Byzantine Studies) 4, Melbourne

Johnsen, S.J., Clausen, H.B., Dansgaard, W., Fuhrer, K., Gundestrup, N., Hammer, C.U. Iversen, P., Jouzel, J., Stauffer, B. and Steffensen, J.P. 1992, 'Irregular Glacial Interstadials Recorded in a New Greenland Ice-Core', *Nature 359*, 311–13

Keay, C.S.L. 1993, 'Progress in Explaining the Mysterious Sounds Produced by Very Large Meteor Fireballs', *Journal of Scientific Exploration 7* (4), 337–54

Keay, C.S.L. 1995, 'Continued Progress in Electrophonic Fireball Investigations', *Earth, Moon and Planets 68*, 361–8

Kelly, S. and Rogers, R. 1995, *Saints Preserve Us!* Robson Books, London

Kelly, P.M. and Sear, C.B. 1985, 'The Climate Impact of Explosive Volcanic Eruptions', in *Third Conference on Climate Variations and Symposium on Contemporary Climate: 1850–2100*, American Meteorological Society, Boston, Mas., 178–9

Keys, D. 1989, 'Fire Stones Support Catastrophe Theory', *The Independent*, London (14 Jan.), 8

Keys, D. 1994, 'Comet May Have Caused Catastrophe on Earth', *The Independent*, London (25 July), 7

Kitchen, K.A. 1991, 'The Chronology of Ancient Egypt', *World Archaeology 23*, 201–8

Klaeber, Fr. 1950, *Beowulf and the Fight at Finnsburg*, DC Heath and Co., Boston

Klein, P., Mehringer, H. and Bauch, J. 1986, 'Dendrochronological and Wood Biological Investigations on String Instruments', *Holzforschung 40*, 197–203

Kobres, R. 1995, 'The Path of a Comet and Phaëton's Ride', *The World and I, (Feb.)*, 394–405

Krinov, E.L. 1960, *Principles of Meteoritics*, Pergamon Press, London

Kugler, see Kobres 1995

Kulik, see Krinov 1960 and Baxter and Adams 1976

Kuniholm, P.I. 1990, Archaeological Evidence and Non-Evidence for

Climatic Change, *Phil. Trans. R. Soc. Lond,* A330, 645–55

Kuniholm, P.I. 1996 'The Prehistoric Aegean: Dendrochronological Progress as of 1995', *Acta Archaeologica Supplementum 1,* Randsborg, K. (ed.), *Absolute Chronology: Archaeological Europe 2500–500 BC,* 327–35

Kuniholm, P.I., Kromer, B., Manning, S.W., Newton, M., Latini, C.E. and Bruce, M.J. 1996, 'Anatolian Tree Rings and the Absolute Chronology of the Eastern Mediterranean, 2220–718 BC', *Nature 381,* 780–3

LaMarche, V.C. Jr 1970, 'Frost-Damage Rings in Subalpine Conifers and Their Application to Tree-Ring Dating Problems', The University of British Columbia, Faculty of Forestry, *Bulletin 7,* 99–100

LaMarche, V.C. Jr. and Harlan, T.P. 1973, 'Accuracy of Tree-Ring Dating of Bristlecone Pine for Calibration of the Radiocarbon Time Scale', *Journal of Geophysical Research 78,* 8849–58

LaMarche, V.C. Jr. and Hirschboeck, K.K. 1984, 'Frost Rings in Trees as Records of Major Volcanic Eruptions', *Nature 307,* 121–6

Larson, D.O. and Michaelson, J. 1990, 'Impacts of Climatic Variability and Population Growth on Virgin Branch Anasazi Cultural Developments', *American Antiquity 55,* 227–49.

Legge, J. 1879, *The Sacred Books of China,* Clarendon Press, Oxford

Leuschner, von H.H. and Delorme, A. 1988, 'Tree-Ring Work in Gottingen – Absolute Oak Chronologies Back to 6255 BC', Pact II.5 *Wood and Archaeology,* 123–32

Levy, D.H. 1995, *The Quest for Comets,* Oxford University Press

Low, D.M. 1960, *The Decline and Fall of the Roman Empire (an abridgment),* The Reprint Society, London

McCrindle, J.W. 1897, *The Christian Topography of Cosmas, An Egyptian Monk,* Hakluyt Society, London

MacKie, E.W. 1984, 'A Late Single-Piece Dug-Out Canoe from Loch Doon, Ayrshire', *Glasgow Archaeological Journal 11,* 132–3

Malalas, see Jeffreys et al. 1986

Mandelkehr, M.M. 1983, 'An Integrated Model for an Earthwide Event at 2300 BC'. Part I: *The Archaeological Evidence, S.I.S. Review 5,* 77–95

Manning, S. 1990, 'The Thera Eruption: The Third Congress and the Problem of the Date', *Archaeometry 32,* 1, 91–100

Manning, S.W. 1992, 'Thera, Sulphur, and Climatic Anomalies', *Oxford Journal of Archaeology 11,* 3, 245–53

Manning, S. 1996, 'Dating the Aegean Bronze Age: Without, With, and Beyond, Radiocarbon', *Acta Archaeologica Supplementum 1,* Randsborg, K. (ed.), *Absolute Chronology: Archaeological Europe 2500–500 BC,* 15–37

Masse, W.B. 1995, 'The Celestial Basis of Civilization', *Vistas in Astronomy 39*

(4), 463–77

Matthews, C. 1995, Mabon, 'The Celtic Divine Child', in Stewart, R.J. and Matthews, J. (eds.), *Merlin Through the Ages*, Blandford, London, 299–310

Niddrie, D. 1961, *When the Earth Shook,* The Scientific Book Club, London

Norwich, J.J. 1990, *Byzantium: The Early Centuries*, Penguin, London

Orcel, A., Orcel, C., Danérol, A. and Ramseyer, D. 1992, 'Contribution to the Study of the Neolithic Forest Dynamic. The Example of Delley/Portalban II (CH)', *Lundqua 34*, 242–6

Palmer, see Sparks et al. 1995

Pang, K.D. 1987, 'Extraordinary Floods in Early Chinese History and Their Absolute Dates', *Journal of Hydrology 96,* 139–55

Pang, K.D. 1991, 'The Legacies of Eruption', *The Sciences 31*, (1), 30–3

Pang, K.D. and Chou, H.-H. 1985, 'Three Very Large Volcanic Eruptions in Antiquity and Their Effects on the Climate of the Ancient World', *EOS Transactions, American Geophysical Union 66*, 816

Pang, K.D., Yau, K., Chou, H.H., and Wolff, R. 1988, 'Computer Analysis of Some Ancient Chinese Sunrise Eclipse Records to Determine the Earth's Rotation Rate', *Vistas in Astronomy 31*, 833–47

Pang, K.D., Yau, K. and Chou, H.H. 1995, 'The Earth's Palaeorotation, Postglacial Rebound and Lower Mantle Viscosity from Analysis of Ancient Chinese Eclipse Records', *PAGEOPH 145*, 459–85

Pankenier, D. 1981, Astronomical Dates in Shang and Western Zhou, *Early China 7 (1981–2)*, 18ff

Pankenier, D. 1995, 'Astrological Origins of Chinese Dynastic Ideology', *Vistas in Astronomy 39 (4)*, 503–16

Pearson, G.W., Pilcher, J.R., Baillie, M.G.L., Corbett, D.M. and Qua, F. 1986, 'High-Precision 14-C Measurement of Irish Oaks to Show the Natural 14-C Variations from AD 1840 to 5210 BC', *Radiocarbon 28*, 911–34

Phillips, B. and Guidoboni, E. 1994, *Catalogue of Ancient Earthquakes in the Mediterranean Area up to the 10th Century*, Inst. Naziolale di Geofisca

Pilcher, J.R., Baillie, M.G.L., Brown, D.M., MacSweeney, P.B. and McLawrence, A. 1995, 'Dendrochronology of Sub-Fossil Pine in the North of Ireland', *Journal of Ecology 83*, 665–71

Post, J. 1977, *The Last Great Subsistence Crisis in the Western World,* Johns Hopkins University Press

Post, J. 1985, *Food Shortage, Climatic Variability and Epidemic Disease in Preindustrial Europe*, Cornell University Press

Pyle, D.M. 1990a, 'The Application of Tree-Ring and Ice-Core Studies to the

Dating of the Minoan Eruption', in Hardy, D.A., (ed.), *Thera and the Aegean World III, vol. 3*, The Thera Foundation, London, 167–73

Pyle, D.M. 1990b, 'New Estimates for the Volume of the Minoan Eruption', in Hardy, D.A., (ed.), *Thera and the Aegean World III, vol. 2*, The Thera Foundation, London, 113–21

Rackham, H. 1949, *Pliny, Natural History*, William Heineman, London

Raftery, B. 1990, *Trackways Through Time: Archaeological Investigations on Irish Bog Roads* 1985–89, Headline, Dublin

Raftery, B. 1996, 'Trackway Excavations in the Mountdillon Bogs, Co. Longford, Irish Archaeological Wetland Unit', *Transactions, vol. 3*, Dept. of Archaeology, University College, Dublin

Rampino, M.R. and Self, S. 1992, 'Volcanic Winter and Accelerated Glaciation Following the Toba Super-Eruption', *Nature 359*, 50–2

Rampino, M.R., Self, S. and Stothers, R.B. 1988, 'Volcanic Winters', *Annual Review of Earth Planet Science 16*, 73–99

Renfrew, C. and Bahn, P. 1991, *Archaeology – Theory, Methods and Practise*, Thames and Hudson, London

Roberts, J.J.M. 1993, *Moses, in Grolier Multimedia Encyclopedia*, for Apple Macintosh

Rogers, R. and Yevi, G. 1996, Hydrate Theory Explains Lake Nyos Disaster. *Second International Conference on Natural Gas Hydrates, 2–6 June 1996*, Toulouse, France

Rohl, D.M. 1995, *A Test of Time*, Century, London

Rose, M.R., Dean, J.S. and Robinson, W.J. 1981, *The Past Climate of Arroyo Hondo, New Mexico, Reconstructed from Tree-Rings*, School of American Research Press, New Mexico

Russell, J.B. 1981, *Satan: The Early Christian Tradition*, Cornell University Press, Ithaca

Sagan, C. and Druyan, A. 1985, *Comet*, Michael Joseph, London

Sagan, C. 1977, 'An Analysis of Worlds in Collision', in D. Goldsmith, (ed.), *Scientists Confront Velikovsky*, Cornell University Press, Ithaca, 41–104

Santillana, G. and Dechend, H. von. 1969, *Hamlet's Mill*, Macmillan, London

Sayers, W. 1986 'Mani, Maidi an Nem … Ringing Changes on a Cosmic Motif', *Erin 37*, 99–117

Schulman, see Ferguson 1969

Scuderi, L.A. 1990, 'Tree-Ring Evidence for Climatically Effective Volcanic Eruptions', *Quaternary Research 34*, 67–85

Scuderi, L.A. 1993, 'A 2000-Year Tree-Ring Record of Annual Temperatures in the Sierra Nevada Mountains', *Science 259*, 1433–6

Sear, C.B., Kelly, P.M., Jones, P.D. and Goodess, C.M 1987, 'Global Surface-

Temperature Responses to Major Volcanic Eruptions,' *Nature 330*, 365–7

Snorri, see Santillana and Dechend 1969

Sparks, R.J., Melhuish, W.D., McKee, J.W.A., Ogden, J., Palmer, J.G. and Molloy, B.P. 1995, 'C14 Calibration in the Southern Hemisphere and the Date of the Taupo Eruption: Evidence from Tree-Ring Sequences', *Radiocarbon 37*, 155–63

Steel, D. 1995, *Rogue Asteroids and Doomsday Comets*, John Wiley and Sons, New York

Stewart, R.J. and Matthews, J. 1995, M*erlin Through the Ages*, Blandford, London

Stothers, R.B. 1984, 'Mystery Cloud of AD 536', *Nature 307*, 344–5

Stothers, R.B. and Rampino, M.R. 1983, 'Volcanic Eruptions in the Mediterranean Before AD 630' from Written and Archaeological Sources, *Journal of Geophysical Research 88*, 6357–71

Stuiver, M. and Pearson, G.W. 1986, 'High-Precision Calibration of the Radiocarbon Timescale AD 1950–500 BC', *Radiocarbon 28*, 805–38

Swetnam, T.W. 1993, 'History and Climate Change in Giant Sequoia Groves', *Science 262*, 885–9

Thorpe, L. 1966, Geoffrey of Monmouth. *The History of the Kings of Britain*, Penguin, London

Tolstoy, N. 1985, *The Quest for Merlin*, Hamish Hamilton, London

Toynbee, A. 1976, *Mankind and Mother Earth*, Oxford University Press

Twigg, G. 1984, *The Black Death: a Biological Reappraisal*, Batsford, London

Velikovsky, I. 1950, *Worlds in Collision*, Victor Gollancz, London

Velikovsky, I. 1973, *Earth in Upheaval*, Abacus, London

Velikovsky, I. 1973, *Ages in Chaos*, Abacus, London

Verdet, J. P. 1992, *The Sky: Order and Chaos*, Thames and Hudson, London

Verschuur, G.L. 1996, *Impact! The Threat of Comets and Asteroids*, Oxford University Press

Walford, C. 1879, *Famines of the World, Past and Present*, Burt Franklin, New York

Walters, D. 1995, *Chinese Mythology: An Encyclopedia of Myth and Legend*, Diamond Books, London

Warner, R.B. 1990, 'The Prehistoric' Irish Annals: Fable or History', *Archaeology Ireland 4, 1,* 30–3

Warner, R.B. 1993, 'Tree-Rings, Catastrophes and Culture in Early Ireland: Some Comments', *Emania 11*, 13–19

Warren, P.M. 1984, 'Absolute Dating of the Bronze Age Eruption of Thera (Santorini)', *Nature 308*, 492–3

Warren, P.M. 1991, 'The Minoan Civilization of Crete and the Volcano of

Thera', *Journal of Ancient Chronology Forum 4*, 29–39

Wazny, see Eckstein et al. 1986

Weisburd, S. 1985, 'Excavating Words: A Geological Tool' *Science News 127*, 91–6

Weiss, H. 1996, in Dalfes, H.N., Kukla, G. and Weiss, H., (eds.), 1996, *Third Millennium BC Climate Change and Old World Collapse*, Springer-Verlag, Berlin

Whiston, W. 1696, *A New Theory of the Earth from its Original to the Consummation of all Things, Wherein the Creation of the World in Six Days, The Universal Deluge, and the General Conflagration, as Laid Down in the Holy Scriptures, are Shown to be Perfectly Agreeable to Reason and Philosophy*, London

Williams, Revd D. 1854, 'The Preceptor's Assistant; or Miscellaneous Questions in General History', *Literature and Science*, Simpkin, Marshall and Co., London

Wilson, I. 1985, *The Exodus Enigma*, Guild Publishing, London

Winterbotham, M. 1978, *Gildas: The Ruin of Britain and Other Works*, Phillimore, London

Zacharias, see Hamilton and Brooks 1899

Zeigler, P. 1970, *The Black Death*, Pelican, London

Zetterberg, P., Eronen, M. and Briffa, K. R. 1994, 'Evidence on Climatic Variability and Prehistoric Human Activities Between 165 BC and AD1400 Derived from Subfossil Scots Pines (*Pinus Sylvestris L.*) Found in a Lake in Utsjoki, Northernmost Finland', *Bulletin of the Geological Society of Finland 66*, 107–24

Zielinski, G. A., Mayewski, P. A., Meeker, L. D., Whitlow, S., Twickler, M. S., Morrison, M., Meese, D. A., Gow, A. J. and Alley, R. B. 1994, 'Record of Volcanism since 7000 BC from the GISP2 Greenland Ice Core and Implications for the Volcano-climate System', *Science 264*, 948–52

INDEX

Note added in proof:

In 1937 C. E. Britton published *A Meteorological Chronology to AD 1450*. Under the year AD 540 he records the following:

Battles in the Air (i.e. auroral appearances). The reference is probably to aurora seen in France. Roger of Wendover has an account of this: 'In the year of grace 541, here appeared a comet in Gaul, so vast that the whole sky seemed on fire. In the same year there dropped real blood from the clouds...and a dreadful mortality ensued.'